MULTIPLICATION & DIVISION WORKBOOK

MULTI-DIGIT MULTIPLICATION & LONG DIVISION

AGES 7+

with

RONNY the FRENCHIE

FREE BONUS

Join me and dive into the captivating stories of extraordinary sport heroes and fearless entrepreneurs. I can't wait to share their remarkable tales of innovation and determination with you. In addition to the inspiring stories, I have included some fantastic coloring pages that will spark your creativity too!

So, what are you waiting for? Claim the freebies by scanning the QR code below or type riccagarden.com/ronny_freebies into your web browser.

(Note: You must be 16 years or older to sign up, so grab your parent for help if you need to.)

Your Frenchie,

RONNY

TABLE OF CONTENTS

Answer Keys Included at the Back

INTRODUCTION

Hey kids! My name is Ronny, and I am a French Bulldog, although some people call us Frenchies.

Even though I am small, I am very curious about the world and cannot wait to start exploring every single part of it—from the tree-tops of the rainforest all the way to the pyramids in Egypt and every-thing in between!

I wasn't always this curious though. I used to be a regular puppy dog, digging for bones and sniffing around for snacks. One day, I got zapped by a huge bolt of lightning!

I got shocked right between my little eyes, which left me feeling all fuzzy. But something amazing happened right after my shock... My brain grew two whole inches! How fantastic! With my new, super smart brain, I started my journey across the world and discovered my favorite food ever—bananas!

However, there is one thing even more bananas than fruit, and that is math! My brain is now extra smart, so I'm here to help you figure out the wild world of multiplication and division!

Multiplication is when we times one number by another. For example, two bananas times three equals six bananas! Yum!

+ +

Division is almost like the cousin of multiplication. Instead of making the numbers larger, we divide them into little numbers. Let's imagine four bones, and we divide them between two Frenchies. That would equal two bones for each Frenchie. Lucky pups!

Now you know what multiplication and division are, we are ready to jump into some super cool exercises which are sure to shape your mind into one big brain full of knowledge!

I promise not to shock you with lightning, but your brain will definitely get bigger with all of my awesome math tricks!

So, let's begin our adventure as we learn to tackle multiplication and division. Grab my paw (and a banana), and let's do this!

MULTIPLICATION

2-DIGIT BY 1-DIGIT

Are you ready? Well, let's get started! When you are multiplying a 2-digit number by a single-digit number, you can't exactly count out the answers on your paws (or fingers)!

1)

	5	2
×		9

2)

	5	2
×		1 9
		8

3)

	5	2
×		9
4	6	8

1. Let's try solving the question 52 x 9!

2. We will first start with the smallest numbers! Take the rightmost digit of the top number, which is 2, and multiply it with the single-digit number, 9. This equals 18. Write down the 8 in the result and carry over the 1 to the next step.

3. Now, we can move to one position to the left in the top number, which is 5, and multiply it by 9. We have the answer 45, but we also need to account for the carryover (1) from the previous step. So, 45 + 1 = 46.

We have the answer: 52 x 9 = 468!

By using my super-duper Frenchie grid magic, you can solve any multiplication ever!

DAY 1

Multiplication: 2-Digit by 1-Digit

Time
:

Score
/20

1)
	6	4
×		6

2)
	8	6
×		4

3)
	9	7
×		7

4)
	9	0
×		9

5)
	5	0
×		9

6)
	6	3
×		3

7)
	8	1
×		6

8)
	8	0
×		6

9)
	7	7
×		5

10)
	1	4
×		9

11)
	2	8
×		5

12)
	2	8
×		3

13)
	6	8
×		8

14)
	4	7
×		8

15)
	4	2
×		6

16)
	6	9
×		9

17)
	7	9
×		9

18)
	9	6
×		9

19)
	3	4
×		5

20)
	3	5
×		2

DAY 2

Multiplication: 2-Digit by 1-Digit

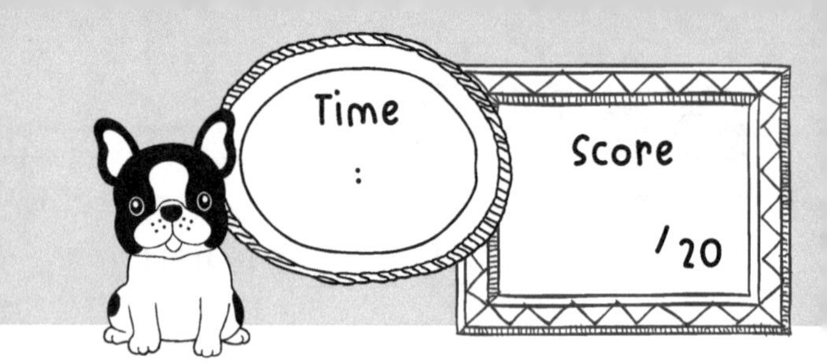

1)

	9	1
×		6

2)

	2	4
×		5

3)

	8	6
×		7

4)

	7	9
×		9

5)

	9	4
×		6

6)

	5	5
×		6

7)

	7	9
×		2

8)

	8	7
×		5

9)

	7	8
×		9

10)

	4	1
×		8

11)

	4	9
×		6

12)

	2	8
×		7

13)

	8	1
×		5

14)

	8	5
×		5

15)

	2	1
×		4

16)

	7	3
×		9

17)

	5	1
×		7

18)

	2	4
×		7

19)

	7	1
×		6

20)

	9	0
×		3

DAY 3

Multiplication: 2-Digit by 1-Digit

1) 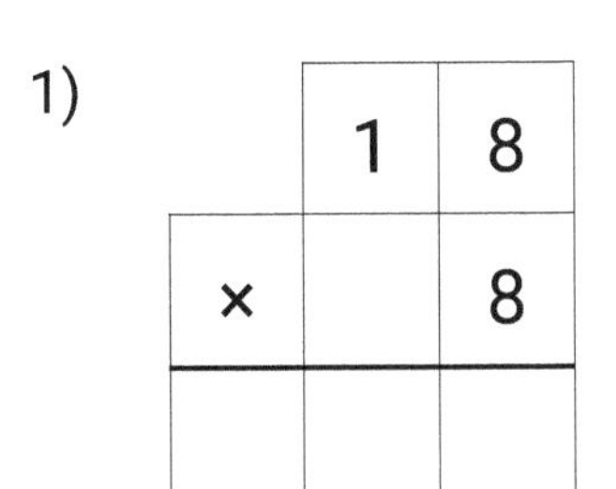

	1	8
×		8

2)

	1	5
×		9

3)

	3	2
×		9

4)

	8	0
×		9

5)

	7	3
×		3

6)

	9	0
×		7

7)

	1	9
×		8

8)

	5	2
×		8

9)

	1	1
×		4

10)

	4	1
×		9

11)

	4	5
×		2

12)

	5	9
×		2

13)

	4	7
×		3

14)

	5	5
×		7

15)

	7	6
×		3

16)

	7	3
×		3

17)

	6	0
×		2

18)

	1	3
×		8

19)

	9	8
×		5

20)

	9	4
×		6

DAY 4

Multiplication: 2-Digit by 1-Digit

1)

	2	3
×		7

2)

	6	7
×		9

3)

	2	6
×		6

4)

	4	6
×		7

5)

	6	4
×		9

6)

	5	7
×		7

7)

	4	4
×		9

8)

	9	5
×		3

9)

	3	9
×		4

10)

	3	7
×		2

11)

	5	1
×		8

12)

	8	6
×		2

13)

	7	2
×		6

14)

	6	4
×		5

15)

	6	3
×		3

16)

	8	1
×		4

17)

	6	0
×		6

18)

	7	6
×		5

19)

	6	0
×		7

20)

	2	7
×		8

DAY 5

Multiplication: 2-Digit by 1-Digit

1) 40×6

2) 66×3

3) 79×8

4) 62×7

5) 98×4

6) 47×4

7) 40×7

8) 75×3

9) 63×3

10) 25×9

11) 26×4

12) 53×8

13) 29×2

14) 64×2

15) 33×9

16) 16×3

17) 92×3

18) 99×2

19) 69×6

20) 91×7

DAY 6

Multiplication: 2-Digit by 1-Digit

1) $85 \times 3 =$

2) $64 \times 2 =$

3) $21 \times 6 =$

4) $84 \times 3 =$

5) $20 \times 6 =$

6) $58 \times 5 =$

7) $65 \times 8 =$

8) $44 \times 9 =$

9) $32 \times 5 =$

10) $71 \times 3 =$

11) $55 \times 8 =$

12) $12 \times 4 =$

13) $80 \times 4 =$

14) $47 \times 4 =$

15) $79 \times 2 =$

16) $55 \times 2 =$

17) $23 \times 9 =$

18) $59 \times 2 =$

19) $53 \times 5 =$

20) $43 \times 8 =$

DAY 7

Multiplication: 2-Digit by 1-Digit

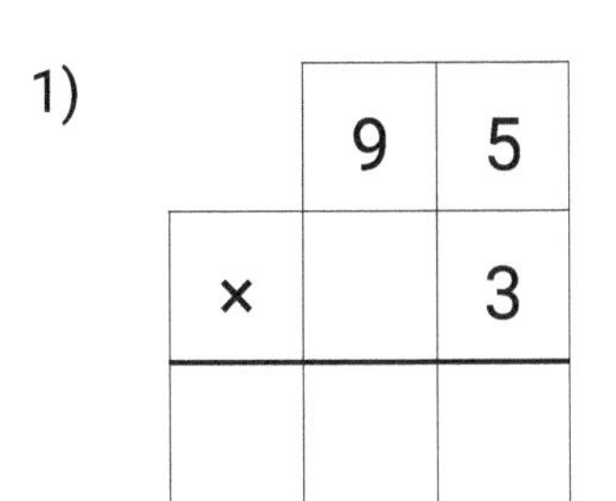

1) 95×3

2) 37×3

3) 63×6

4) 15×6

5) 81×6

6) 29×6

7) 99×9

8) 83×3

9) 62×4

10) 95×2

11) 43×7

12) 18×4

13) 31×4

14) 30×9

15) 67×2

16) 73×4

17) 52×5

18) 39×8

19) 53×4

20) 84×4

DAY 8

Multiplication: 2-Digit by 1-Digit

1)

	4	1
×		3

2)

	6	5
×		8

3)

	5	3
×		2

4)

	2	9
×		7

5)

	7	8
×		8

6)

	8	2
×		3

7)

	2	1
×		3

8)

	9	6
×		5

9)

	6	1
×		5

10)

	5	3
×		4

11)

	7	9
×		9

12)

	7	8
×		2

13)

	8	6
×		7

14)

	1	1
×		8

15)

	8	5
×		3

16)

	3	7
×		4

17)

	5	3
×		5

18)

	1	3
×		7

19)

	5	6
×		9

20)

	9	3
×		7

DAY 9

Multiplication: 2-Digit by 1-Digit

1)

	7	1
×		4

2)

	6	3
×		7

3)

	6	9
×		9

4)

	5	4
×		3

5)

	9	8
×		7

6)

	1	8
×		2

7)

	5	2
×		6

8)

	1	7
×		2

9)

	4	2
×		3

10)

	3	1
×		4

11)

	1	5
×		6

12)

	8	0
×		8

13)

	9	9
×		4

14)

	2	3
×		3

15)

	4	7
×		6

16)

	7	7
×		9

17)

	7	4
×		7

18)

	5	0
×		7

19)

	8	0
×		3

20)

	6	1
×		3

DAY 10

Multiplication: 2-Digit by 1-Digit

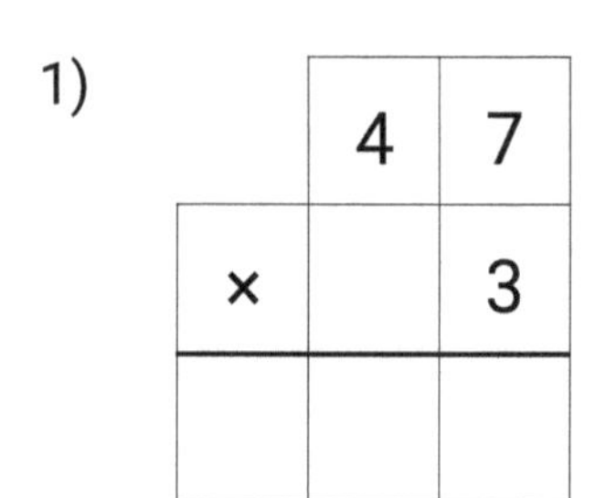

1) 47×3

2) 60×5

3) 15×9

4) 66×3

5) 98×2

6) 19×8

7) 94×2

8) 77×5

9) 28×3

10) 60×7

11) 11×9

12) 53×2

13) 22×5

14) 33×5

15) 76×7

16) 48×3

17) 83×4

18) 20×3

19) 34×5

20) 20×9

DIVISION

NO REMAINDER

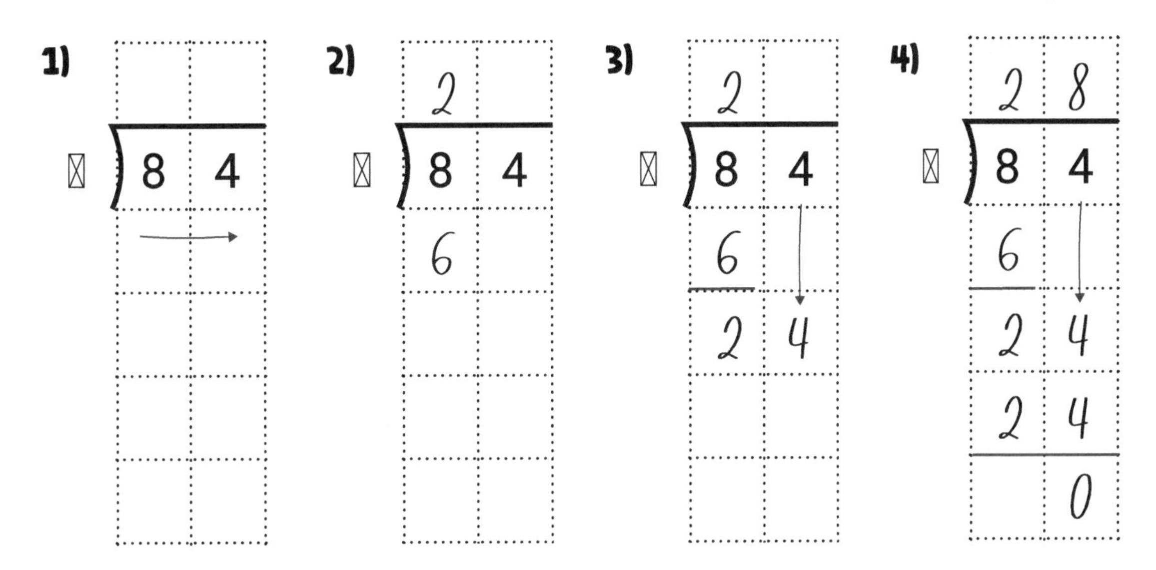

1. Just like reading, we will be tackling this pawesome problem from left to right!

2. We will start by dividing 8 by the divisor 3. How many times does 3 fit into 8? It fits 2 times, write this above the division symbol. Write the result of 2 times 3 below the 8 (6).

3. Next, subtract 6 from 8 to get the remainder, 2. Now we can welcome down the 4 and get 24.

4. Uh-oh, even more dividing! Now, divide 24 by 3. It is exactly 8 times that 3 fits into 24. Write this number above the division symbol. Since there are no more digits to welcome to the party and the division is complete, write the final answer above the division symbol. The final result is 28!

Look at that! You could divide bananas across the whole universe now!

DAY 11

Division: 2-Digit by 1-Digit with No Reminders

1)

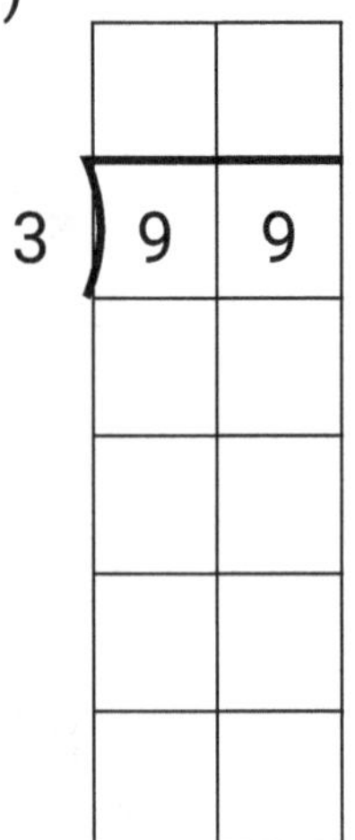

3) 9 9

2)

2) 9 4

3)

2) 8 2

4)

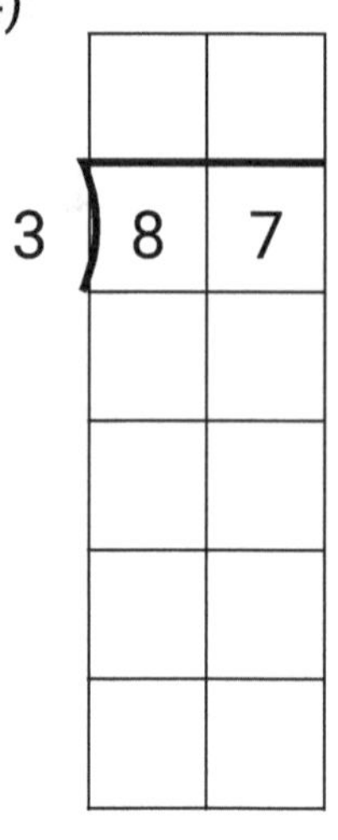

3) 8 7

5)

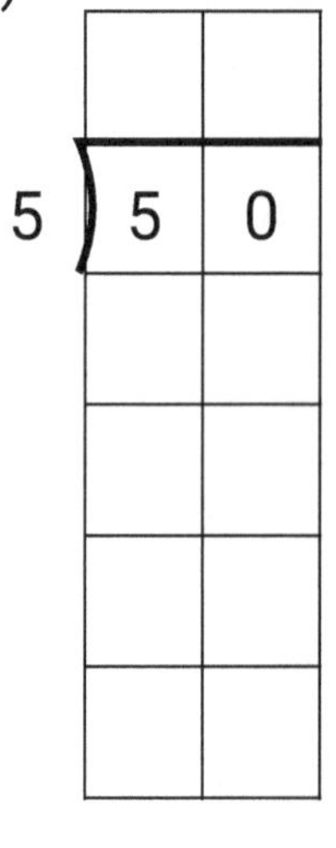

5) 5 0

6)

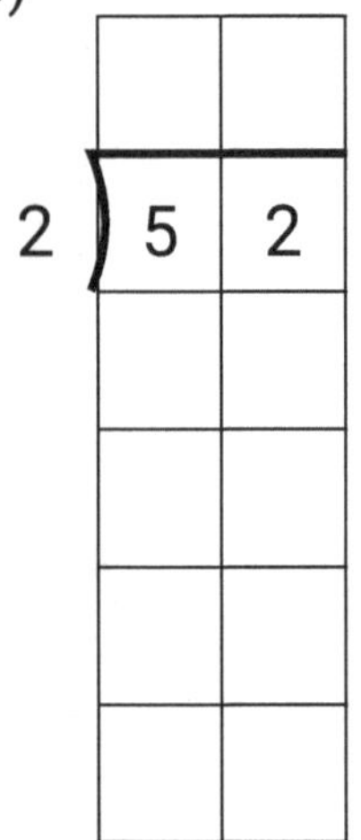

2) 5 2

7)

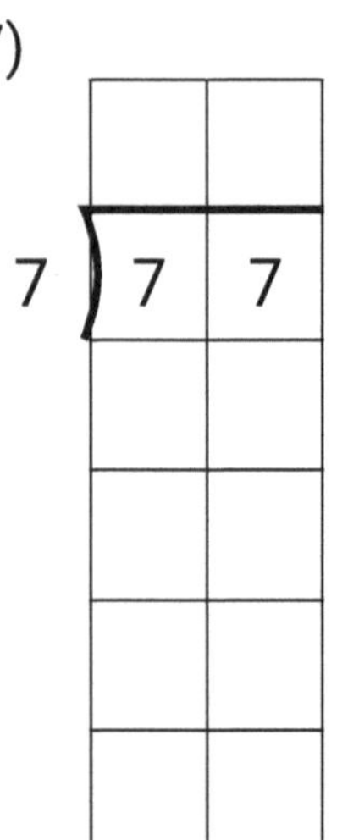

7) 7 7

8)

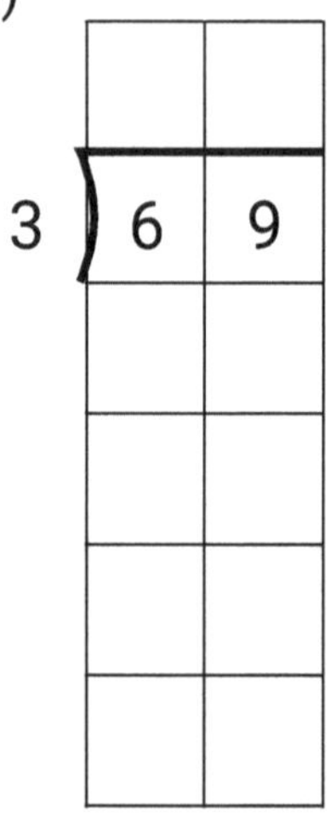

3) 6 9

9)

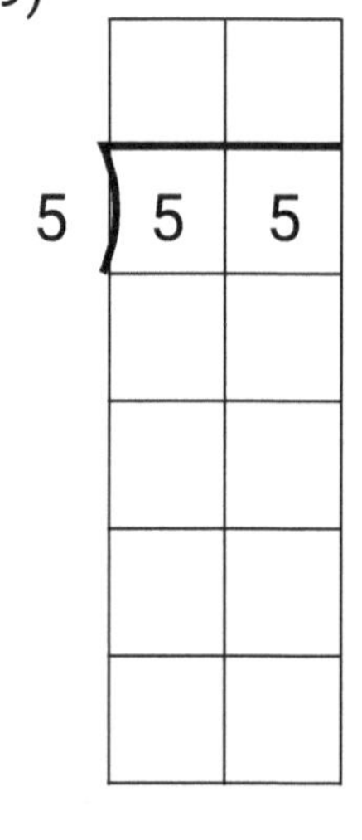

5) 5 5

10)

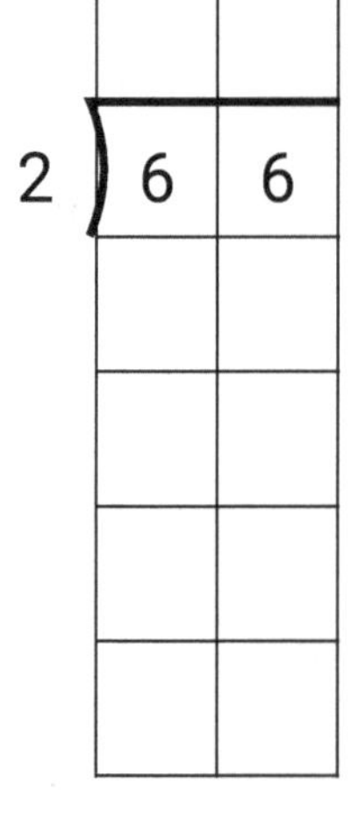

2) 6 6

11)

2) 7 6

12)

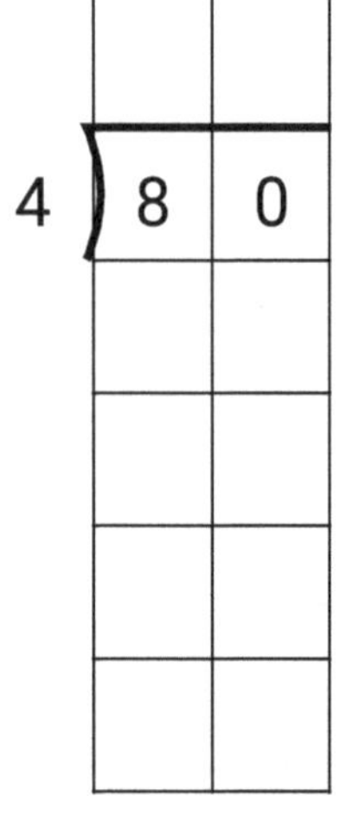

4) 8 0

13)

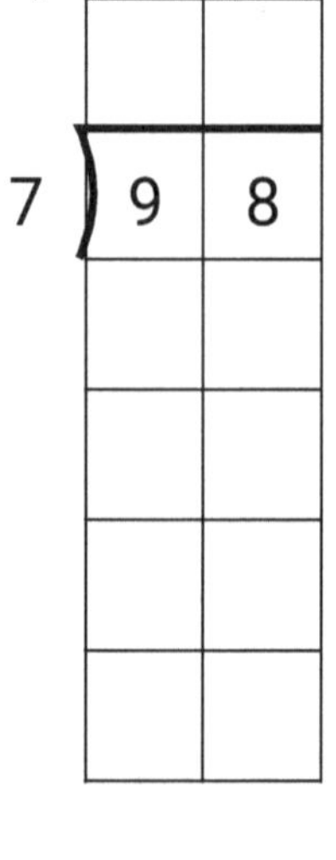

7) 9 8

14)

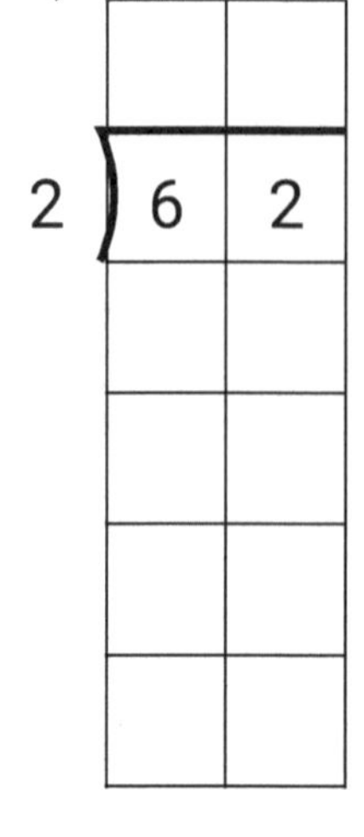

2) 6 2

15)

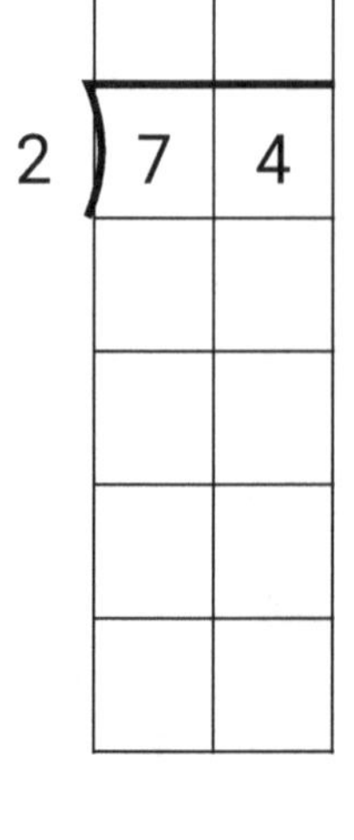

2) 7 4

DAY 12

Division: 2-Digit by 1-Digit with No Reminders

1)

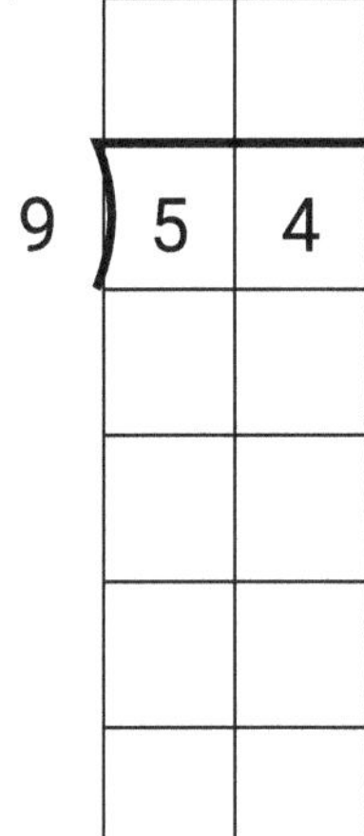

2)

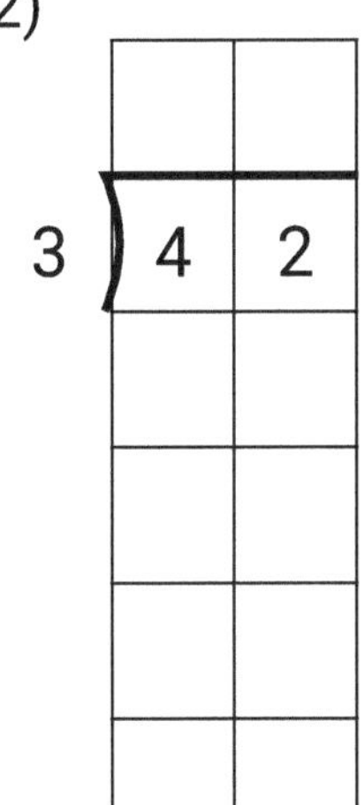

3)

5) 5 5

4)

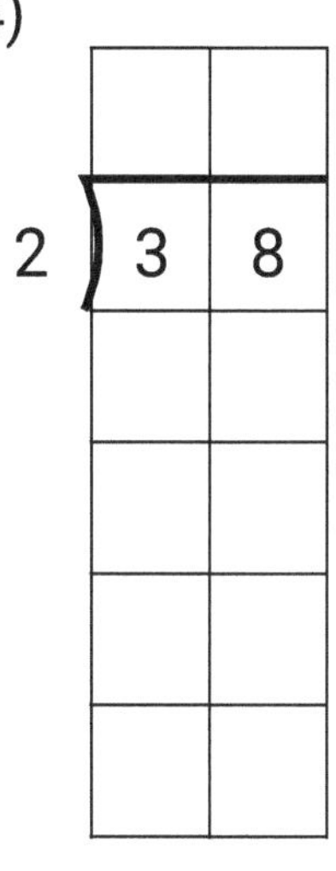

5)

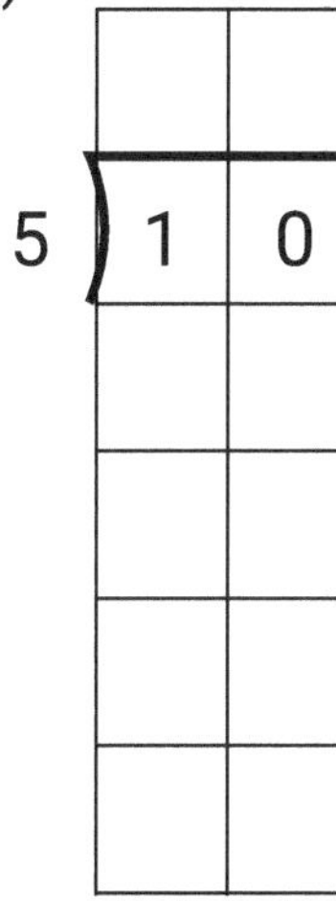

6)

7) 5 6

7)

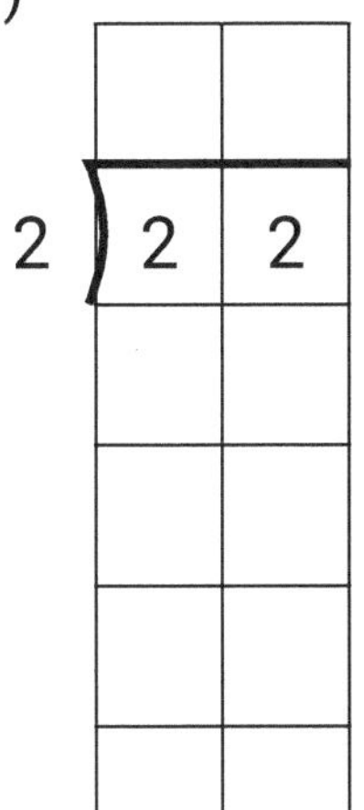

8)

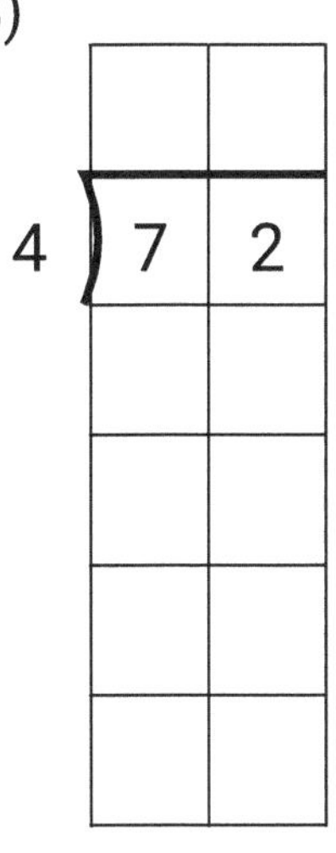

9)

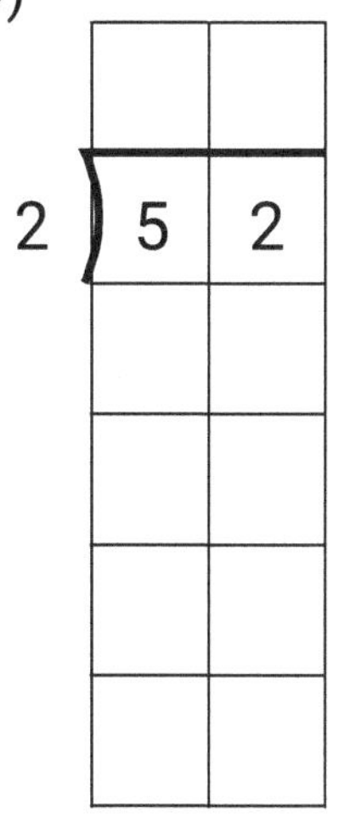

10)

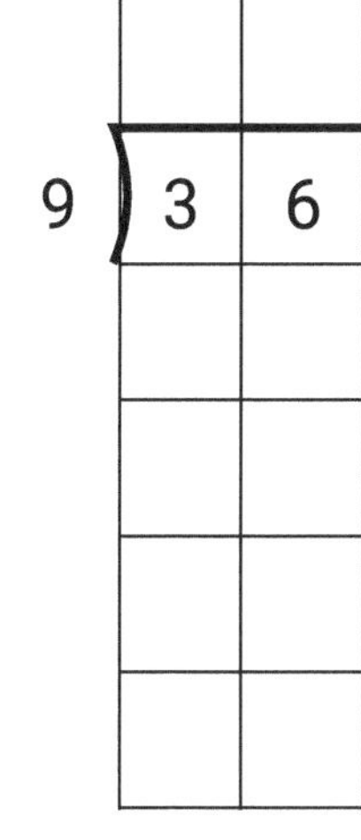

11)

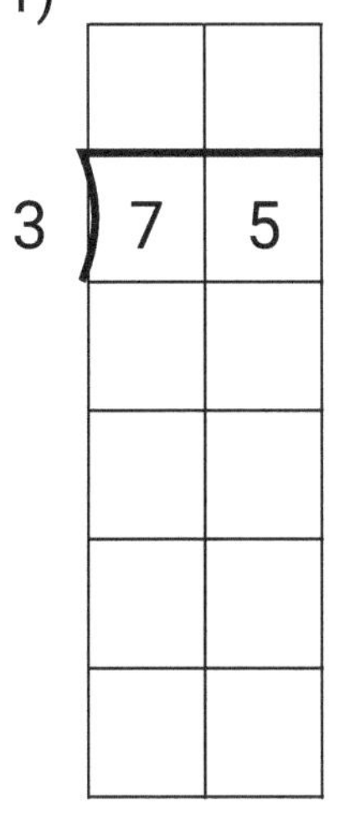

12)

8) 3 2

13)

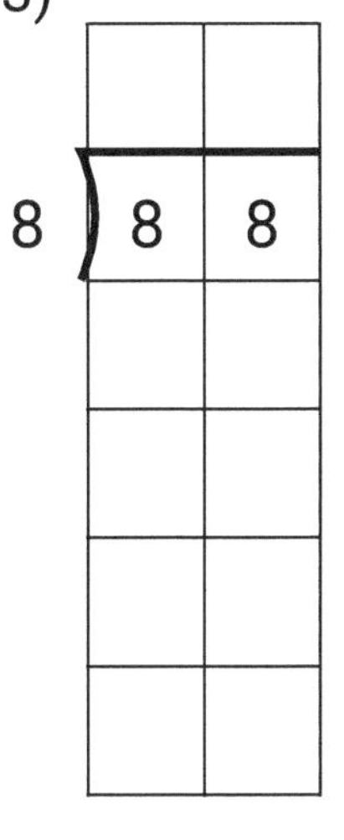

14)

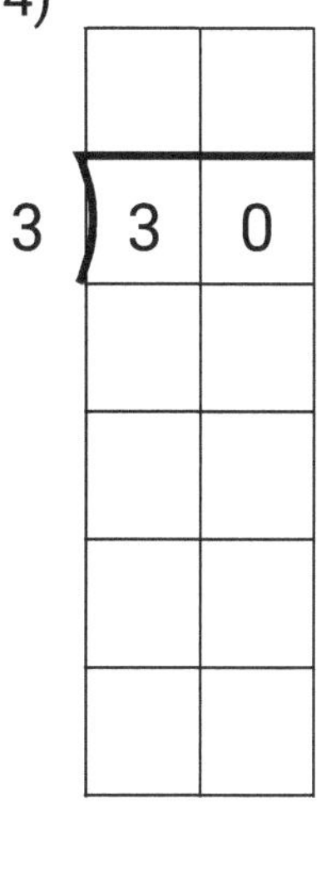

15)

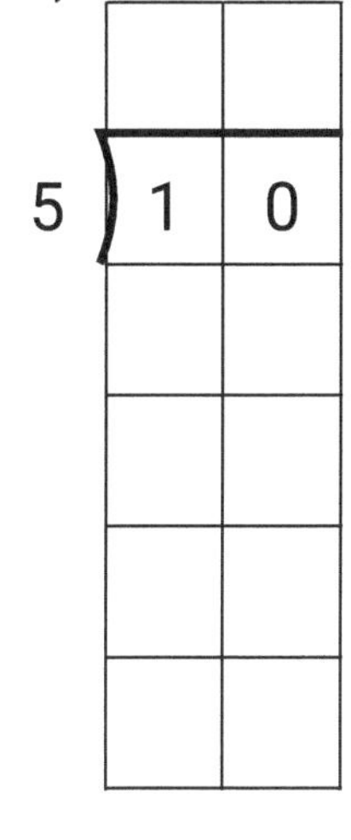

DAY 13

Division: 2-Digit by 1-Digit with No Reminders

1) 2) 3 8

2) 9) 2 7

3)
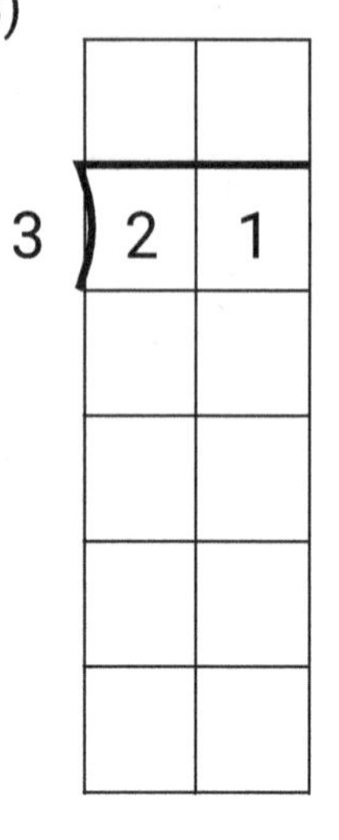

4)
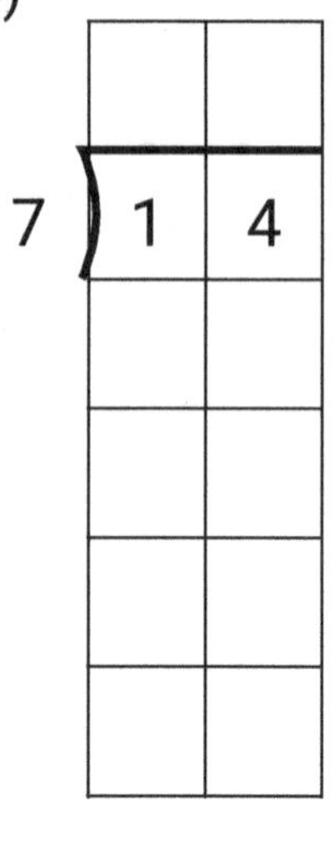

5) 3) 8 7

6)
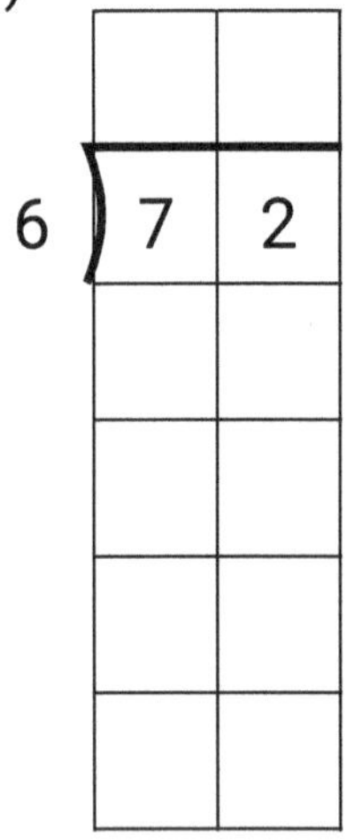

7)
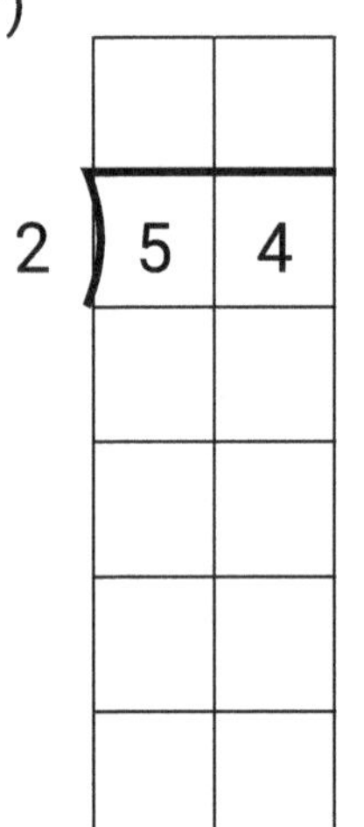

8)
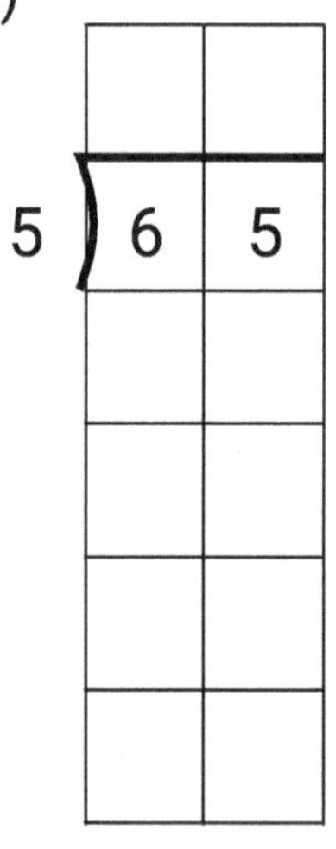

9)
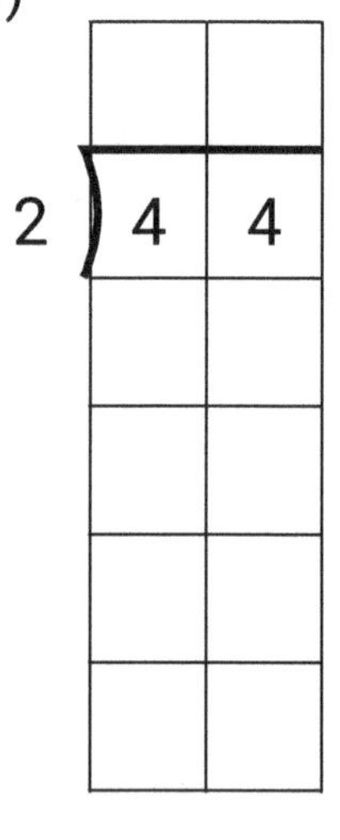

10)
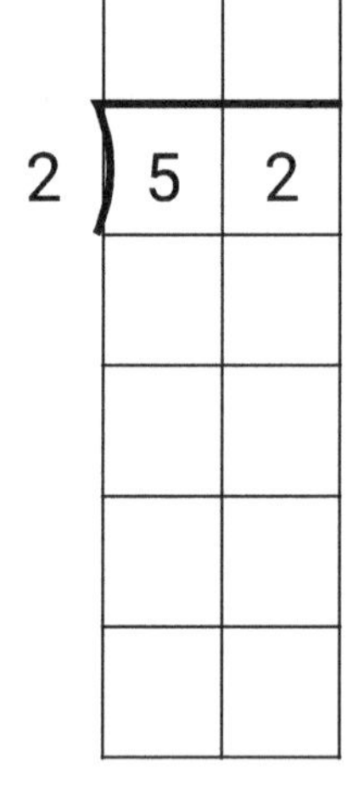

11)
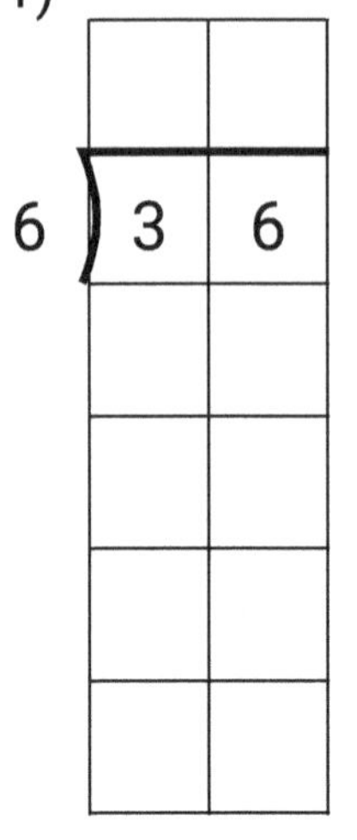

12) 4) 5 2

13)
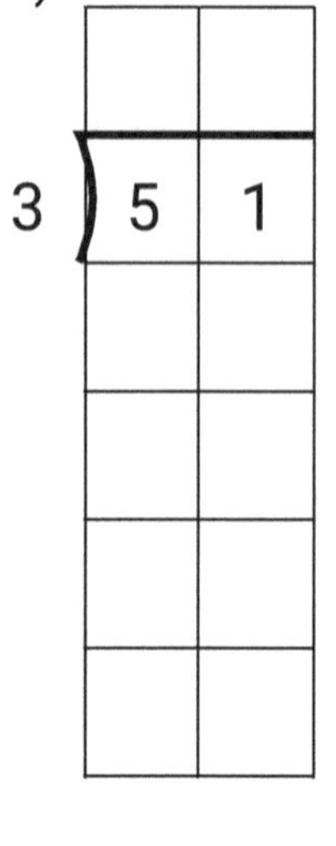

14)
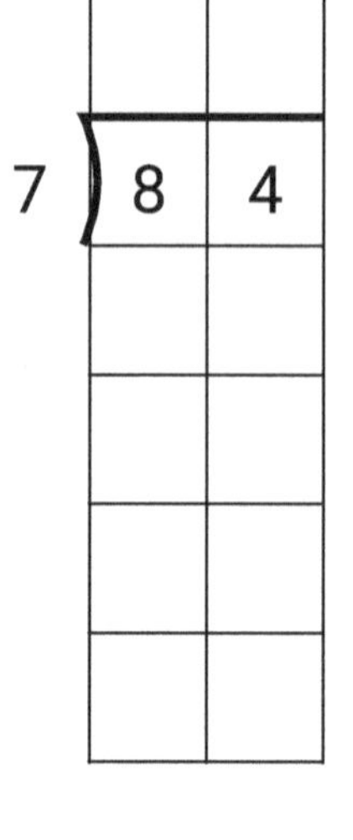

15)
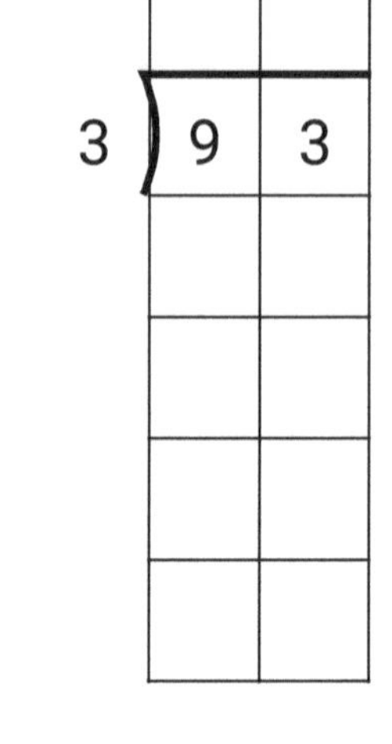

DAY 14

Division: 2-Digit by 1-Digit with No Reminders

1) 2) 38

2) 2) 44

3) 7) 35

4) 7) 49

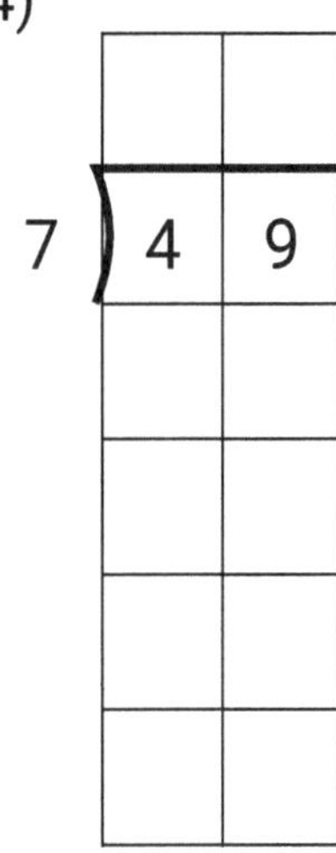

5) 4) 36

6) 5) 50

7) 4) 72

8) 2) 26

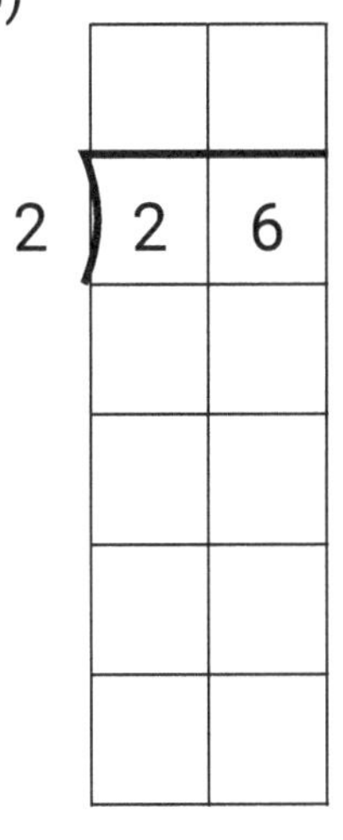

9) 7) 84

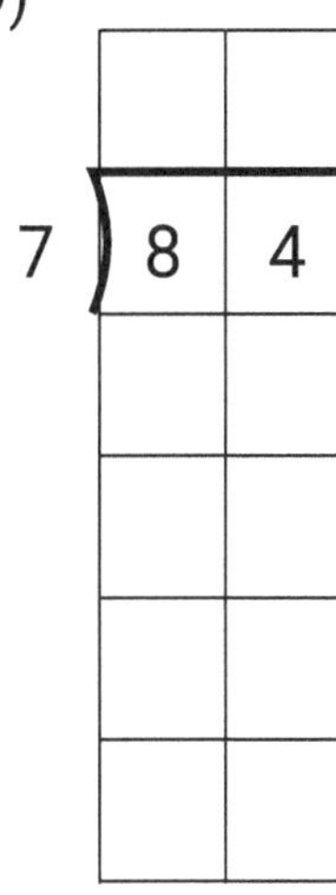

10) 9) 63

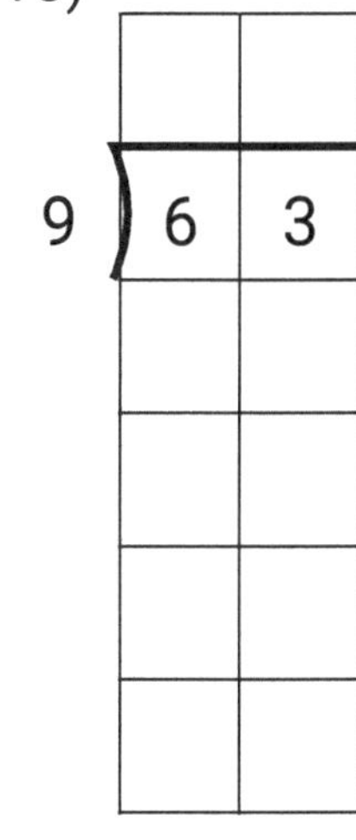

11) 5) 55

12) 7) 84

13) 9) 81

14) 5) 40

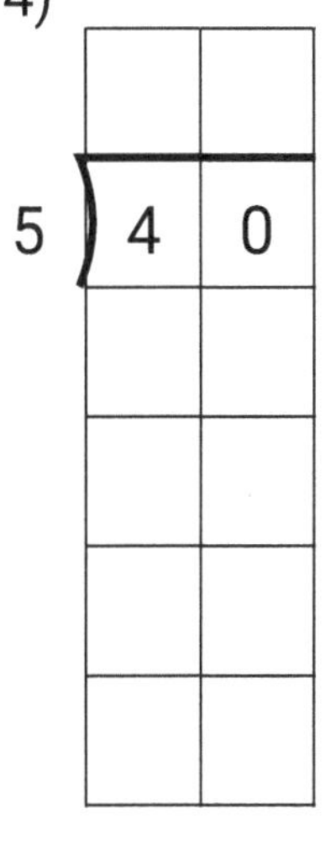

15) 2) 16

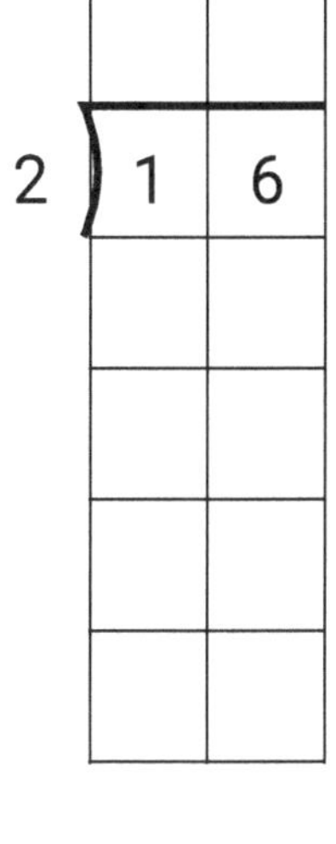

DAY 15

Division: 2-Digit by 1-Digit with No Reminders

1)

3) 3 3

2)

3) 1 8

3)

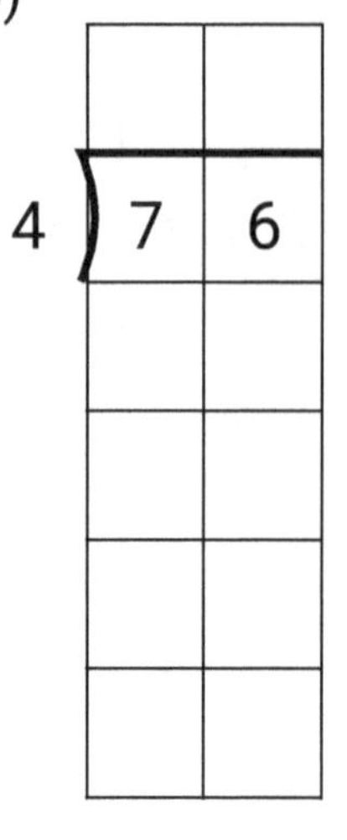

4)

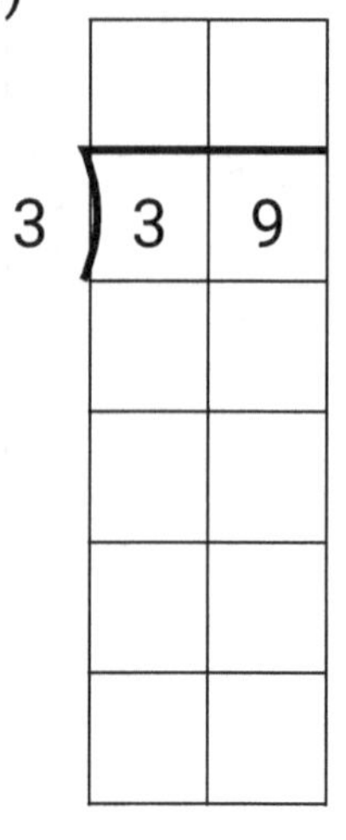

5)

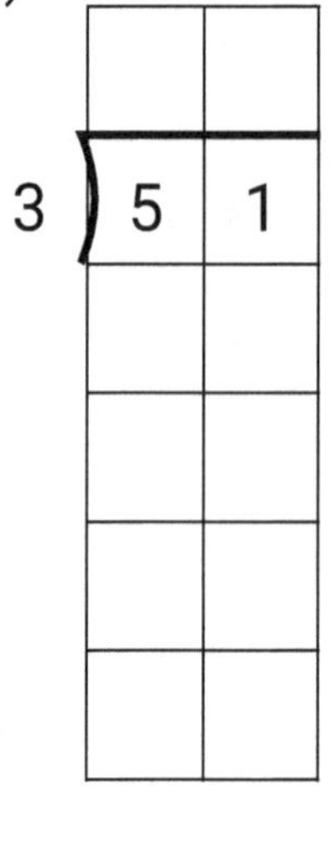

6)

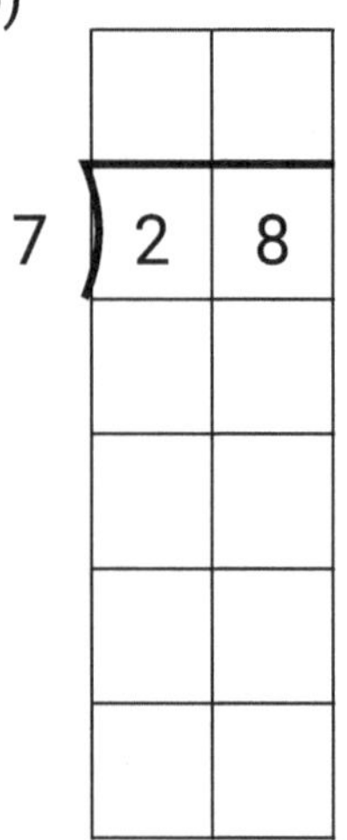

7)

4) 5 2

8)

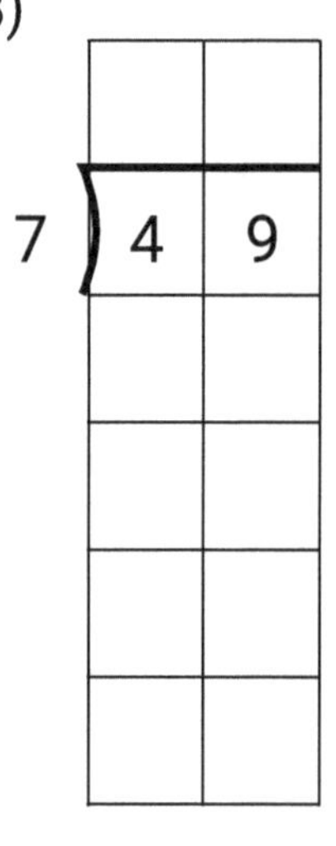

9)

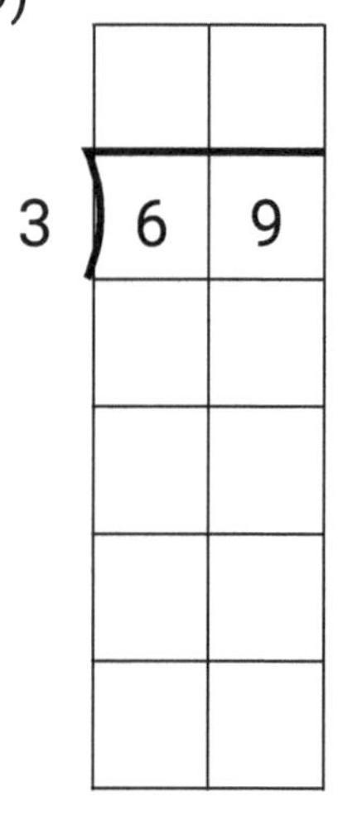

10)

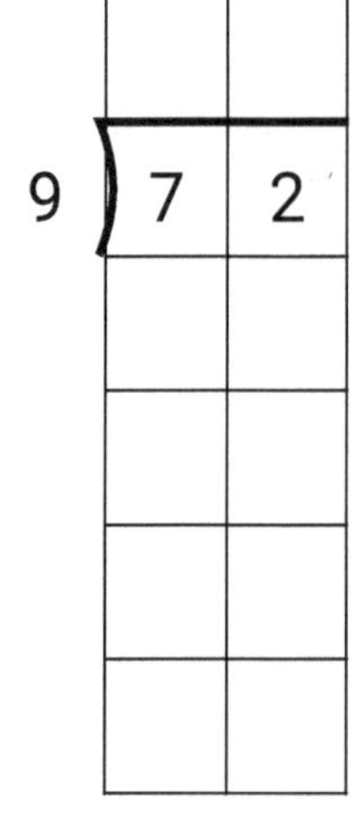

11)

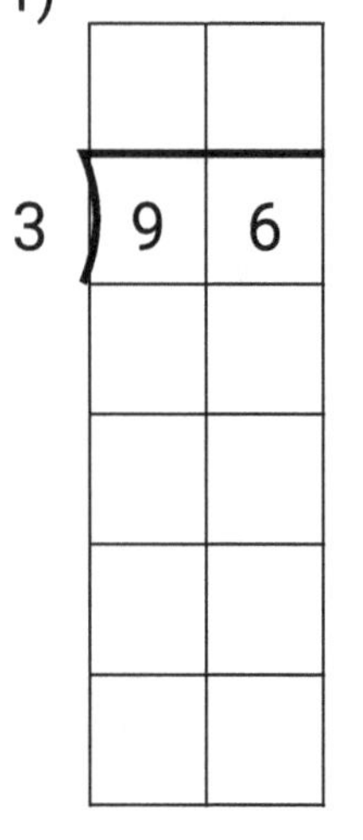

12)

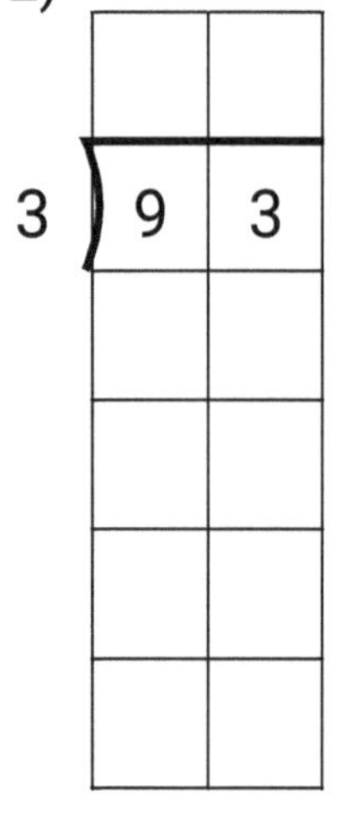

13)

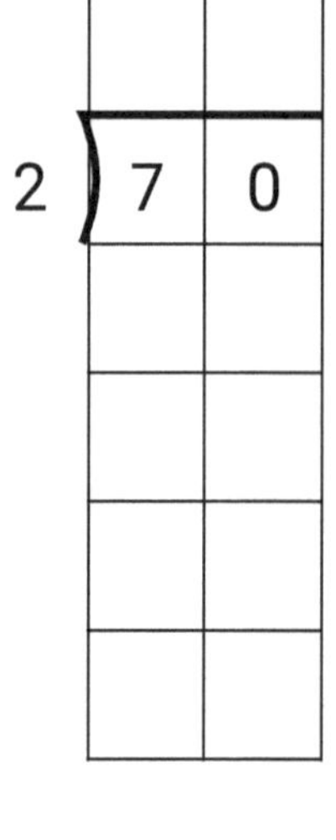

14)

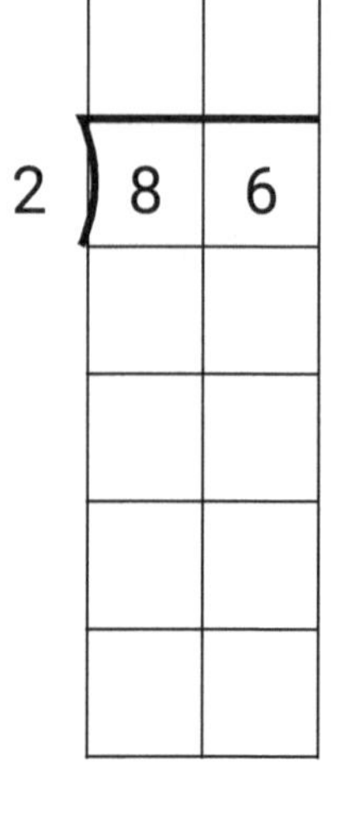

15)

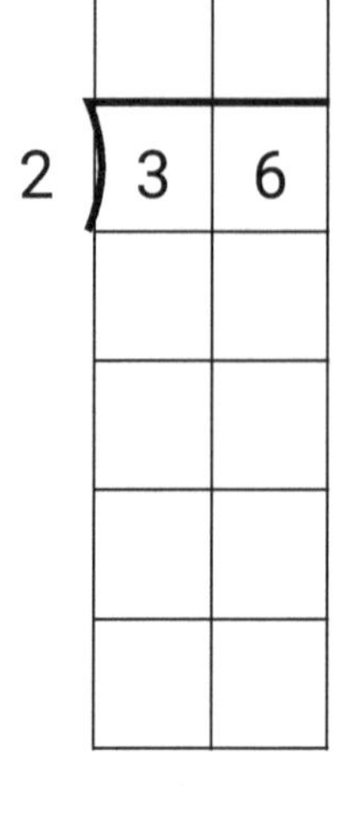

DIVISION
WITH REMAINDER

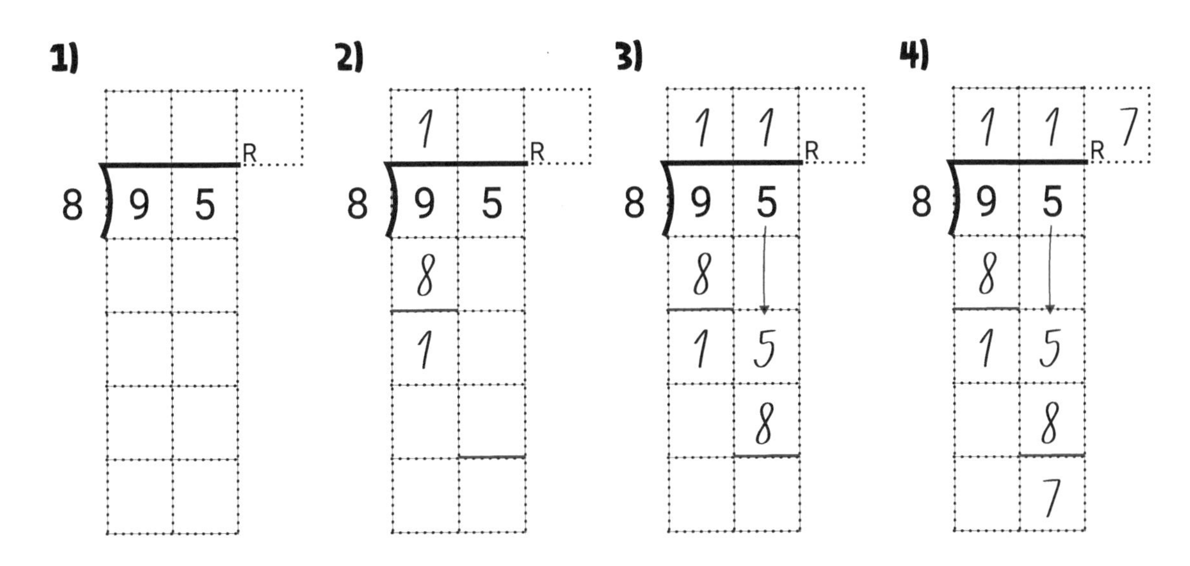

1. Let's find out how we can share 95 bananas among 8 friends.

2. We start by asking, "How many times can 8 go into 9?" Well, it can go 1 time. So, we write 1 above the division symbol and write 8 under the 9. We then subtract 9 from 8, which leaves us with 1.

3. Next, we bring down the next number to the party, which is 5. So, we now have 15 to work with. Now, we ask, "How many times can 8 go into 15?" It can go 1 time again. So, we write 1 above the division symbol.

4. We subtract 15 from 8, which leaves us with 7. This is like giving 8 more bananas to our friends, but we can't give another full set of 8, so we have 7 bananas left. In the end, we could give each friend 11 bananas, and we had 7 bananas left that we couldn't share evenly. This is our final answer: 11 with a remainder of 7.

DAY 16

Division: 2-Digit by 1-Digit with Reminders

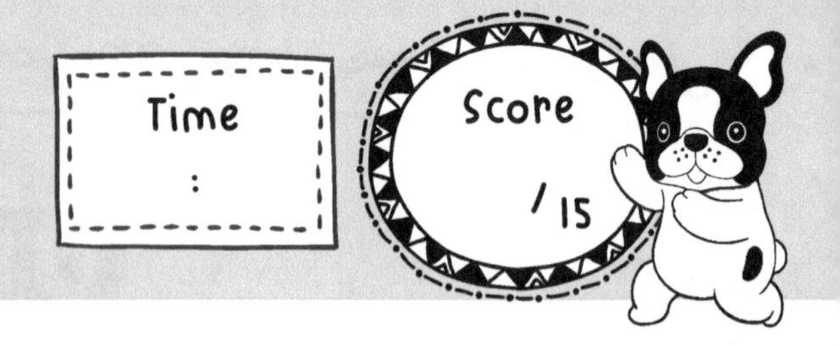

1) 8) 1 1 R

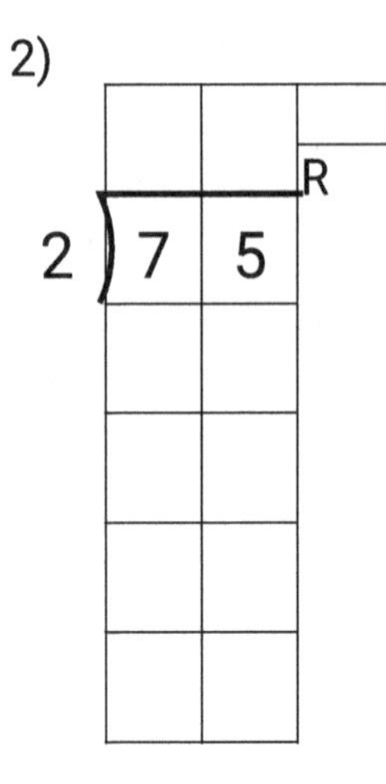

2) 2) 7 5 R

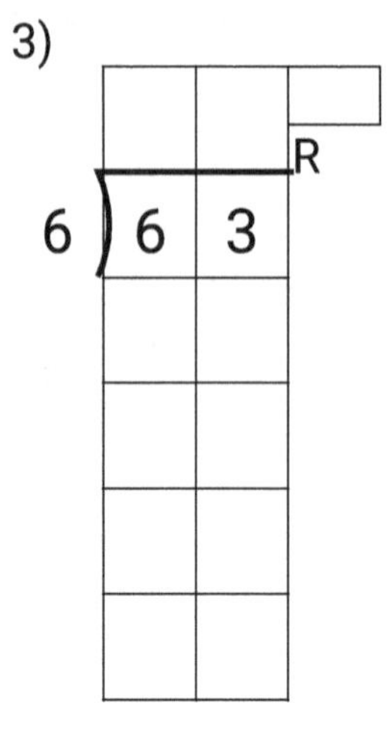

3) 6) 6 3 R

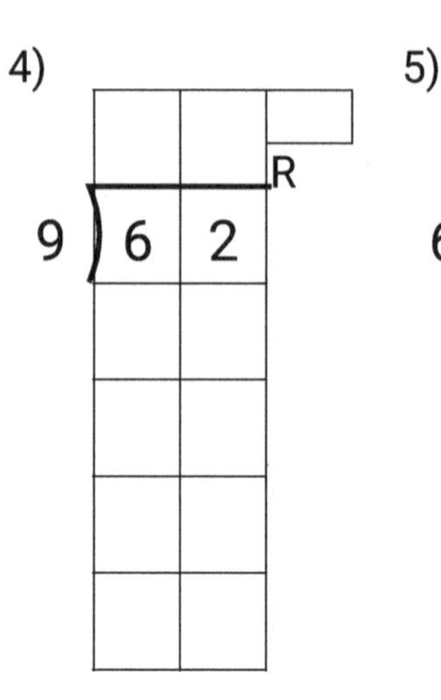

4) 9) 6 2 R

5) 6) 6 0 R

6) 7) 9 0 R

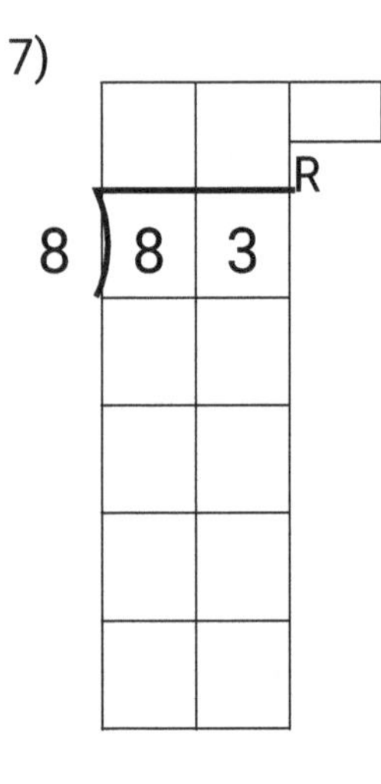

7) 8) 8 3 R

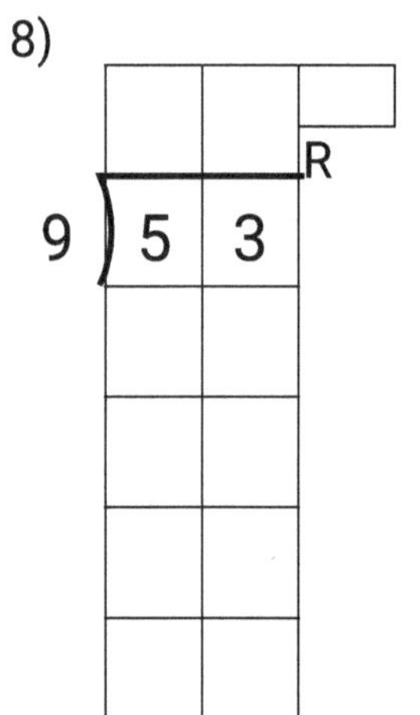

8) 9) 5 3 R

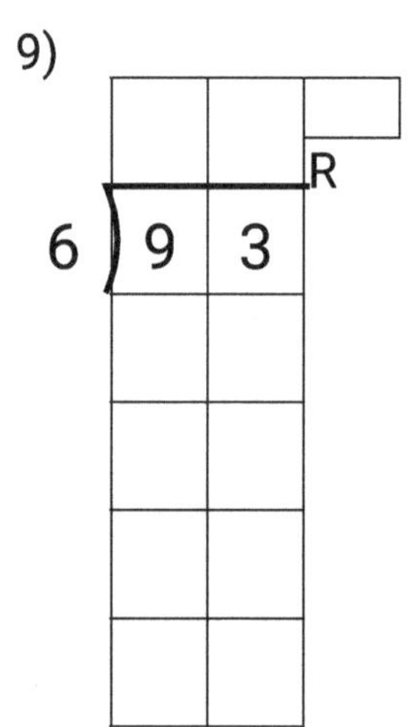

9) 6) 9 3 R

10) 9) 3 3 R

11) 4) 5 1 R

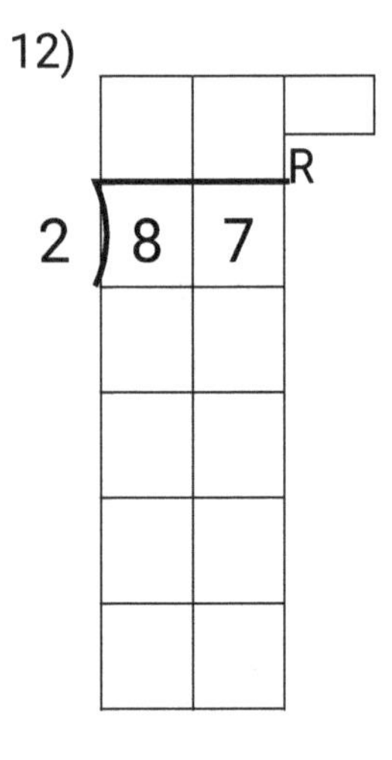

12) 2) 8 7 R

13) 7) 3 3 R

14) 4) 6 6 R

15) 8) 9 3 R

DAY 17

Division: 2-Digit by 1-Digit with Reminders

1) $96 \div 5 =$ ___ R ___

2) $36 \div 4 =$ ___ R ___

3) $20 \div 3 =$ ___ R ___

4) $55 \div 8 =$ ___ R ___

5) $48 \div 3 =$ ___ R ___

6) $61 \div 2 =$ ___ R ___

7) $58 \div 4 =$ ___ R ___

8) $50 \div 7 =$ ___ R ___

9) $70 \div 4 =$ ___ R ___

10) $78 \div 7 =$ ___ R ___

11) $38 \div 2 =$ ___ R ___

12) $29 \div 7 =$ ___ R ___

13) $78 \div 2 =$ ___ R ___

14) $38 \div 8 =$ ___ R ___

15) $47 \div 6 =$ ___ R ___

DAY 18

Division: 2-Digit by 1-Digit with Reminders

1) 9) 9 0 R

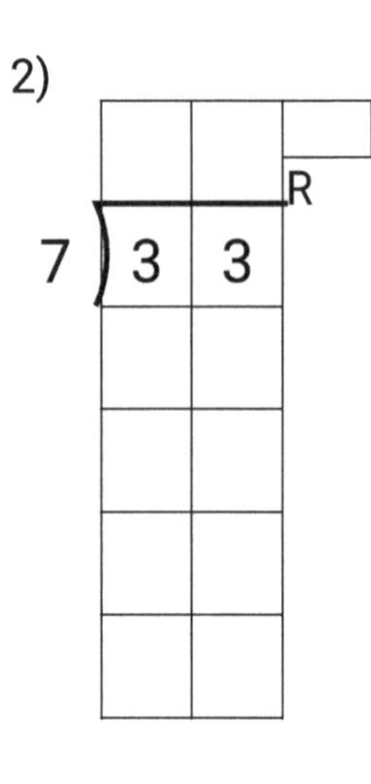

2) 7) 3 3 R

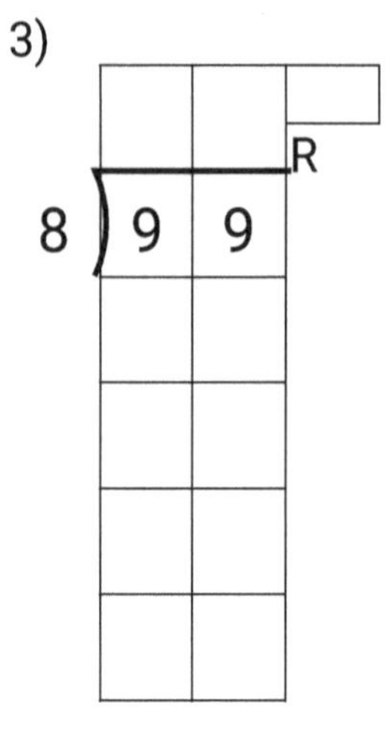

3) 8) 9 9 R

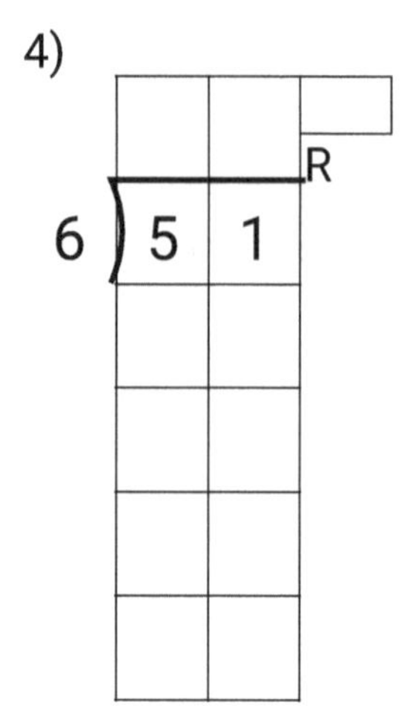

4) 6) 5 1 R

5) 5) 6 5 R

6) 6) 9 8 R

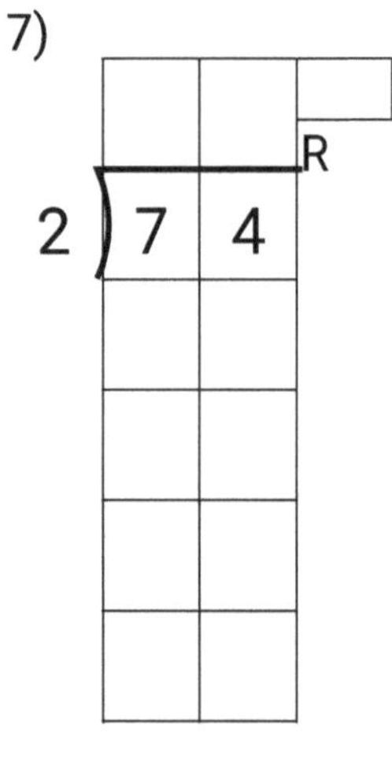

7) 2) 7 4 R

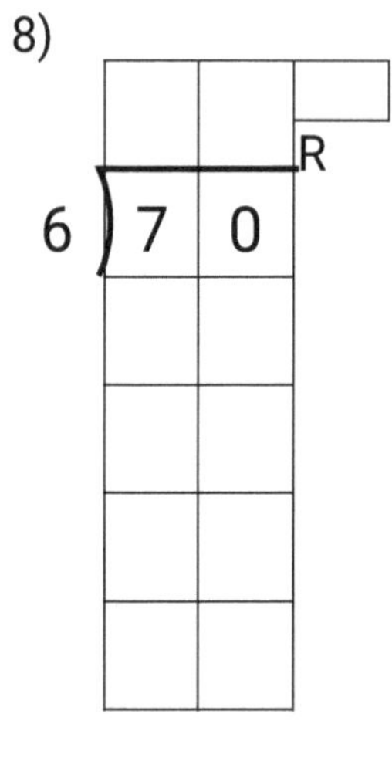

8) 6) 7 0 R

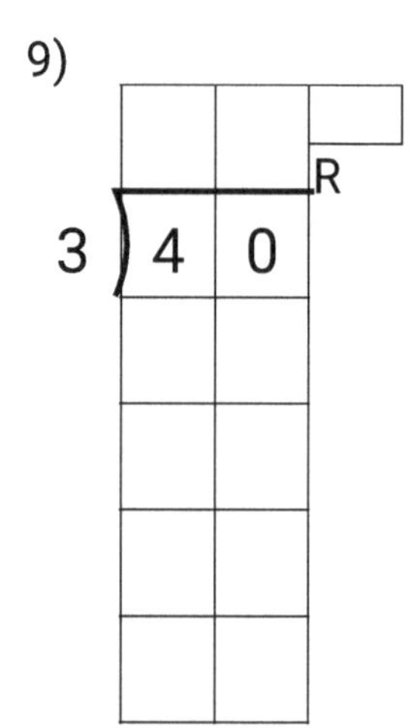

9) 3) 4 0 R

10) 5) 8 7 R

11) 4) 2 1 R

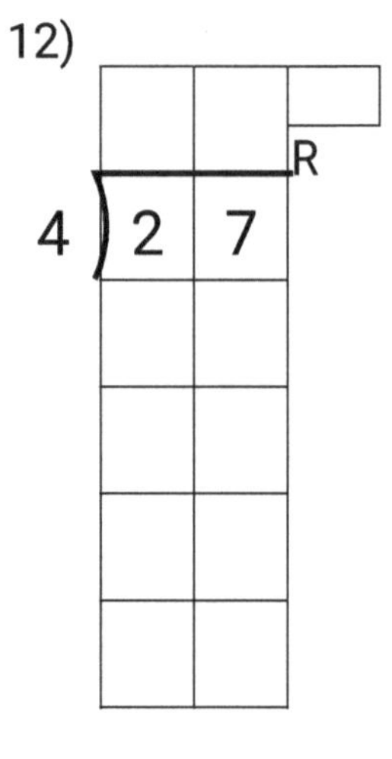

12) 4) 2 7 R

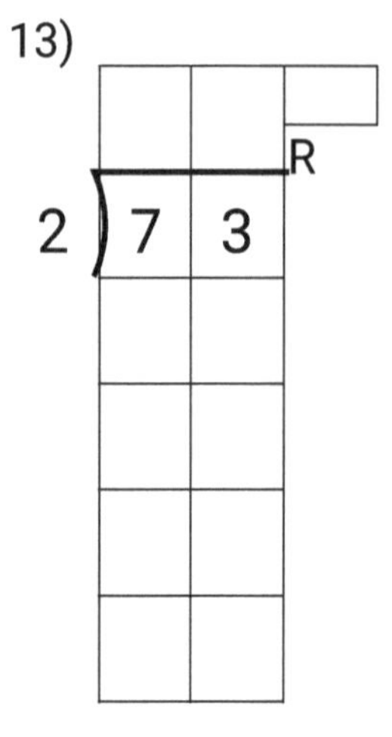

13) 2) 7 3 R

14) 6) 8 3 R

15) 4) 8 9 R

DAY 19

Division: 2-Digit by 1-Digit with Reminders

1) 3) 7 6 R

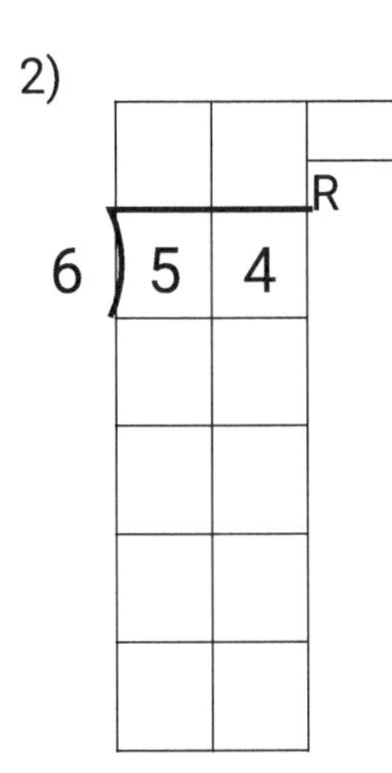

2) 6) 5 4 R

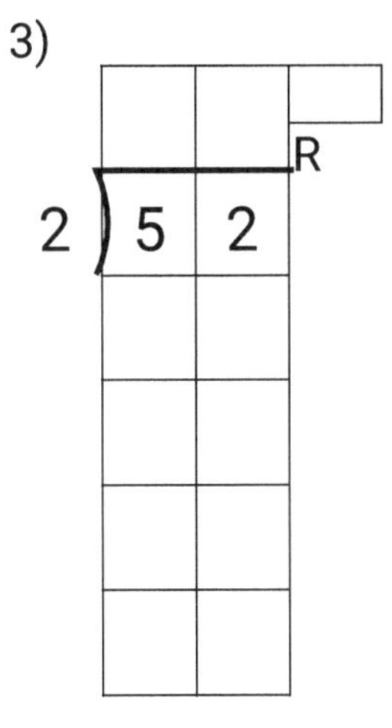

3) 2) 5 2 R

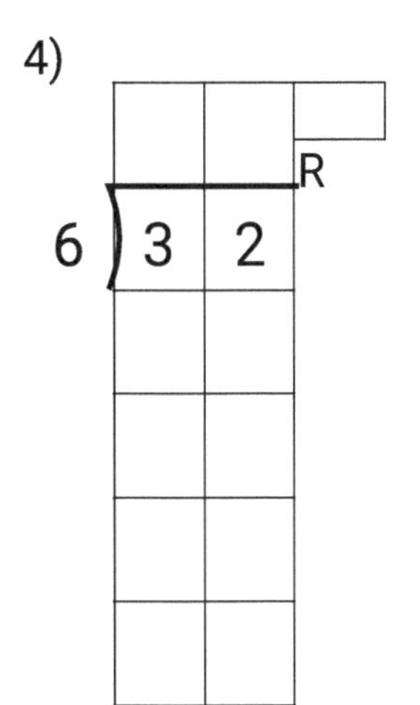

4) 6) 3 2 R

5) 2) 4 5 R

6) 5) 5 9 R

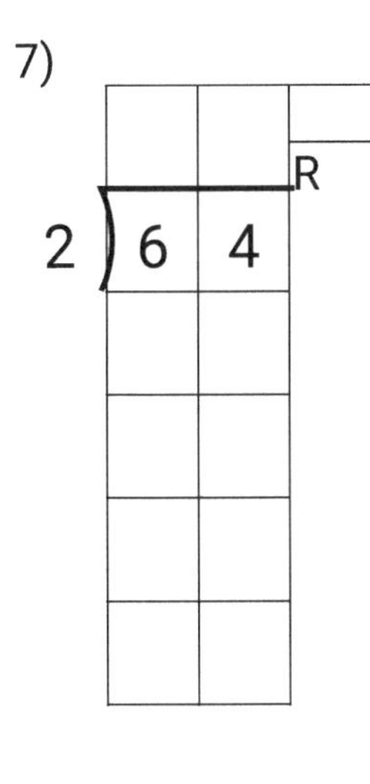

7) 2) 6 4 R

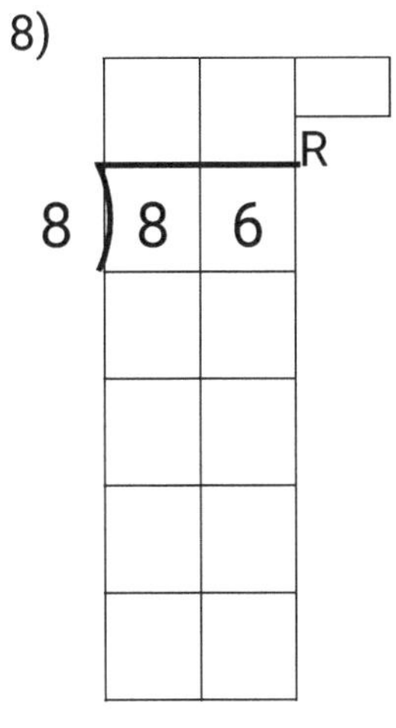

8) 8) 8 6 R

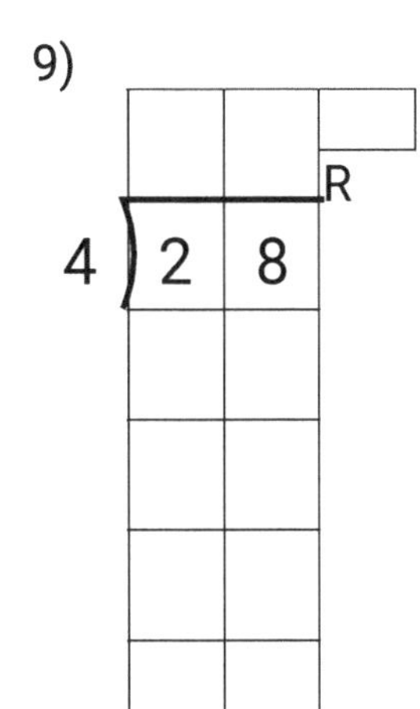

9) 4) 2 8 R

10) 3) 3 6 R

11) 3) 7 4 R

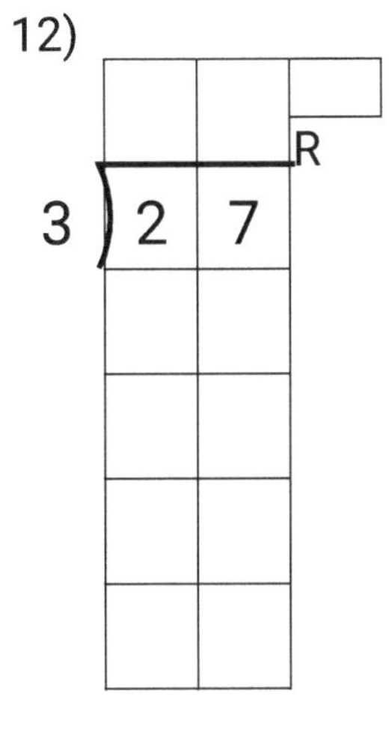

12) 3) 2 7 R

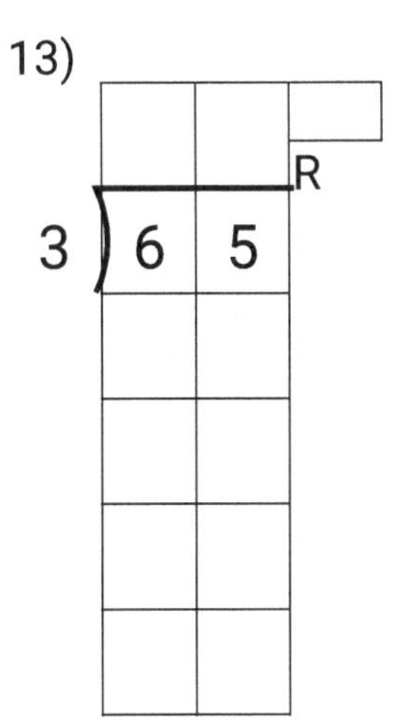

13) 3) 6 5 R

14) 2) 7 5 R

15) 8) 2 4 R

DAY 20

Division: 2-Digit by 1-Digit with Reminders

1) $68 \div 3$ = ___ R ___

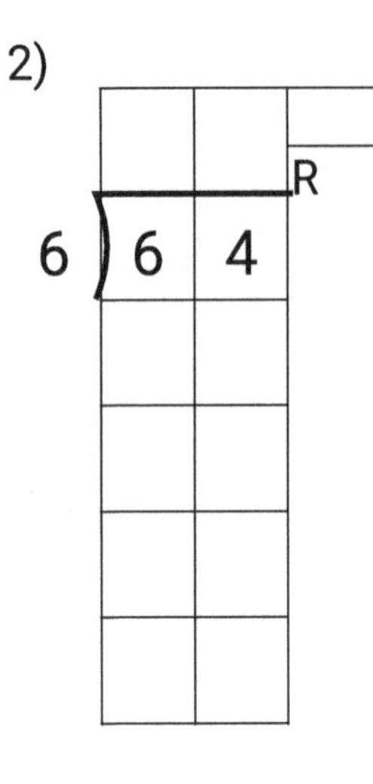

2) $64 \div 6$ = ___ R ___

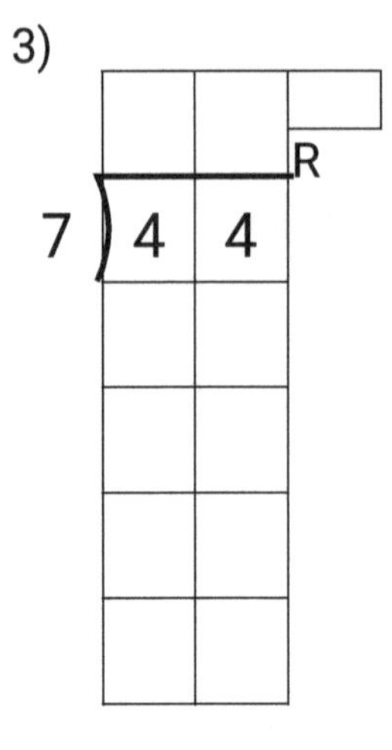

3) $44 \div 7$ = ___ R ___

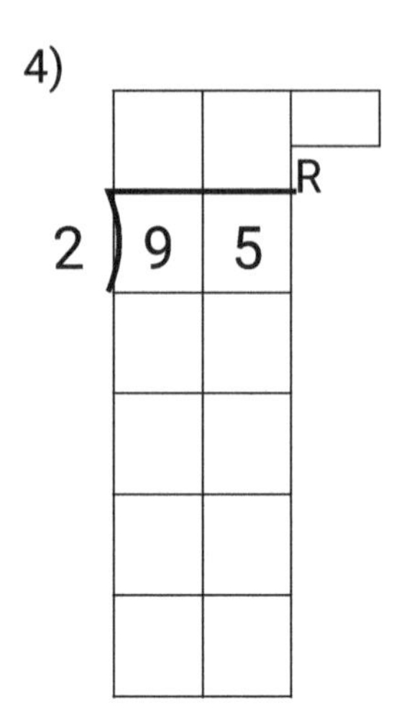

4) $95 \div 2$ = ___ R ___

5) $63 \div 9$ = ___ R ___

6) $85 \div 8$ = ___ R ___

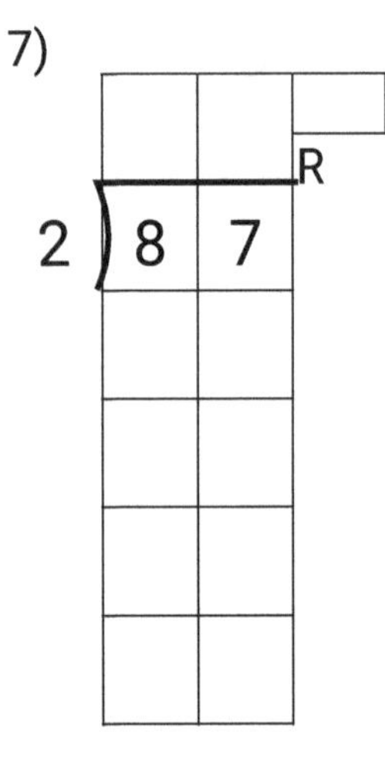

7) $87 \div 2$ = ___ R ___

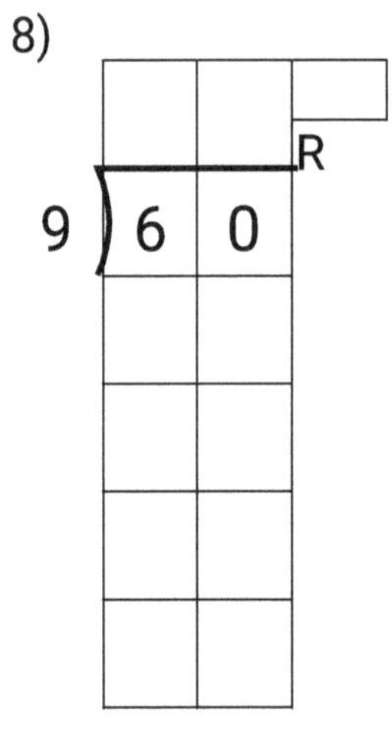

8) $60 \div 9$ = ___ R ___

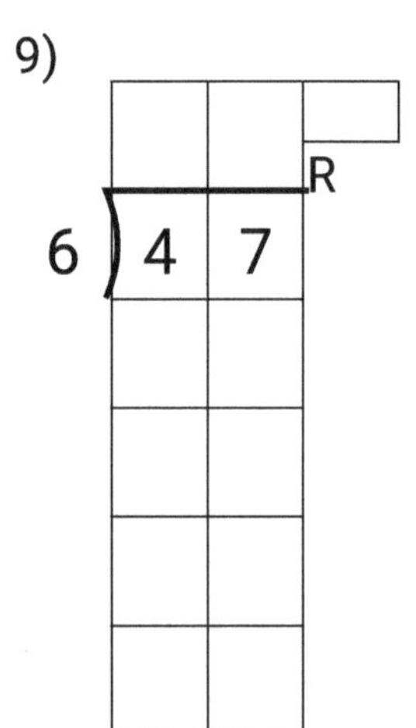

9) $47 \div 6$ = ___ R ___

10) $49 \div 3$ = ___ R ___

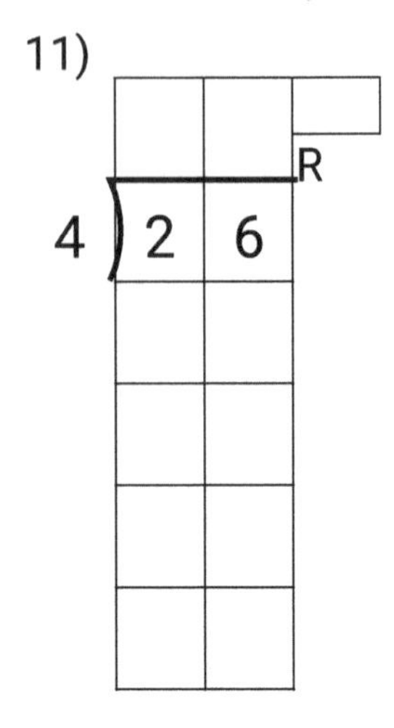

11) $26 \div 4$ = ___ R ___

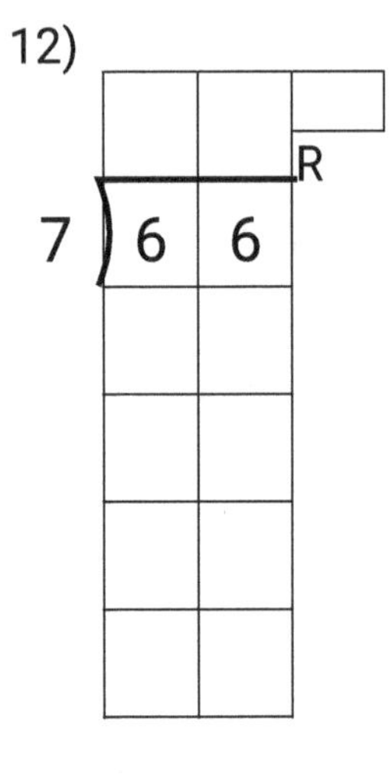

12) $66 \div 7$ = ___ R ___

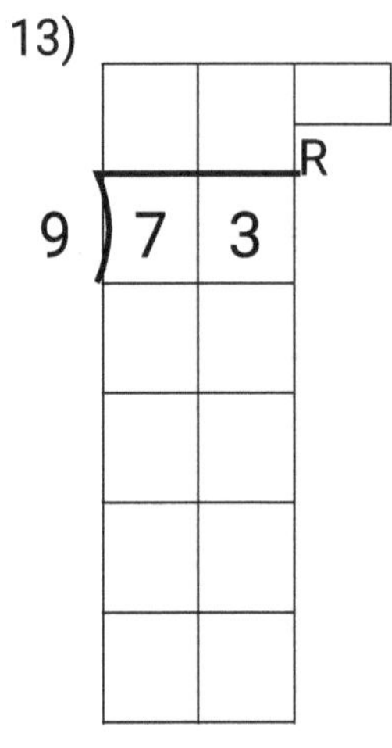

13) $73 \div 9$ = ___ R ___

14) $99 \div 7$ = ___ R ___

15) $90 \div 7$ = ___ R ___

DID YOU KNOW THAT THE NUMBER 2 IS THE ONLY NATURAL NUMBER EQUALING ITSELF WHEN ADDED AND MULTIPLIED?

A natural number means any positive number (above 0). The number 2 is the only number that satisfies this equation: $2 + 2 = 2 \times 2$. If you put any other number in here it just wouldn't work. How unique is that!

DAY 21

Multiplication: 3-Digit by 1-Digit

1) 198 × 2 =

2) 598 × 3 =

3) 986 × 2 =

4) 598 × 2 =

5) 359 × 3 =

6) 132 × 4 =

7) 180 × 4 =

8) 917 × 4 =

9) 799 × 7 =

10) 626 × 4 =

11) 594 × 9 =

12) 298 × 5 =

13) 121 × 2 =

14) 487 × 9 =

15) 569 × 7 =

16) 592 × 8 =

17) 300 × 2 =

18) 311 × 3 =

19) 312 × 2 =

20) 443 × 6 =

21) 462 × 2 =

22) 269 × 3 =

23) 742 × 2 =

24) 344 × 9 =

DAY 22

Multiplication: 3-Digit by 1-Digit

1) 574×2

2) 561×4

3) 896×9

4) 288×4

5) 641×5

6) 433×9

7) 137×4

8) 619×9

9) 586×7

10) 754×2

11) 547×6

12) 692×5

13) 457×9

14) 560×4

15) 269×3

16) 458×5

17) 255×2

18) 820×8

19) 143×2

20) 447×6

21) 762×4

22) 662×2

23) 594×9

24) 576×5

DAY 23

Multiplication: 3-Digit by 1-Digit

1)

	5	2	8
×			3

2)

	1	7	7
×			4

3)

	8	7	5
×			9

4)

	1	6	2
×			8

5)

	4	7	8
×			8

6)

	4	6	1
×			5

7)

	3	0	6
×			2

8)

	3	9	7
×			6

9)

	4	4	7
×			7

10)

	3	9	7
×			9

11)

	5	5	1
×			2

12)

	3	0	9
×			5

13)

	6	2	5
×			8

14)

	1	6	2
×			5

15)

	4	9	5
×			2

16)

	3	4	3
×			6

17)

	9	6	3
×			8

18)

	5	7	2
×			6

19)

	6	8	9
×			4

20)

	9	4	6
×			9

21)

	3	0	2
×			5

22)

	5	5	8
×			9

23)

	7	5	7
×			6

24)

	6	5	6
×			9

DAY 24

Multiplication: 3-Digit by 1-Digit

1) 662 × 2

2) 637 × 8

3) 817 × 4

4) 653 × 5

5) 557 × 7

6) 848 × 8

7) 809 × 8

8) 146 × 5

9) 316 × 2

10) 772 × 2

11) 574 × 6

12) 331 × 5

13) 288 × 8

14) 831 × 9

15) 435 × 8

16) 747 × 5

17) 144 × 2

18) 968 × 5

19) 751 × 8

20) 725 × 3

21) 627 × 8

22) 856 × 8

23) 135 × 3

24) 930 × 5

DAY 25

Multiplication: 3-Digit by 1-Digit

1)

	8	1	8
×			2

2)

	6	8	4
×			7

3)

	2	6	2
×			8

4)

	2	4	8
×			8

5)

	6	1	1
×			2

6)

	3	9	0
×			8

7)

	8	8	5
×			5

8)

	3	6	4
×			8

9)

	4	5	4
×			9

10)

	2	1	1
×			9

11)

	5	5	9
×			7

12)

	1	5	6
×			8

13)

	5	7	5
×			2

14)

	1	3	6
×			2

15)

	6	3	2
×			3

16)

	1	3	2
×			9

17)

	1	8	1
×			5

18)

	1	8	1
×			3

19)

	7	7	1
×			7

20)

	7	7	1
×			7

21)

	6	0	5
×			5

22)

	3	3	6
×			7

23)

	3	6	4
×			7

24)

	4	0	2
×			3

DAY 26

Multiplication: 3-Digit by 1-Digit

1) $336 \times 2 =$

2) $858 \times 5 =$

3) $578 \times 5 =$

4) $151 \times 2 =$

5) $420 \times 3 =$

6) $890 \times 7 =$

7) $763 \times 6 =$

8) $480 \times 3 =$

9) $698 \times 9 =$

10) $557 \times 5 =$

11) $163 \times 8 =$

12) $508 \times 8 =$

13) $457 \times 8 =$

14) $247 \times 5 =$

15) $692 \times 4 =$

16) $451 \times 3 =$

17) $192 \times 3 =$

18) $659 \times 6 =$

19) $326 \times 5 =$

20) $642 \times 9 =$

21) $651 \times 7 =$

22) $531 \times 4 =$

23) $980 \times 7 =$

24) $535 \times 3 =$

DAY 27

Multiplication: 3-Digit by 1-Digit

1)

	2	2	3
×			3

2)

	3	0	2
×			4

3)

	8	7	7
×			5

4)

	3	9	0
×			8

5)

	3	1	3
×			3

6)

	5	5	0
×			4

7)

	2	8	4
×			3

8)

	3	3	7
×			6

9)

	8	4	0
×			6

10)

	2	8	4
×			5

11)

	7	0	7
×			2

12)

	8	7	6
×			7

13)

	4	6	1
×			9

14)

	7	7	2
×			7

15)

	2	5	1
×			3

16)

	4	3	7
×			7

17)

	2	7	5
×			4

18)

	8	4	0
×			6

19)

	9	3	7
×			9

20)

	9	9	0
×			4

21)

	2	4	7
×			7

22)

	2	8	8
×			6

23)

	9	4	1
×			9

24)

	3	2	7
×			3

DAY 28

Multiplication: 3-Digit by 1-Digit

1)

	8	4	0
×			8

2)

	2	8	0
×			9

3)

	5	3	9
×			5

4)

	7	0	8
×			2

5)

	7	6	4
×			3

6)

	2	5	4
×			3

7)

	8	1	8
×			2

8)

	4	9	4
×			3

9)

	1	1	3
×			7

10)

	7	9	5
×			2

11)

	2	9	6
×			4

12)

	2	0	0
×			2

13)

	9	5	0
×			2

14)

	8	2	8
×			4

15)

	2	2	1
×			5

16)

	2	1	2
×			5

17)

	6	2	7
×			5

18)

	2	1	2
×			8

19)

	1	1	2
×			6

20)

	8	4	9
×			9

21)

	3	5	1
×			9

22)

	7	0	1
×			3

23)

	5	4	9
×			9

24)

	2	6	4
×			4

DAY 29

Multiplication: 3-Digit by 1-Digit

1) 454 × 9

2) 533 × 9

3) 747 × 2

4) 957 × 2

5) 420 × 8

6) 341 × 3

7) 201 × 2

8) 531 × 5

9) 843 × 3

10) 422 × 3

11) 552 × 5

12) 563 × 3

13) 353 × 2

14) 605 × 3

15) 987 × 7

16) 792 × 4

17) 993 × 6

18) 570 × 7

19) 900 × 4

20) 521 × 4

21) 373 × 3

22) 226 × 4

23) 878 × 2

24) 756 × 4

DAY 30

Multiplication: 3-Digit by 1-Digit

1)

	6	6	9
×			2

2)

	5	4	9
×			2

3)

	2	9	8
×			8

4)

	6	2	0
×			3

5)

	9	1	7
×			6

6)

	5	0	9
×			5

7)

	2	9	0
×			4

8)

	2	6	9
×			8

9)

	5	7	8
×			9

10)

	5	6	8
×			5

11)

	2	6	3
×			8

12)

	9	6	8
×			7

13)

	1	8	0
×			4

14)

	8	3	5
×			8

15)

	1	4	9
×			4

16)

	4	3	1
×			3

17)

	3	2	8
×			4

18)

	8	3	3
×			2

19)

	5	0	0
×			5

20)

	8	5	9
×			2

21)

	6	8	2
×			8

22)

	8	4	7
×			5

23)

	1	9	0
×			8

24)

	6	3	6
×			7

WHAT COMES AFTER A MILLION, BILLION, AND TRILLION?

A quadrillion, quintillion, sextillion, septillion, octillion, nonillion, decillion, and undecillion. Those are some positively huge numbers!

The best bit is, to get from one to the next you can multiply them all by the same number. Can you guess what it is?

One thousand! That's right, there are 1000 million in 1 billion, and 1000 billion in 1 trillion.

DAY 31

Division: 3-Digit by 1-Digit with No Reminders

1) $711 \div 3$

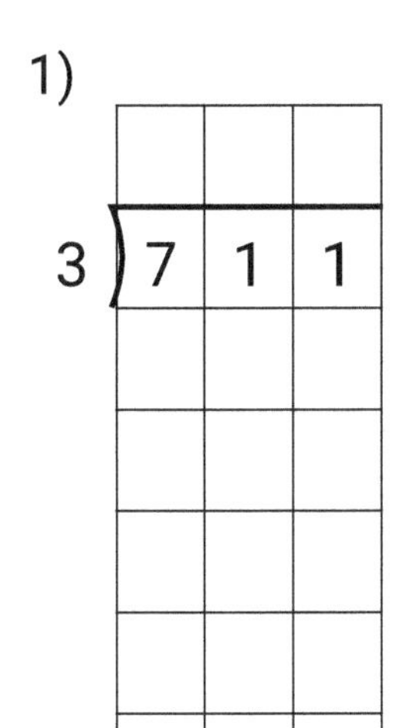

2) $445 \div 5$

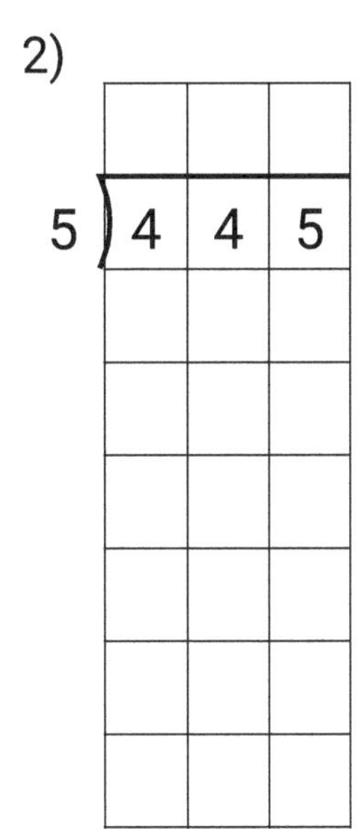

3) $404 \div 4$

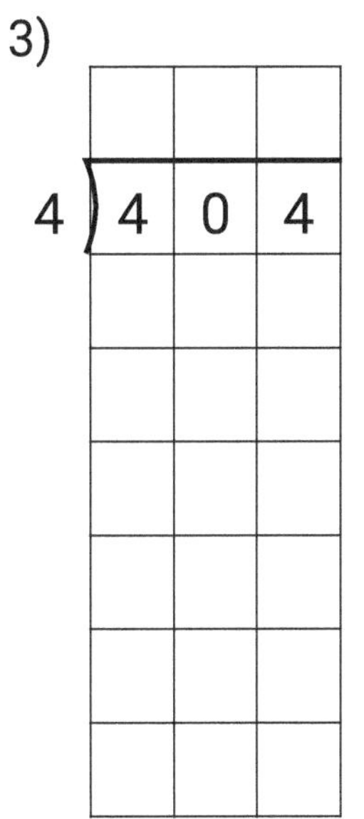

4) $625 \div 5$

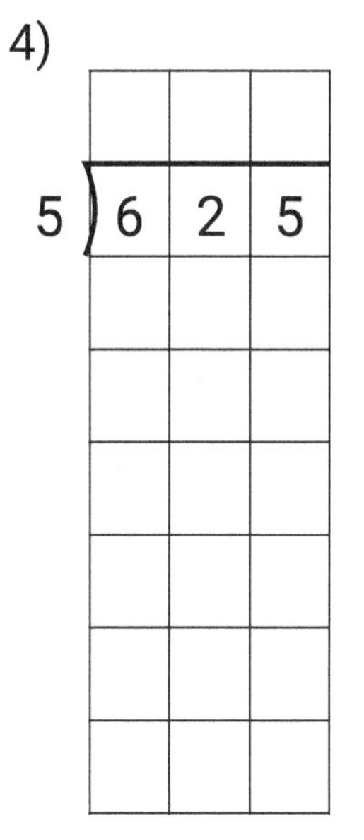

5) $464 \div 8$

6) $726 \div 2$

7) $581 \div 7$

8) $660 \div 4$

9) $608 \div 8$

10) $816 \div 2$

11) $458 \div 2$

12) $921 \div 3$

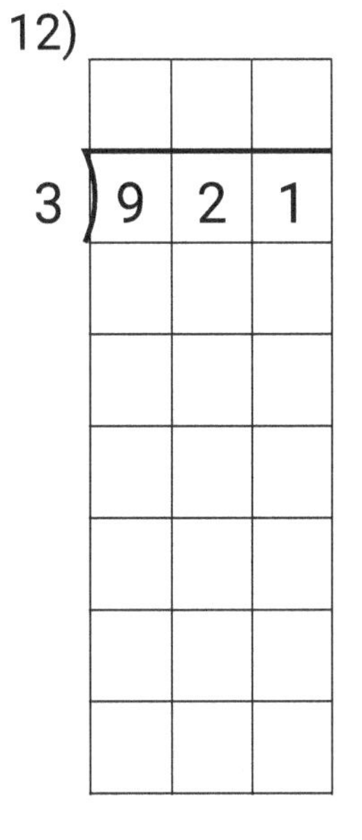

13) $256 \div 4$

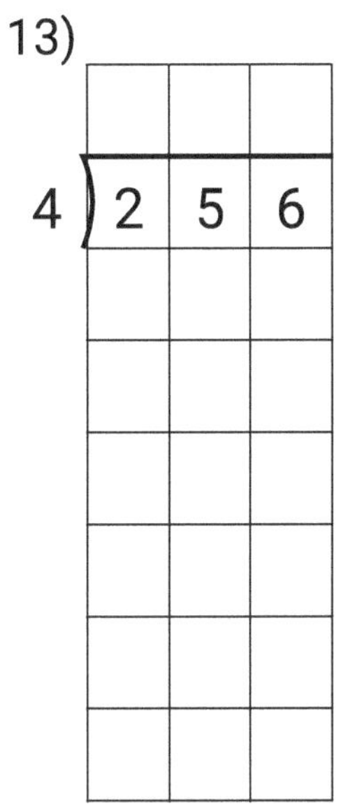

14) $326 \div 2$

15) $914 \div 2$

DAY 32

Division: 3-Digit by 1-Digit with No Reminders

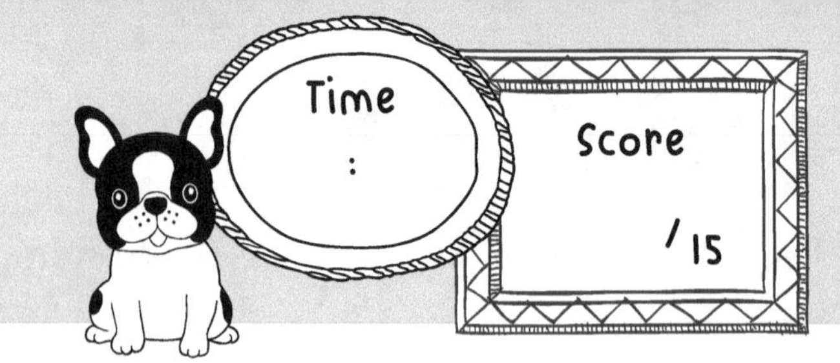

1) $2\overline{)526}$

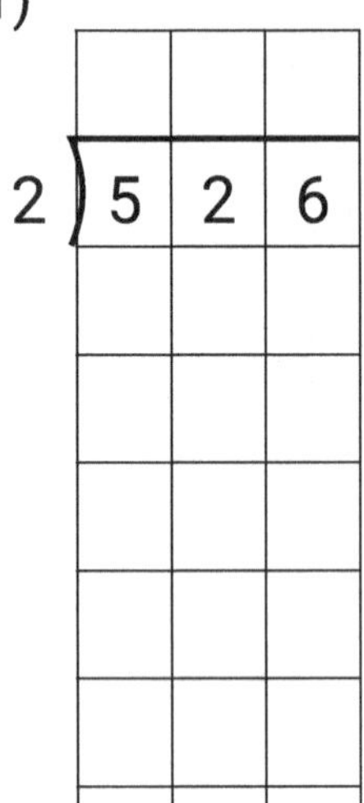

2) $2\overline{)570}$

3) $5\overline{)540}$

4) $7\overline{)385}$

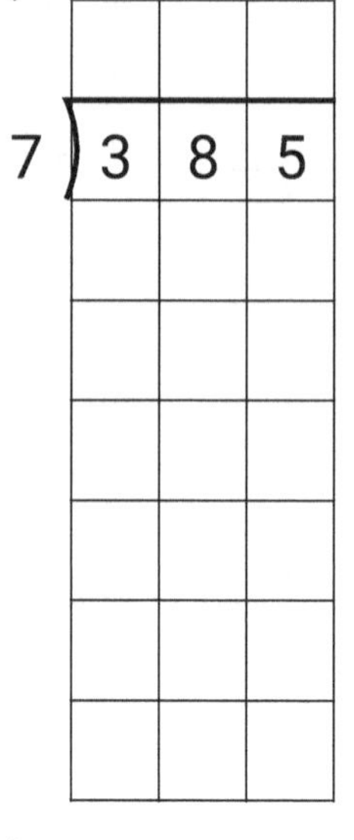

5) $2\overline{)616}$

6) $5\overline{)195}$

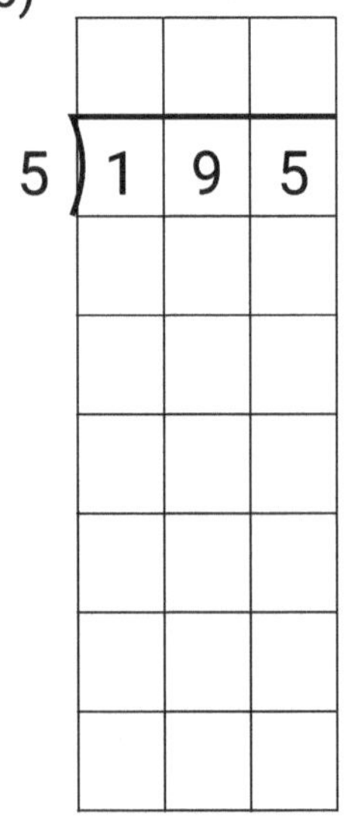

7) $5\overline{)125}$

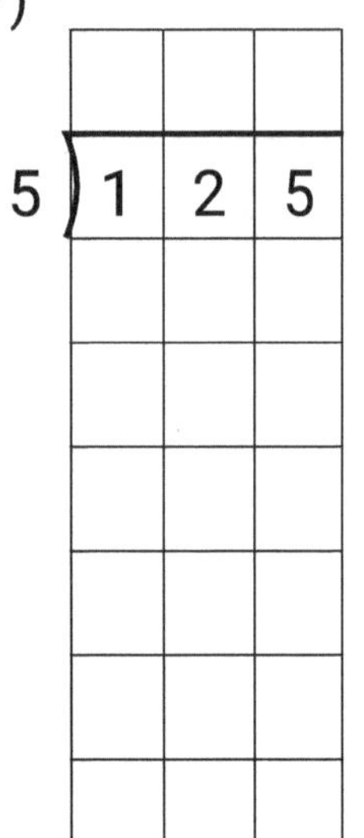

8) $3\overline{)525}$

9) $3\overline{)813}$

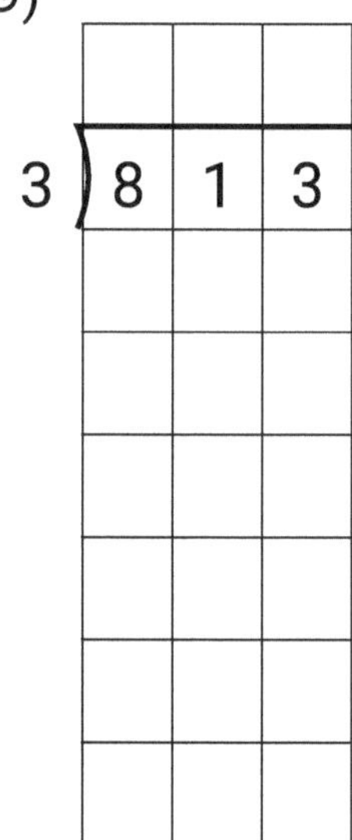

10) $3\overline{)975}$

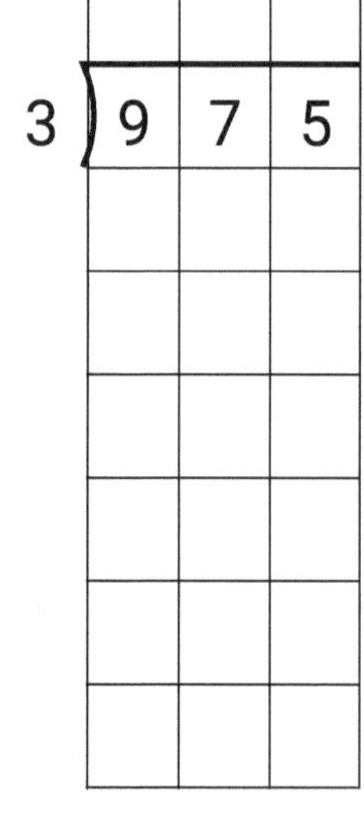

11) $2\overline{)398}$

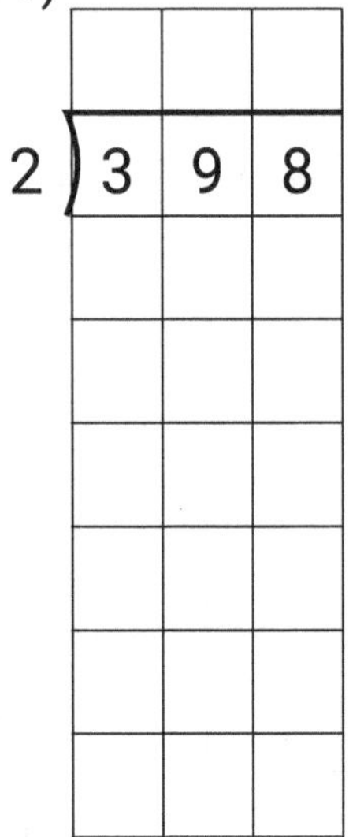

12) $3\overline{)309}$

13) $9\overline{)783}$

14) $3\overline{)897}$

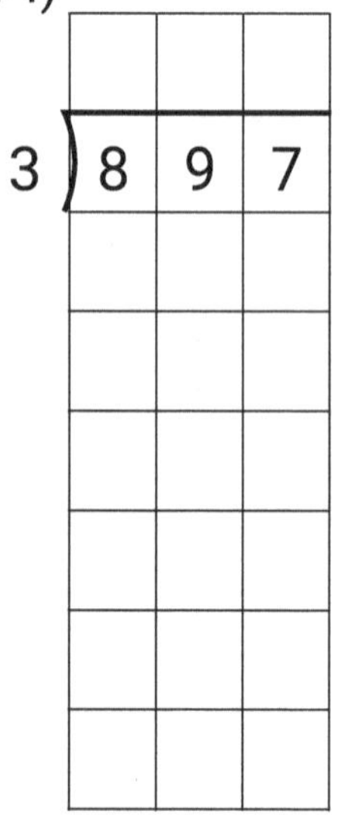

15) $2\overline{)308}$

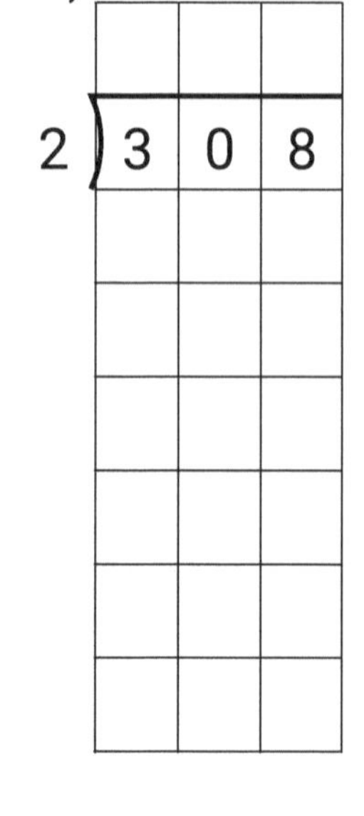

DAY 33

Division: 3-Digit by 1-Digit with No Reminders

1)
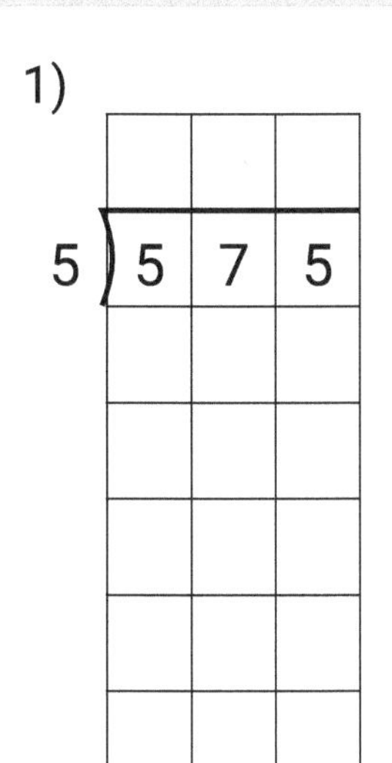

2)
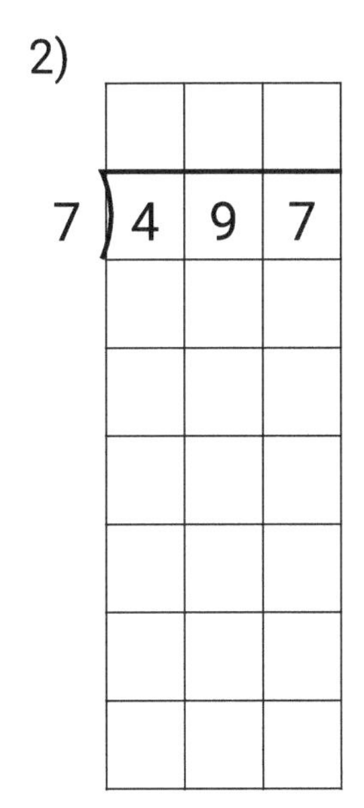

3) 2) 8 8 4

4) 3) 8 9 7

5) 7) 9 8 7

6) 2) 6 9 2

7) 7) 7 2 1

8) 5) 2 0 5

9)
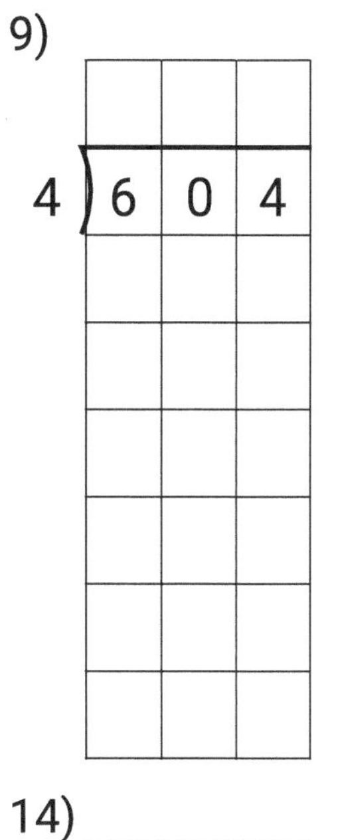

10) 5) 2 6 5

11) 9) 3 7 8

12)
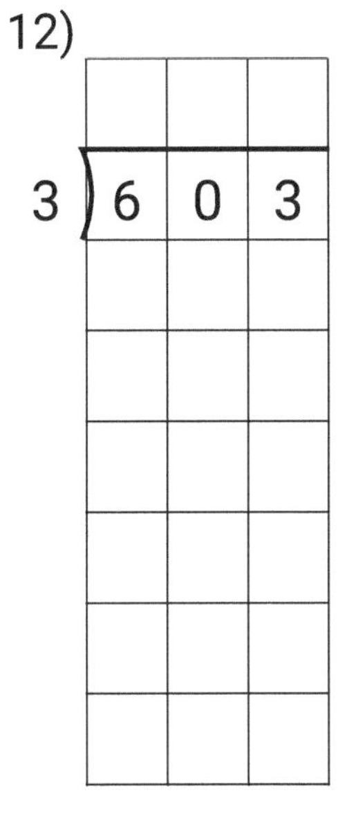

13)
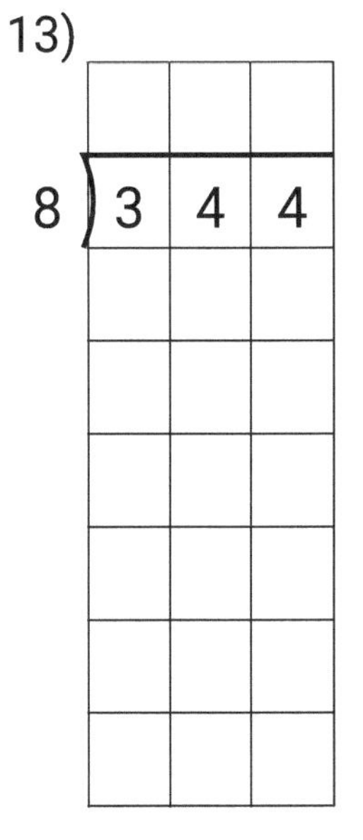

14) 5) 5 1 5

15) 7) 4 5 5

DAY 34

Division: 3-Digit by 1-Digit with No Reminders

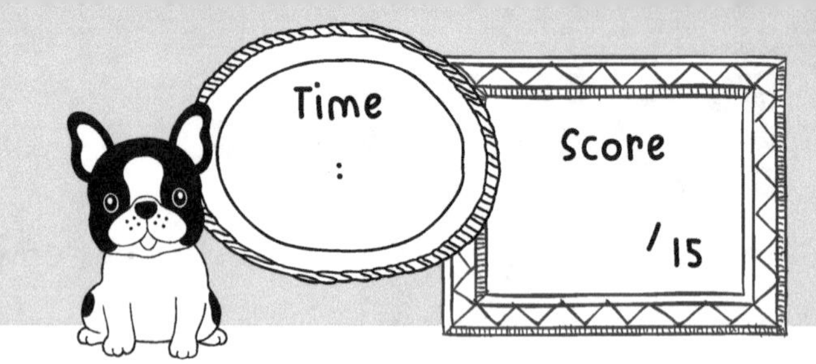

1) 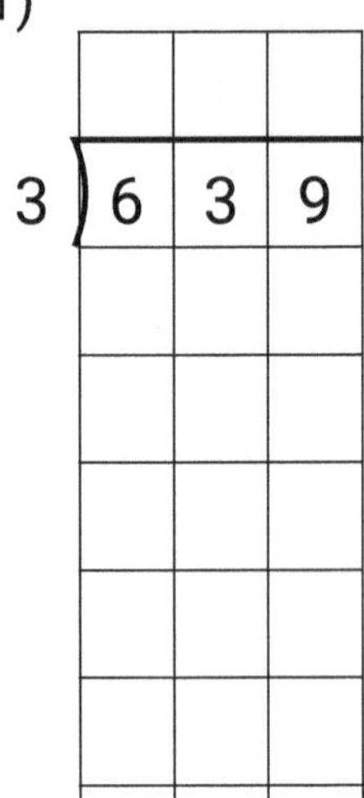

3) 6 3 9

2) 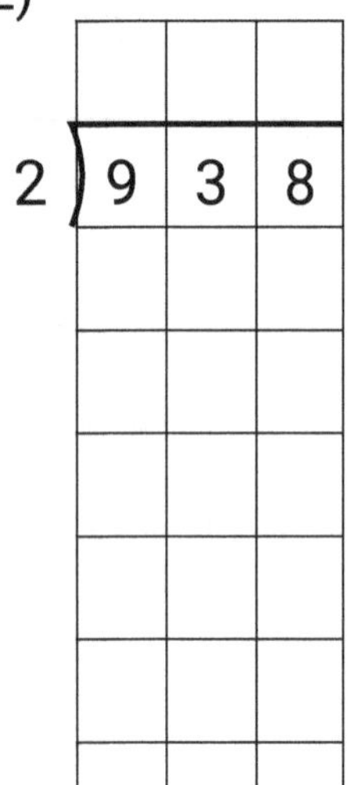

2) 9 3 8

3) 5) 2 9 5

4) 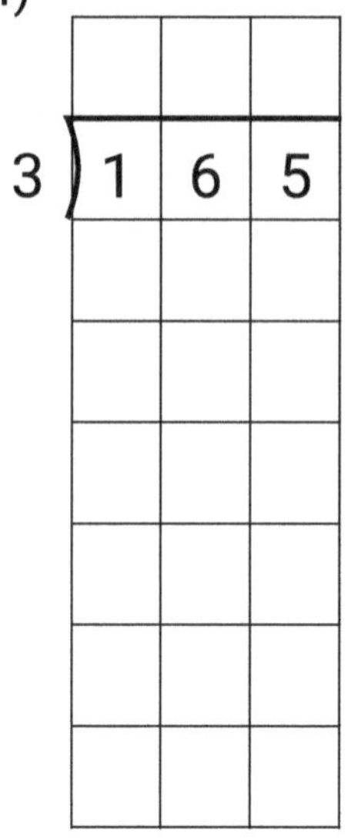

3) 1 6 5

5) 2) 9 1 8

6) 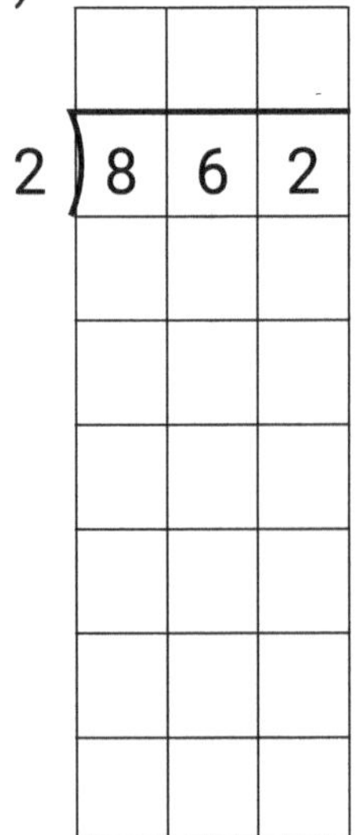

2) 8 6 2

7) 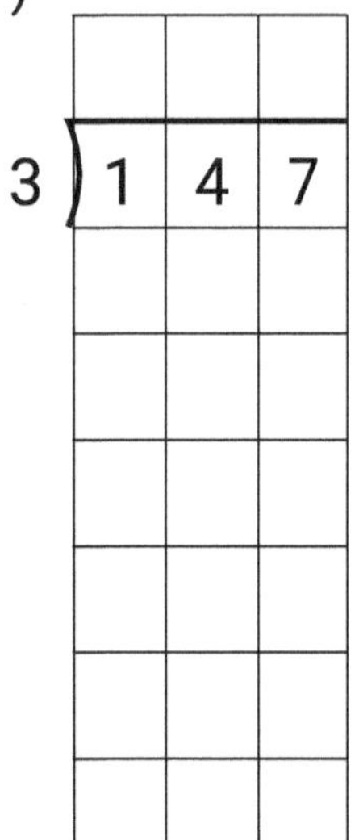

3) 1 4 7

8) 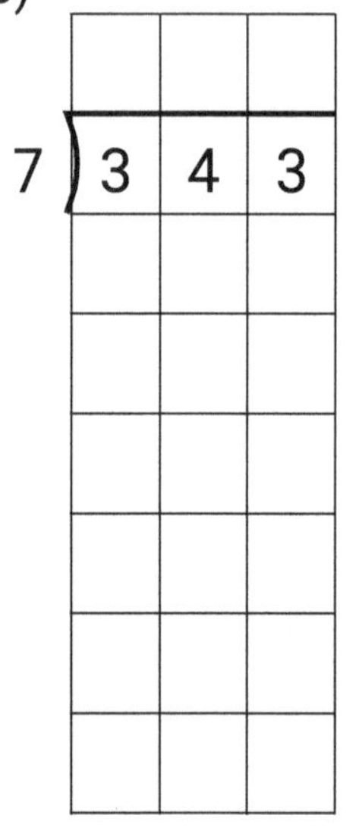

7) 3 4 3

9) 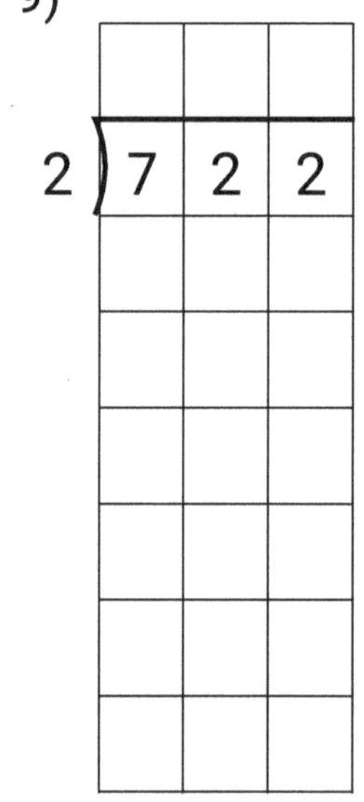

2) 7 2 2

10) 2) 4 8 4

11) 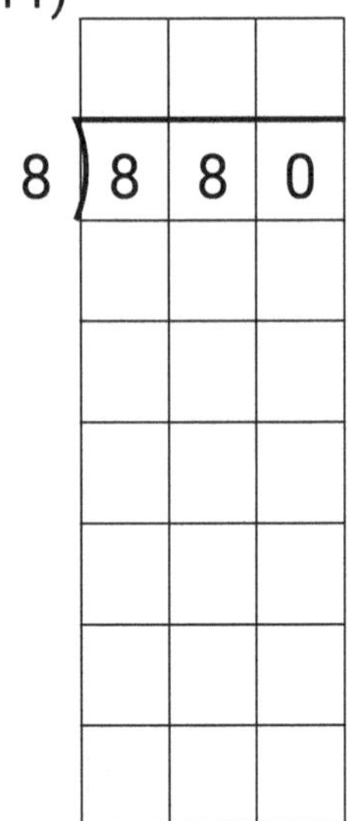

8) 8 8 0

12) 2) 1 2 2

13) 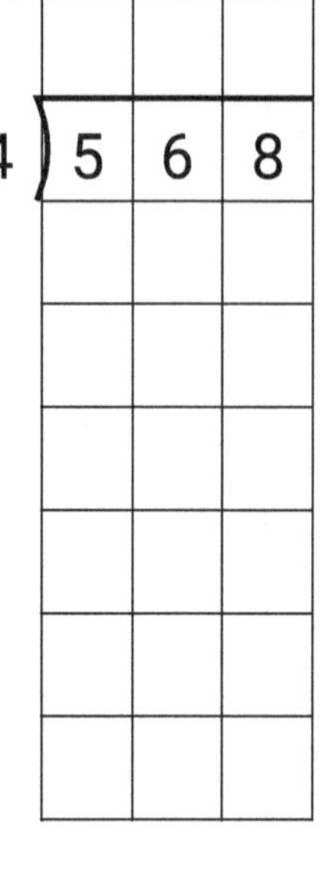

4) 5 6 8

14) 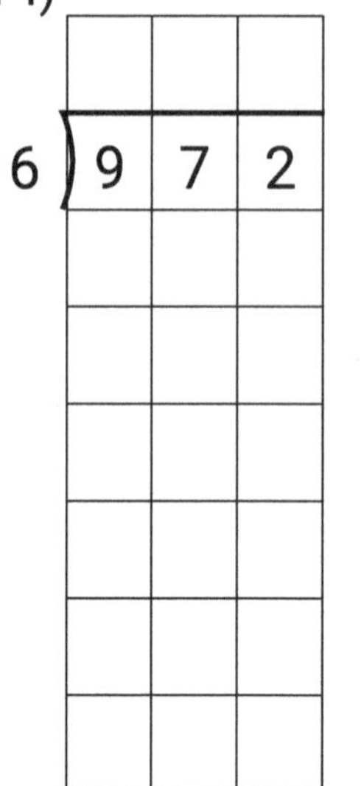

6) 9 7 2

15) 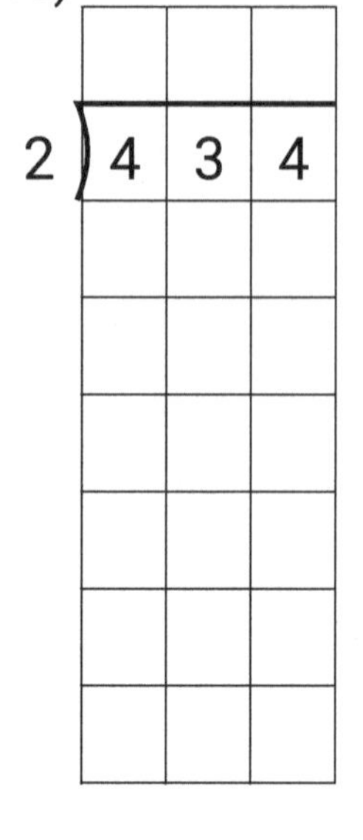

2) 4 3 4

DAY 35

Division: 3-Digit by 1-Digit with No Reminders

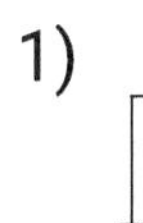

1)
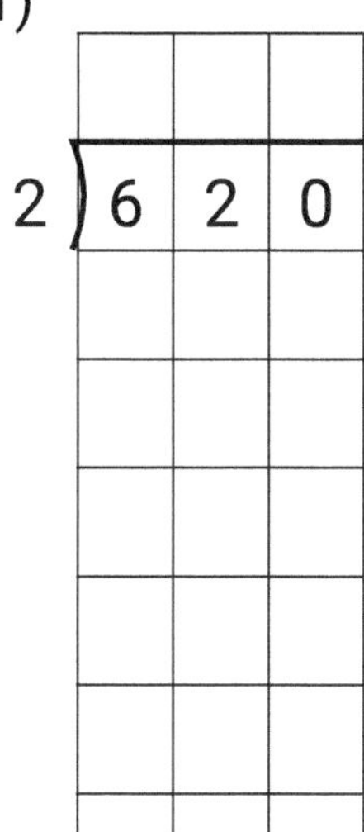

2) 7)469

3) 2)768

4)
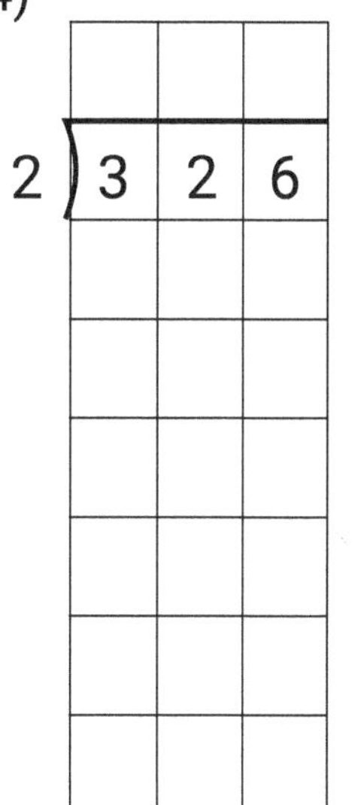

5)
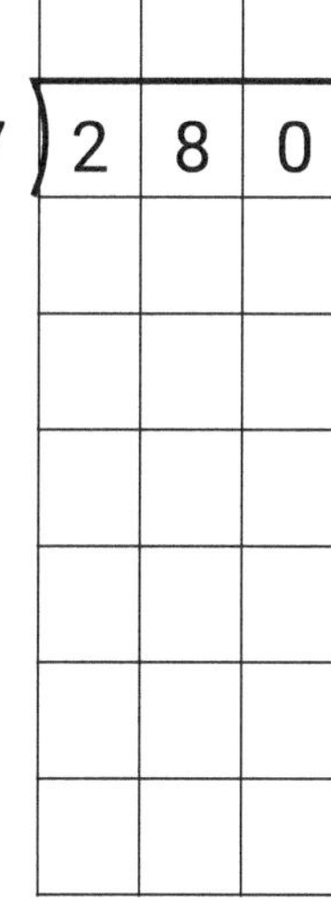

6)
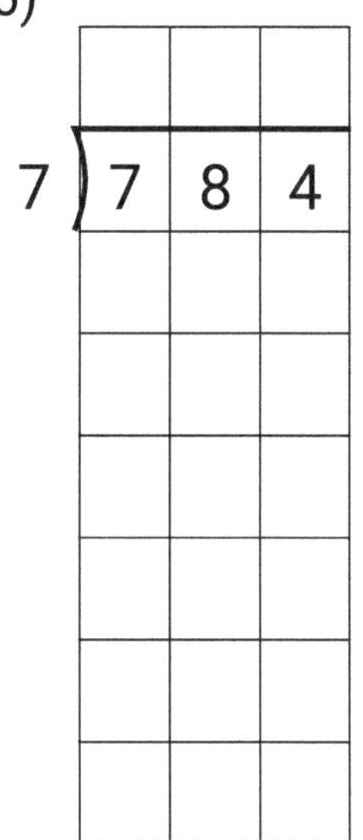

7)
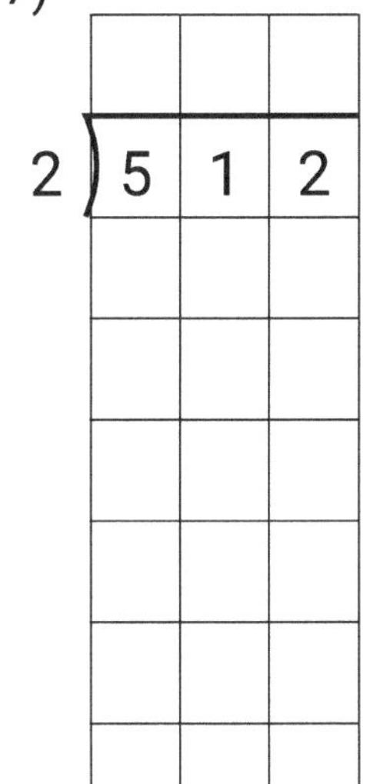

8) 5)620

9)
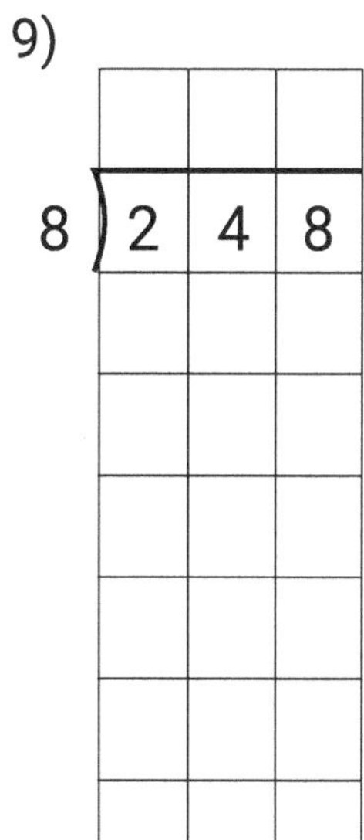

10) 7)581

11)
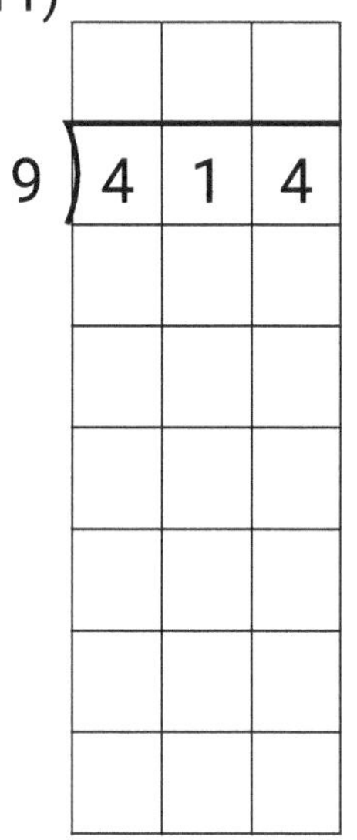

12)
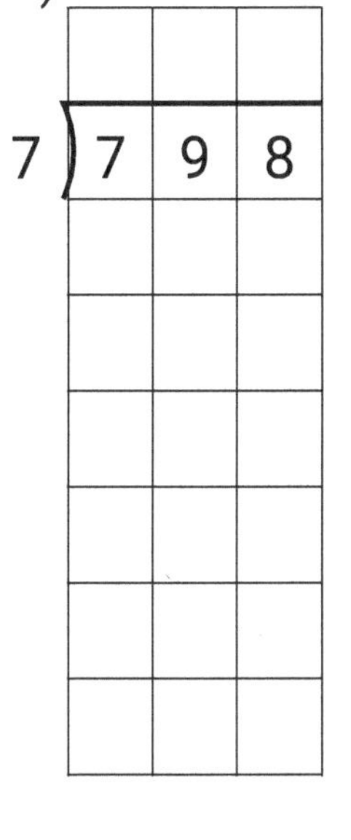

13) 5)785

14)
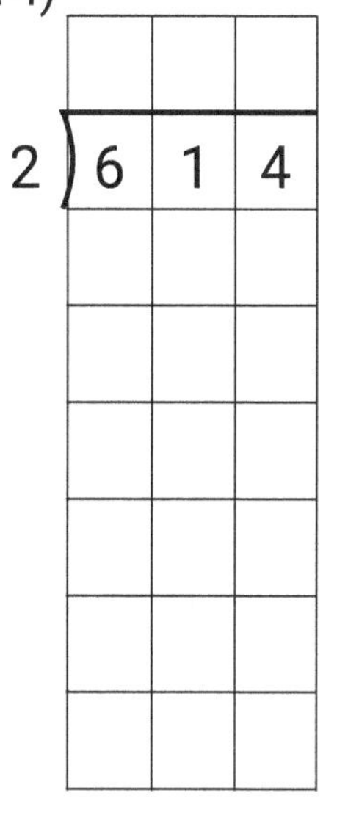

15)
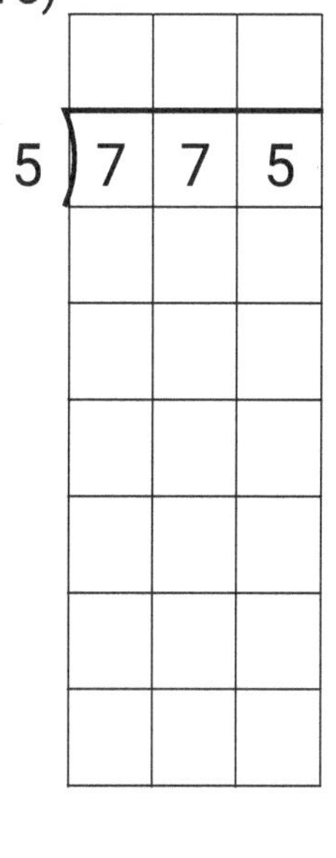

DAY 36

Division: 3-Digit by 1-Digit with Reminders

1) 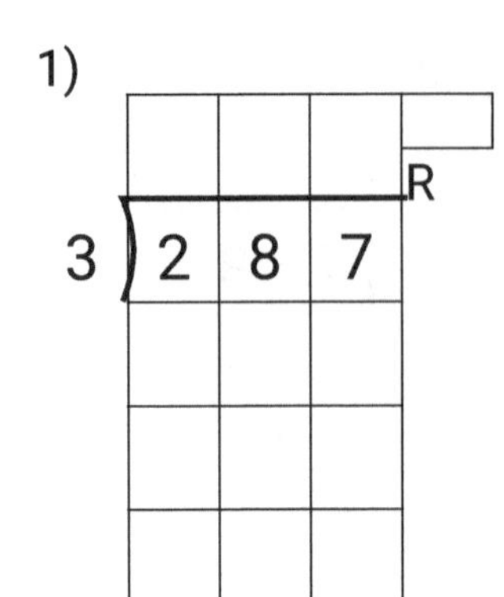
3) 2 8 7 R

2) 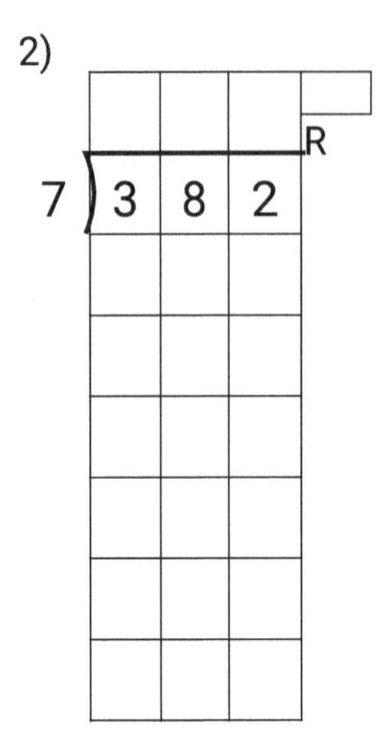
7) 3 8 2 R

3) 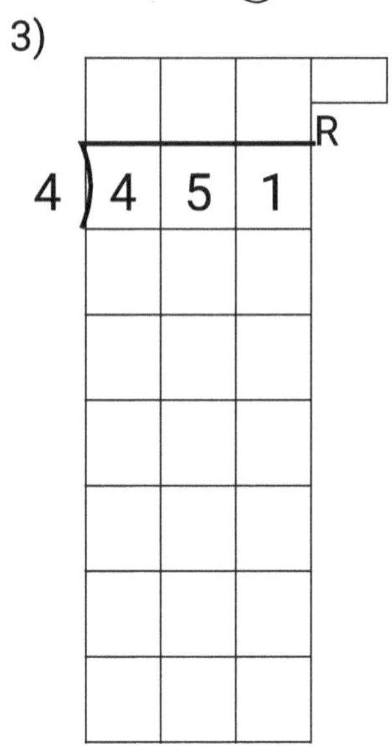
4) 4 5 1 R

4) 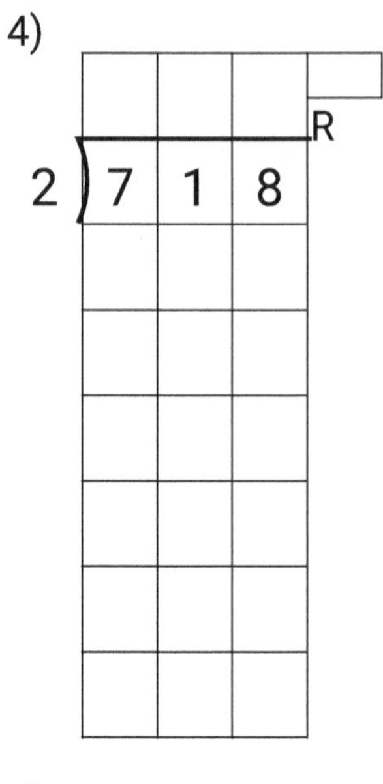
2) 7 1 8 R

5)
8) 3 7 7 R

6) 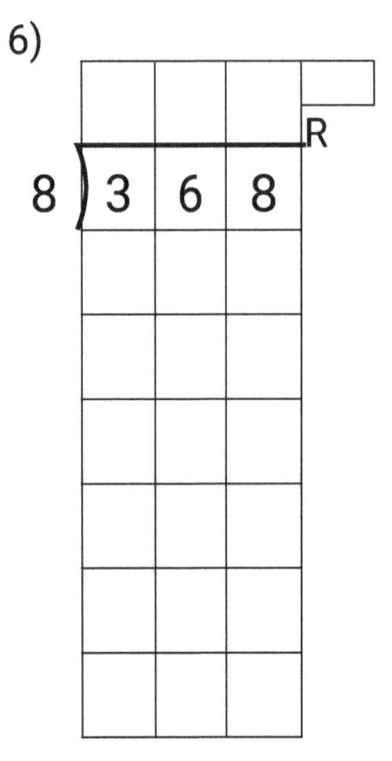
8) 3 6 8 R

7) 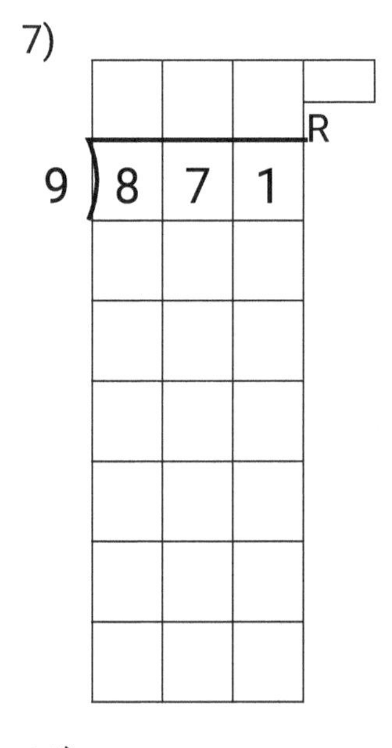
9) 8 7 1 R

8)
2) 3 8 0 R

9) 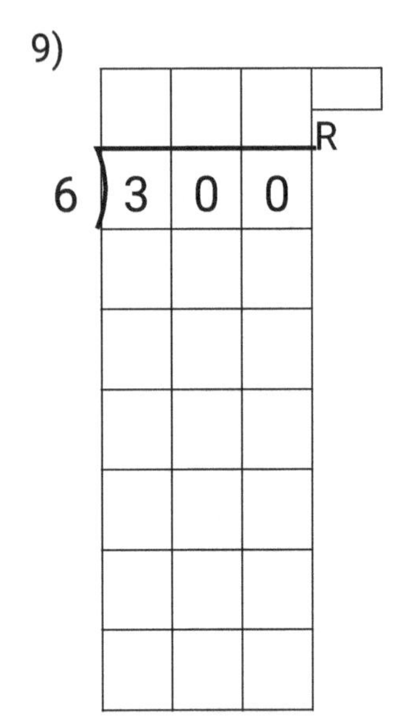
6) 3 0 0 R

10) 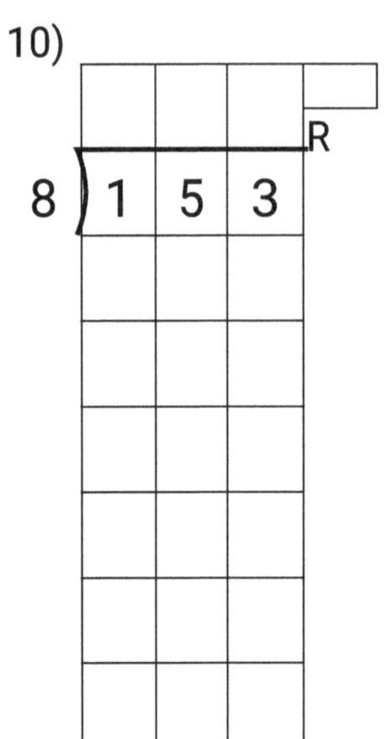
8) 1 5 3 R

11) 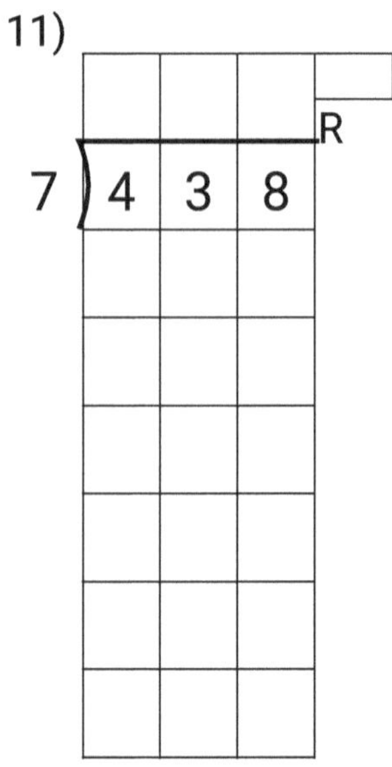
7) 4 3 8 R

12) 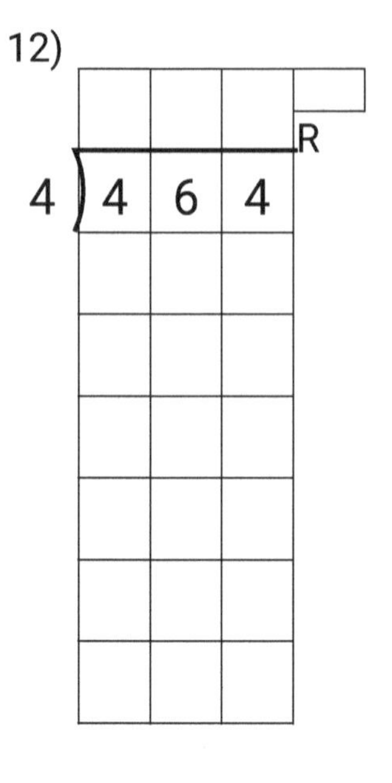
4) 4 6 4 R

DAY 37

Division: 3-Digit by 1-Digit with Reminders

1)
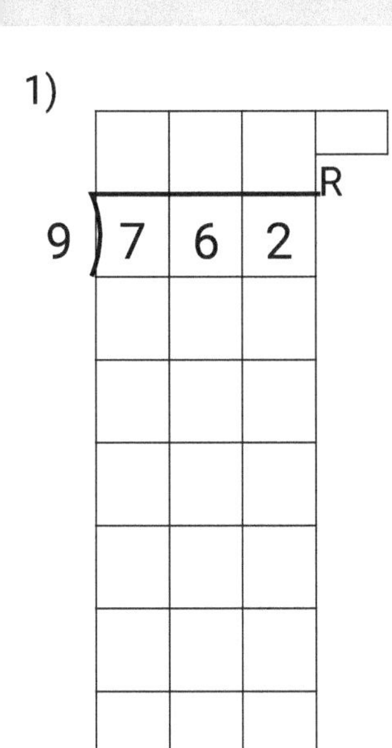

2)
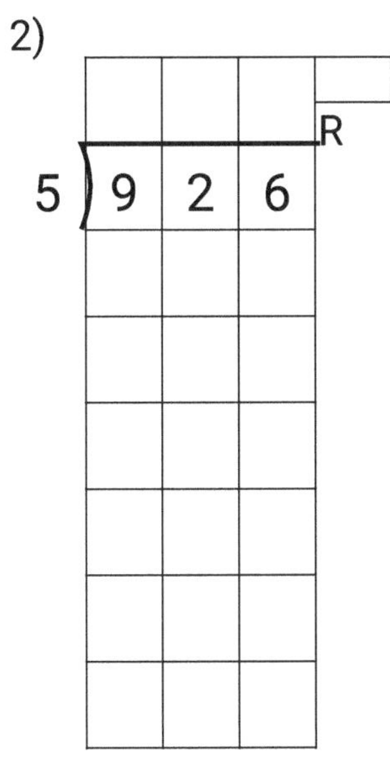

3)
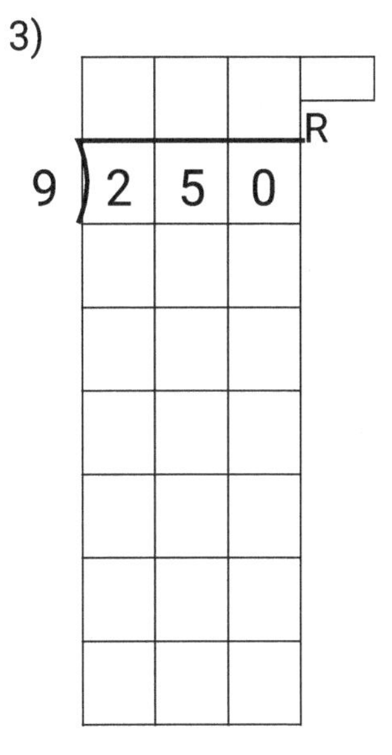

4)
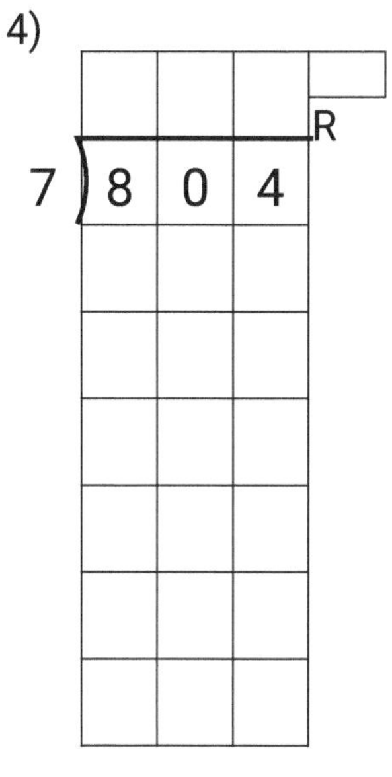

5)

R

9) 5 7 9

6)
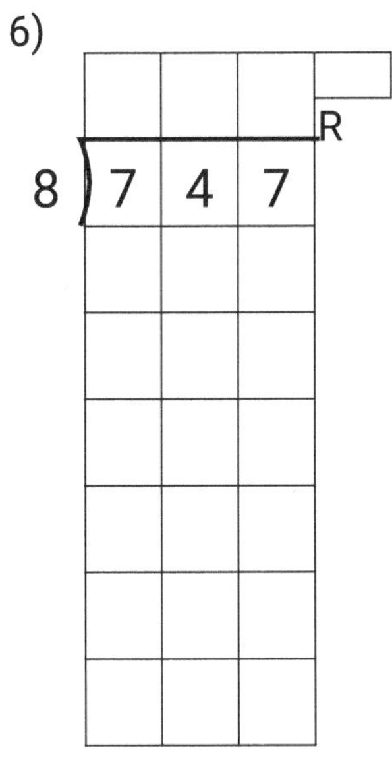

7)
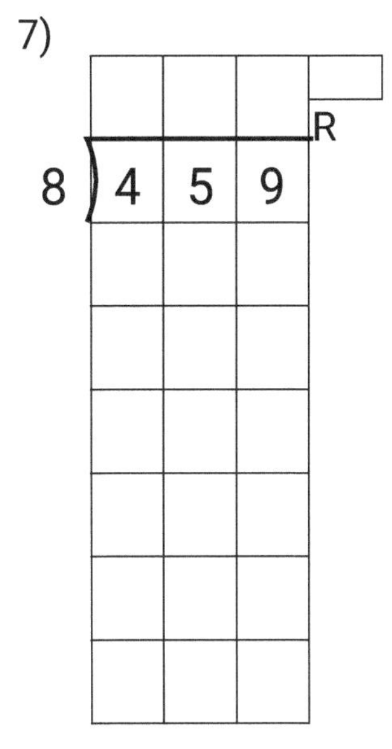

8)

R

9) 2 7 1

9)

R

4) 8 6 5

10)
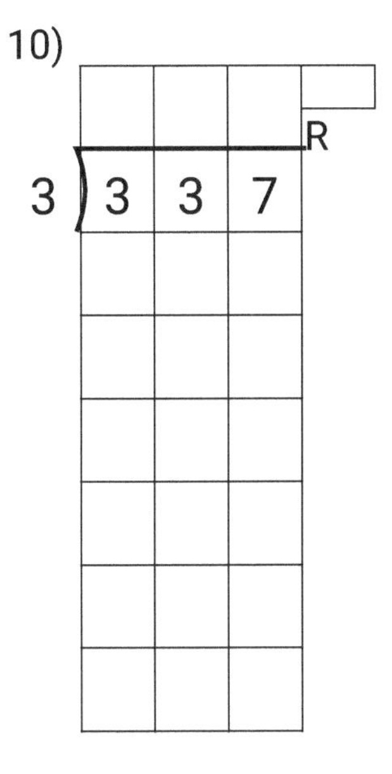

11)
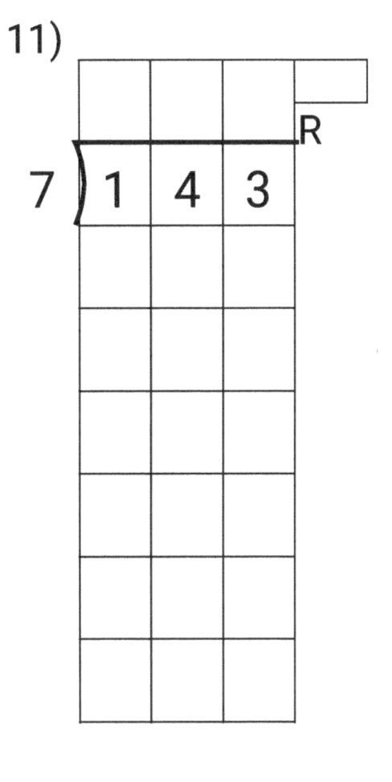

12)

R

7) 1 3 8

DAY 38

Division: 3-Digit by 1-Digit with Reminders

1) 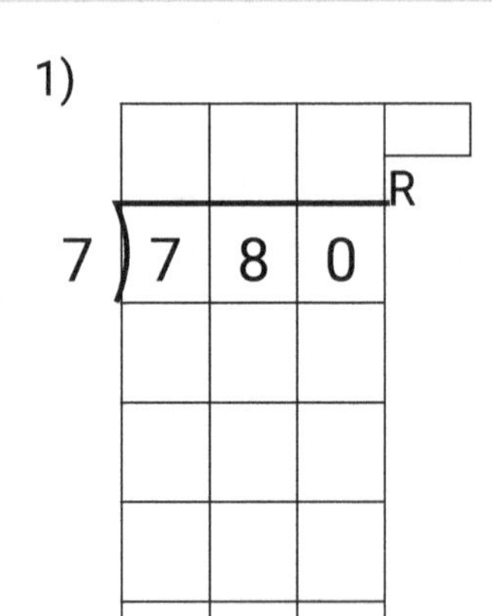

7) 7 8 0 R

2) 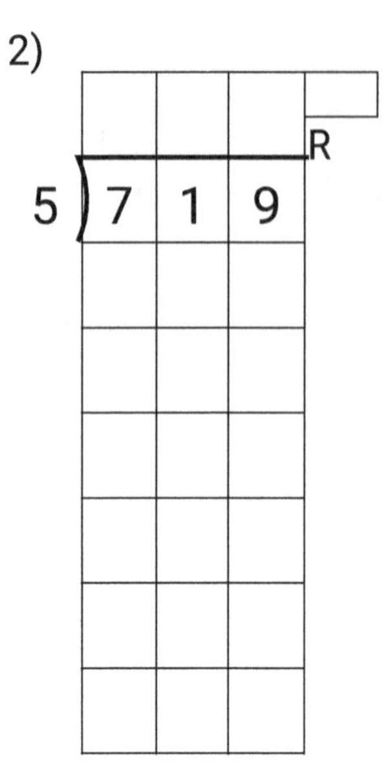

5) 7 1 9 R

3) 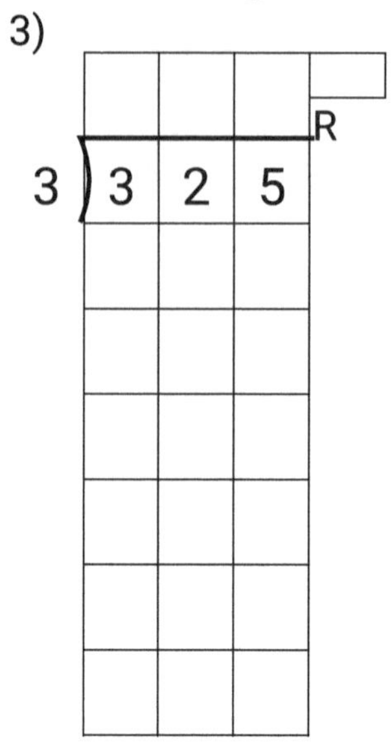

3) 3 2 5 R

4) 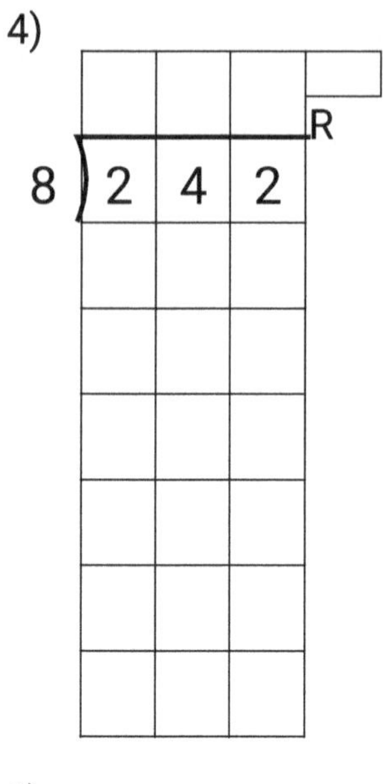

8) 2 4 2 R

5) 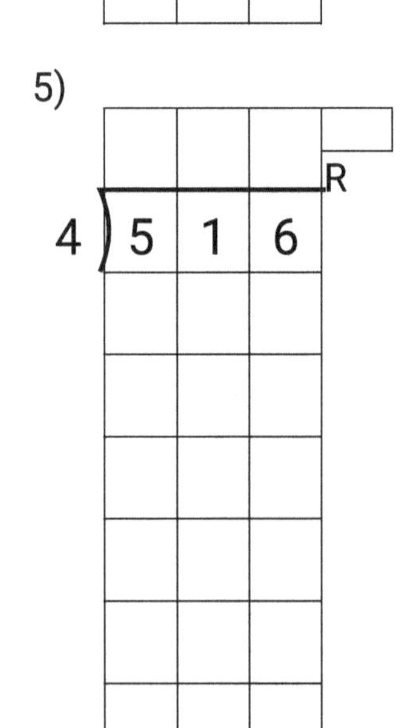

4) 5 1 6 R

6) 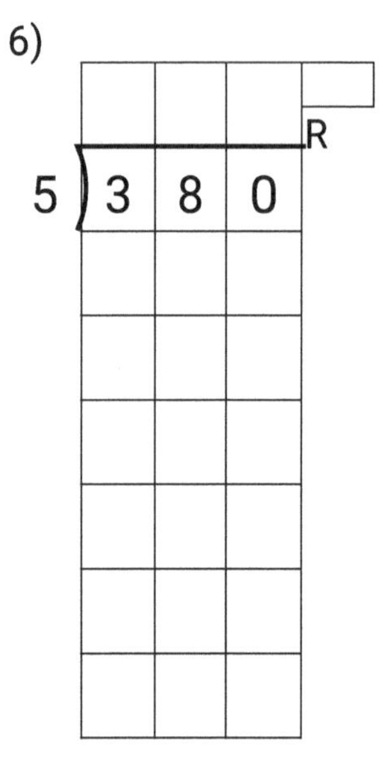

5) 3 8 0 R

7) 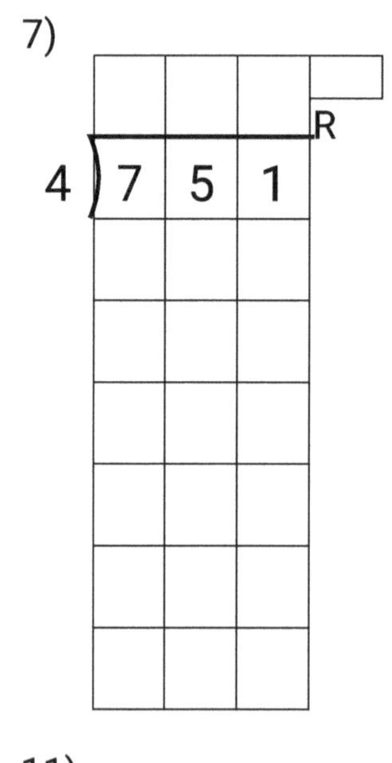

4) 7 5 1 R

8) 8) 6 9 6 R

9) 3) 1 1 6 R

10) 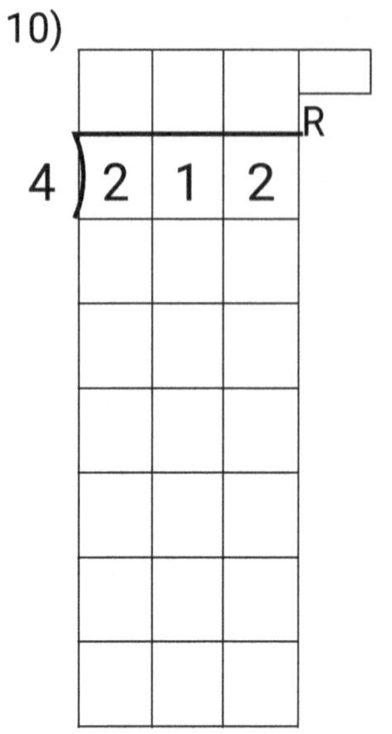

4) 2 1 2 R

11) 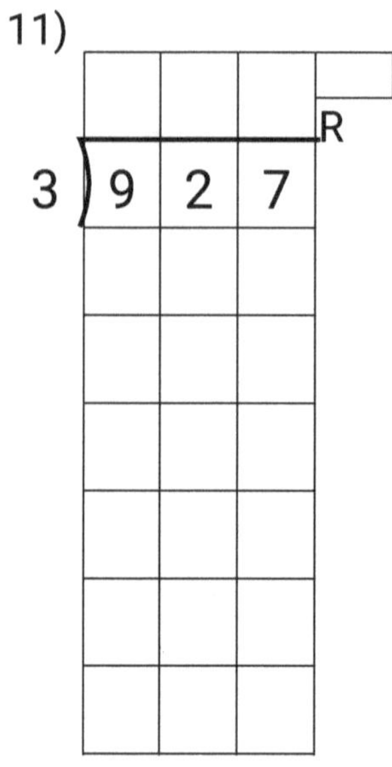

3) 9 2 7 R

12) 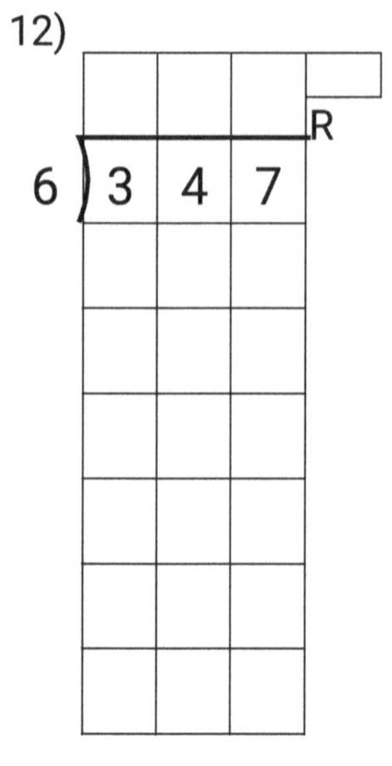

6) 3 4 7 R

DAY 39

Division: 3-Digit by 1-Digit with Reminders

1)
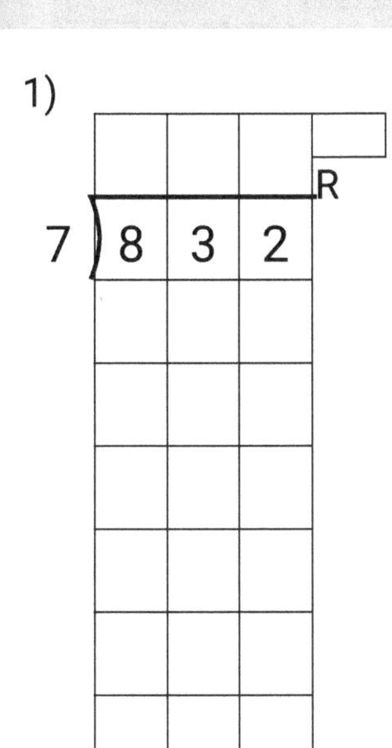

2)
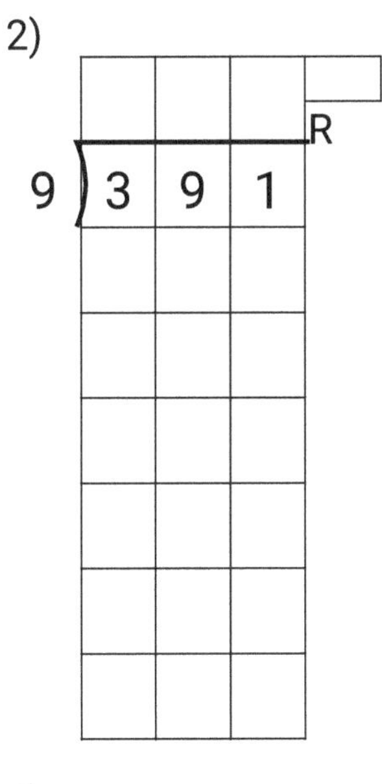

3)
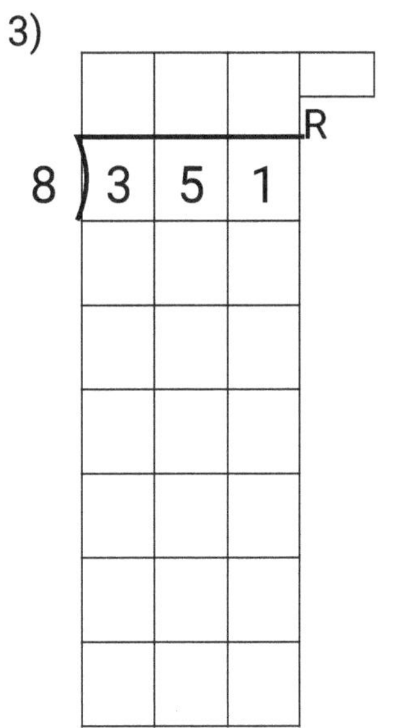

4)
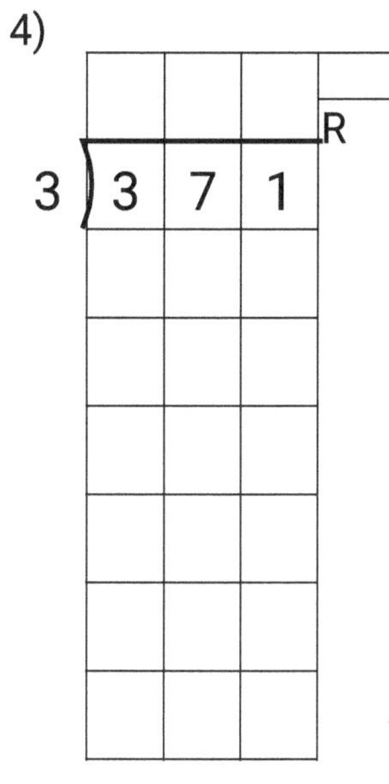

5)
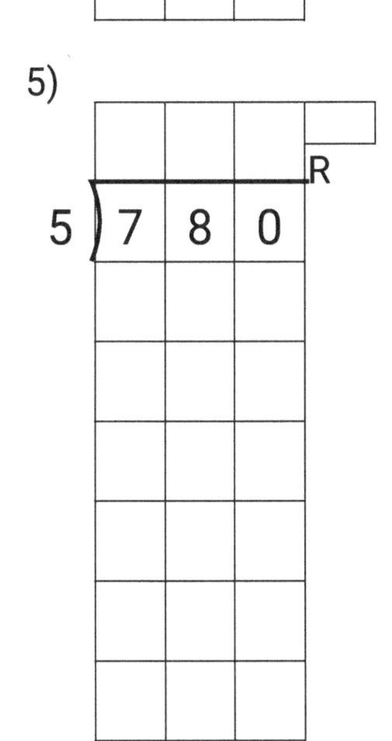

6)
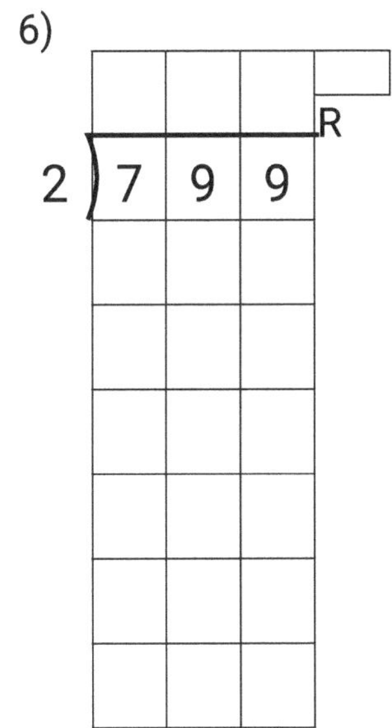

7)
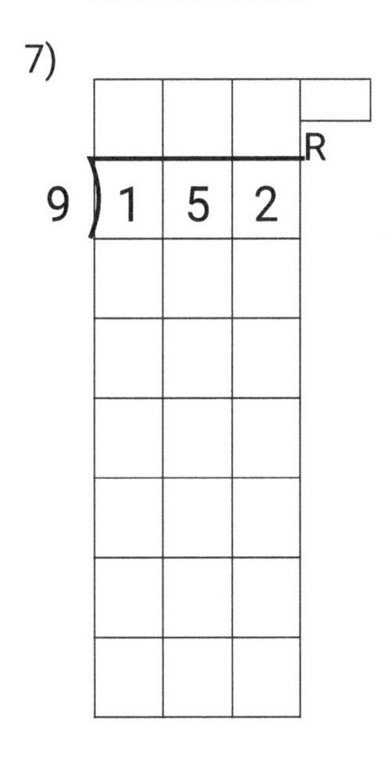

8)
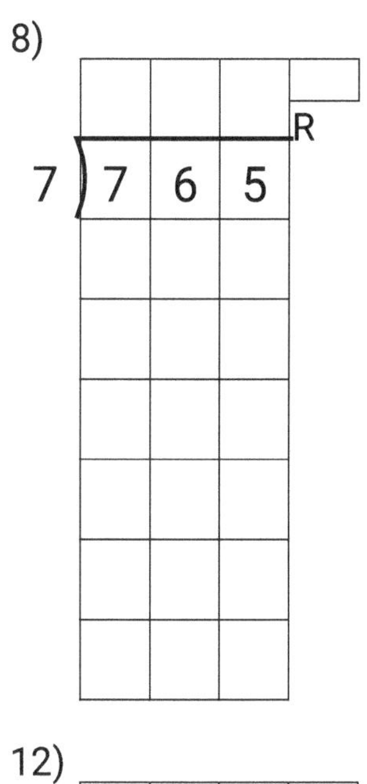

9)
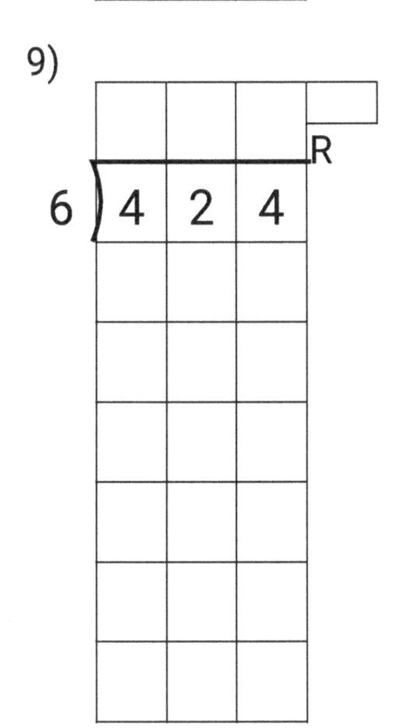

10)
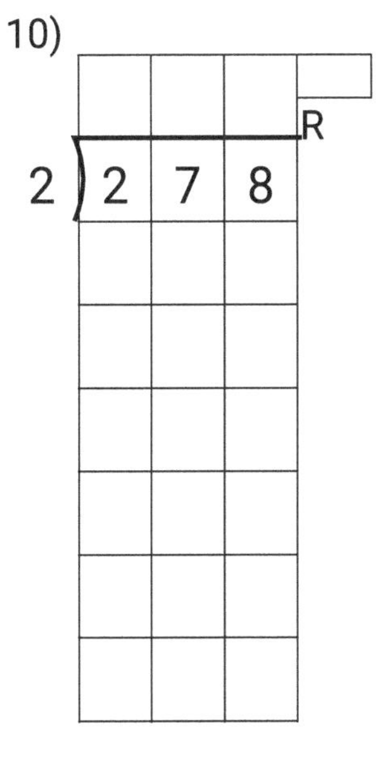

11)
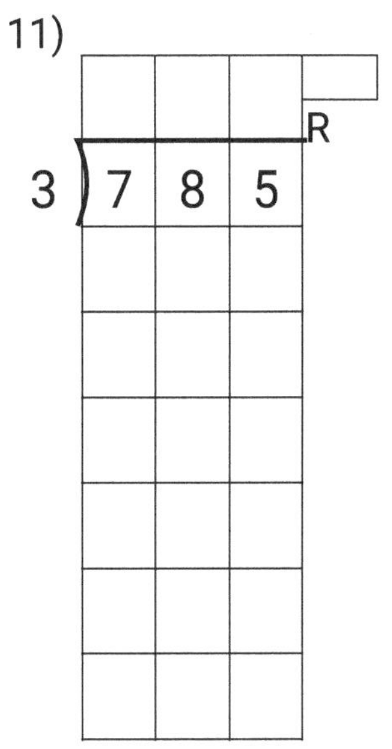

12)

DAY 40

Division: 3-Digit by 1-Digit with Reminders

1) 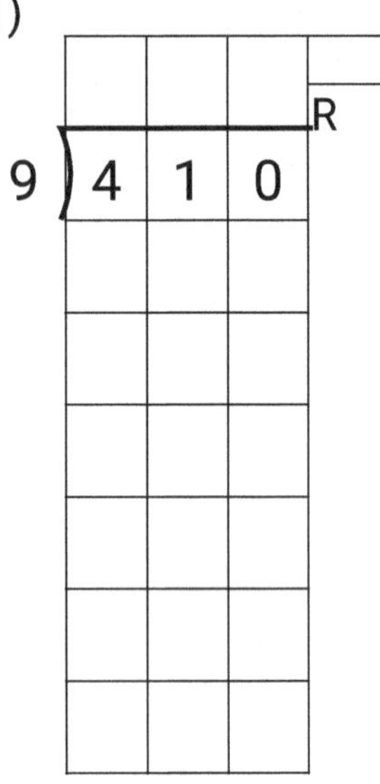

2) 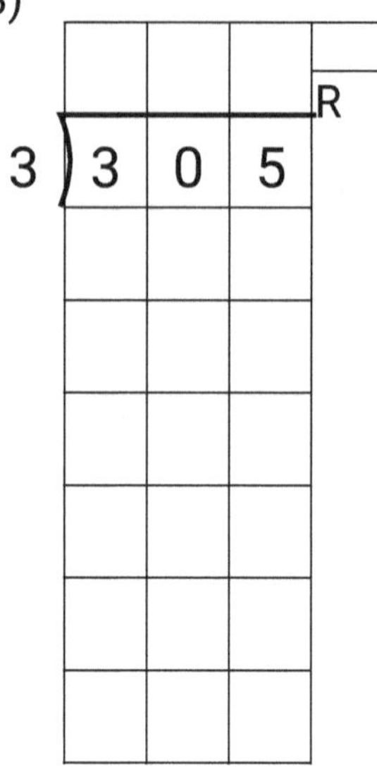

3) 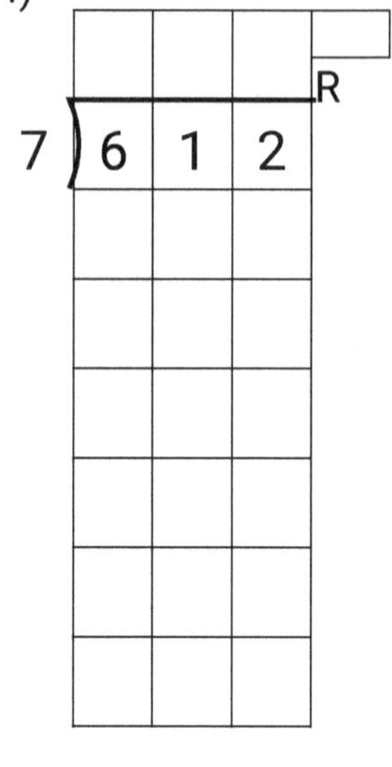

4)
7) 6 1 2

5) 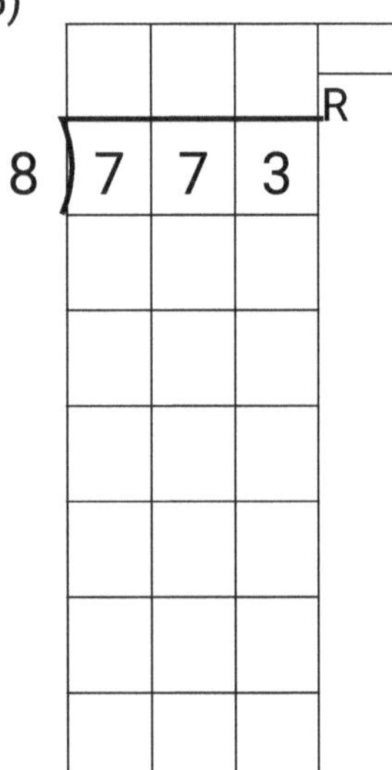

6) 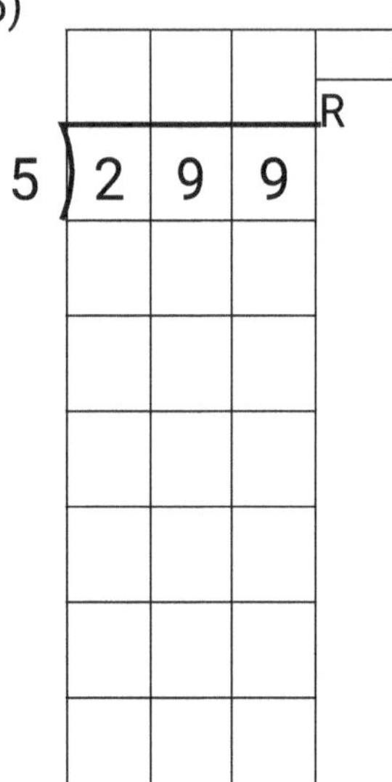

7) 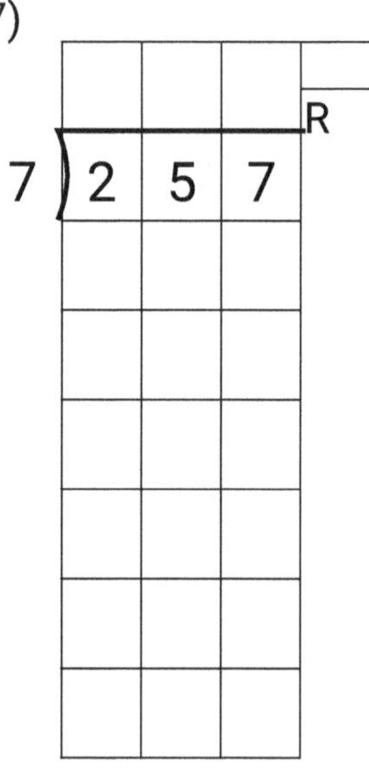

8) 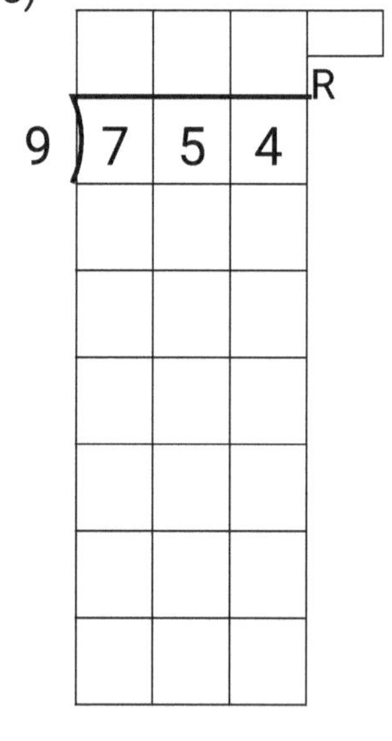

9) 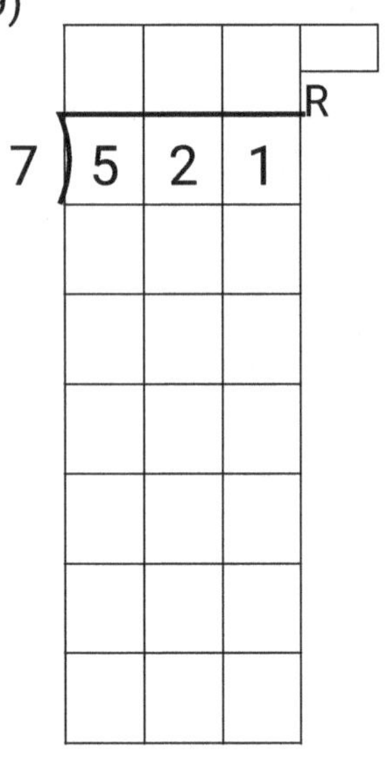

10) 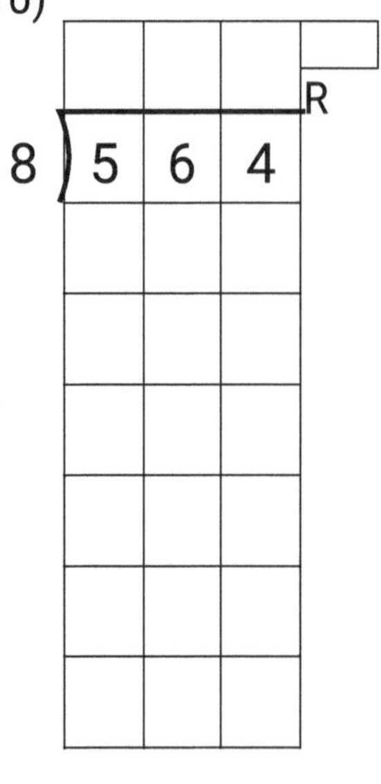

11) 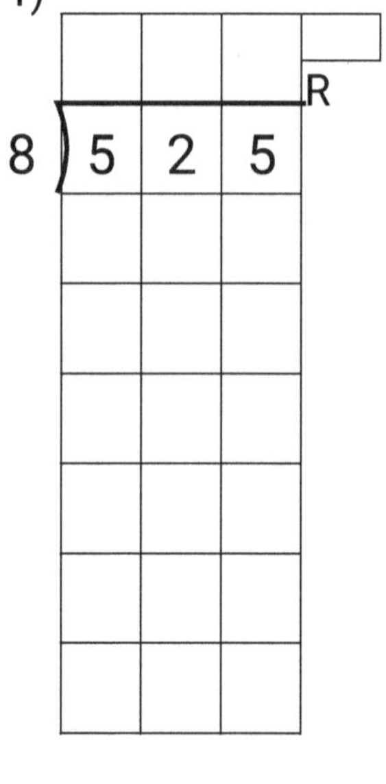

12) 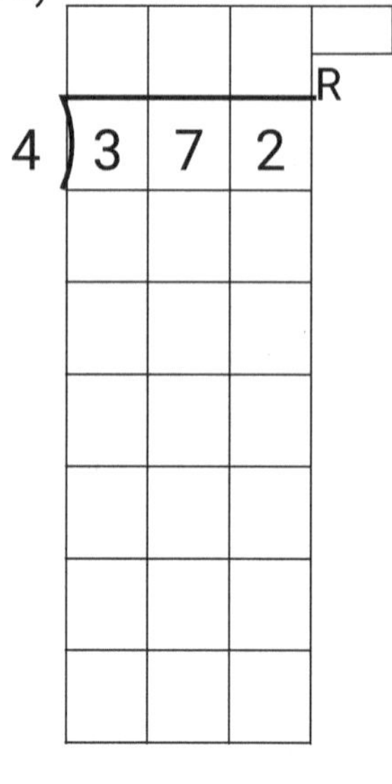

HOW WELL DO YOU KNOW YOUR ROMAN NUMERALS?

What is the Roman numeral for the number 4?

IV! Now go look at a clock or watch that uses Roman numerals on its face. Does it have an IV?

Probably not because most clocks use IIII instead of IV. While the real reason is unknown, one potential reason is that when ancient Romans made their sundials, they also used IIII as they used to write the number that way. The reason they did this is because they worshipped Jupiter, king of the gods in ancient Roman religion, whose name was spelled IVPPITER, and they did not want to insult the name. I certainly would not want to be insulting to a god who could take all my bananas away!

DAY 41

Multiplication: 4-Digit by 1-Digit

1)

	3	9	0	0
×				6

2)

	9	0	5	2
×				2

3)

	7	2	0	9
×				5

4)

	7	0	6	3
×				8

5)

	1	9	0	0
×				7

6)

	4	2	3	9
×				9

7)

	5	3	8	8
×				4

8)

	9	1	1	4
×				2

9)

	2	3	4	7
×				2

10)

	6	8	7	4
×				6

11)

	2	4	5	5
×				7

12)

	7	6	8	1
×				5

13)

	5	1	0	3
×				4

14)

	1	9	4	1
×				3

15)

	6	3	7	5
×				5

16)

	2	5	0	1
×				3

17)

	8	9	9	6
×				9

18)

	8	7	0	2
×				4

DAY 42

Multiplication: 4-Digit by 1-Digit

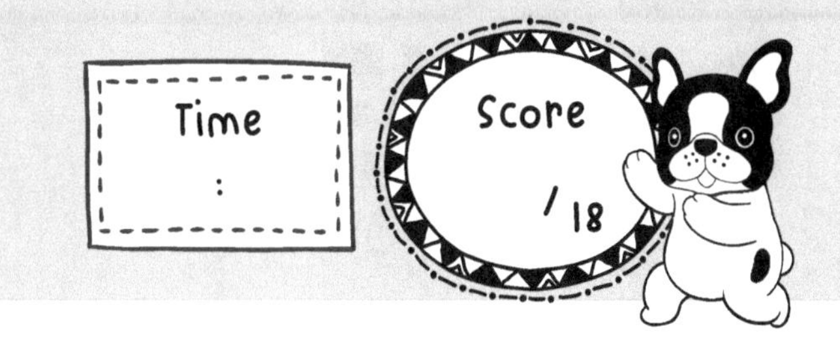

1)

	7	0	0	4
×				2

2)

	7	3	4	6
×				4

3)

	3	8	2	5
×				5

4)

	7	0	0	6
×				7

5)

	9	7	5	1
×				9

6)

	1	0	9	5
×				4

7)

	3	9	4	4
×				8

8)

	2	7	1	2
×				2

9)

	2	5	4	3
×				6

10)

	9	2	0	5
×				7

11)

	6	8	7	8
×				4

12)

	6	4	8	5
×				7

13)

	5	8	2	5
×				2

14)

	9	1	1	1
×				4

15)

	1	3	9	4
×				4

16)

	9	9	5	4
×				2

17)

	9	9	5	5
×				7

18)

	2	0	0	5
×				7

DAY 43

Multiplication: 4-Digit by 1-Digit

1)

	6	8	5	0
×				8

2)

	1	4	7	5
×				7

3)

	7	4	5	9
×				9

4)

	3	4	9	1
×				6

5)

	1	2	9	0
×				4

6)

	3	3	2	3
×				2

7)

	9	1	4	4
×				6

8)

	2	3	5	7
×				8

9)

	3	3	2	5
×				5

10)

	4	2	4	6
×				8

11)

	6	8	2	6
×				9

12)

	6	8	3	1
×				9

13)

	8	6	6	3
×				9

14)

	8	9	1	2
×				6

15)

	1	8	5	8
×				2

16)

	1	9	7	7
×				2

17)

	1	3	3	5
×				6

18)

	8	3	4	0
×				8

DAY 44

Multiplication: 4-Digit by 1-Digit

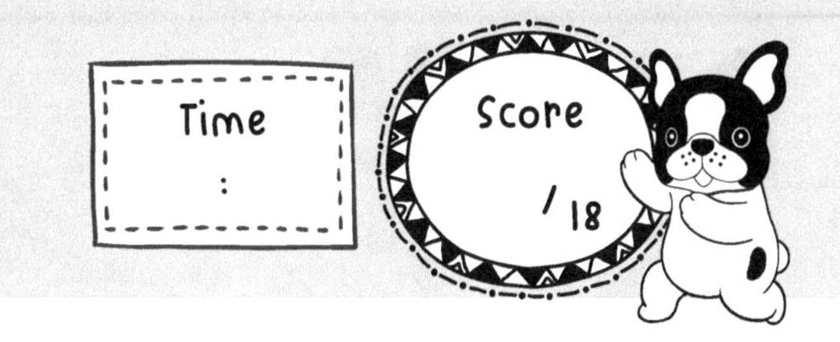

1)

	6	2	0	3
×				5

2)

	5	1	4	5
×				3

3)

	4	9	0	5
×				2

4)

	1	9	2	0
×				7

5)

	2	5	0	4
×				7

6)

	6	7	6	4
×				5

7)

	8	0	3	8
×				8

8)

	4	6	8	2
×				5

9)

	1	5	5	1
×				9

10)

	2	6	0	0
×				7

11)

	6	1	8	3
×				7

12)

	5	1	4	3
×				9

13)

	2	4	5	9
×				7

14)

	4	8	8	6
×				9

15)

	2	6	6	2
×				8

16)

	5	5	5	3
×				4

17)

	6	0	2	7
×				9

18)

	4	6	0	7
×				7

DAY 45

Multiplication: 4-Digit by 1-Digit

Time
:

Score
/18

1)

	4	1	4	6
×				7

2)

	8	0	7	0
×				7

3)

	9	7	3	7
×				2

4)

	7	4	6	4
×				9

5)

	1	7	6	0
×				5

6)

	2	9	0	8
×				2

7)

	4	0	8	1
×				2

8)

	5	9	9	8
×				4

9)

	7	9	5	8
×				6

10)

	1	4	4	0
×				7

11)

	6	9	1	1
×				7

12)

	2	8	3	8
×				6

13)

	9	3	7	3
×				4

14)

	6	0	3	1
×				9

15)

	9	9	9	5
×				5

16)

	8	3	3	6
×				2

17)

	3	0	1	5
×				6

18)

	9	1	2	2
×				6

DAY 46

Multiplication: 4-Digit by 1-Digit

Time :

Score / 18

1)

	3	8	0	8
×				9

2)

	3	9	9	1
×				7

3)

	4	0	9	6
×				5

4)

	1	3	6	4
×				8

5)

	9	5	1	9
×				2

6)

	1	7	7	6
×				3

7)

	1	0	6	1
×				7

8)

	6	9	4	2
×				5

9)

	6	4	7	2
×				8

10)

	4	8	3	5
×				8

11)

	2	3	6	3
×				4

12)

	5	0	9	2
×				8

13)

	4	2	5	9
×				4

14)

	7	9	2	1
×				9

15)

	3	6	3	6
×				5

16)

	4	4	0	0
×				8

17)

	5	3	6	1
×				3

18)

	9	0	1	1
×				6

DAY 47

Multiplication: 4-Digit by 1-Digit

Time :

Score / 18

1)

	9	7	2	5
×				8

2)

	1	1	4	5
×				8

3)

	8	0	2	2
×				7

4)

	3	8	2	4
×				9

5)

	7	9	2	2
×				7

6)

	8	1	4	5
×				7

7)

	4	4	7	4
×				8

8)

	5	8	5	3
×				7

9)

	8	0	8	6
×				5

10)

	5	7	8	9
×				6

11)

	8	7	6	3
×				6

12)

	3	2	6	1
×				6

13)

	8	3	3	5
×				3

14)

	5	3	9	9
×				2

15)

	2	4	5	1
×				6

16)

	9	1	5	3
×				7

17)

	6	1	0	7
×				2

18)

	9	5	2	3
×				7

DAY 48

Multiplication: 4-Digit by 1-Digit

Time :

Score / 18

1) 9705 × 5 =

2) 4027 × 4 =

3) 6852 × 2 =

4) 7675 × 5 =

5) 6043 × 8 =

6) 6014 × 3 =

7) 8237 × 9 =

8) 4384 × 3 =

9) 7564 × 3 =

10) 9657 × 4 =

11) 1422 × 7 =

12) 7776 × 3 =

13) 6903 × 5 =

14) 7344 × 3 =

15) 9488 × 5 =

16) 8489 × 4 =

17) 8290 × 6 =

18) 4427 × 9 =

DAY 49

Multiplication: 4-Digit by 1-Digit

1)

	4	9	1	0
×				6

2)

	7	1	9	2
×				4

3)

	4	7	1	6
×				6

4)

	1	5	5	4
×				5

5)

	1	8	1	6
×				7

6)

	1	9	5	2
×				4

7)

	1	3	6	6
×				3

8)

	6	7	9	7
×				9

9)

	2	4	1	5
×				7

10)

	3	2	2	7
×				9

11)

	2	8	4	2
×				8

12)

	2	7	4	5
×				7

13)

	4	1	6	4
×				8

14)

	7	2	5	5
×				3

15)

	7	5	3	2
×				4

16)

	1	9	4	0
×				4

17)

	6	4	5	0
×				7

18)

	2	1	6	0
×				4

DAY 50

Multiplication: 4-Digit by 1-Digit

Time :

Score / 18

1)

	9	8	1	2
×				6

2)

	5	3	8	8
×				9

3)

	7	2	1	4
×				6

4)

	4	1	8	2
×				8

5)

	5	4	4	2
×				5

6)

	2	6	0	3
×				9

7)

	9	7	3	2
×				5

8)

	8	3	5	6
×				9

9)

	6	0	8	7
×				2

10)

	6	1	5	2
×				3

11)

	1	9	0	8
×				9

12)

	9	3	0	6
×				6

13)

	7	2	2	1
×				9

14)

	7	9	5	5
×				8

15)

	4	0	8	3
×				9

16)

	1	1	8	6
×				3

17)

	7	6	1	0
×				7

18)

	2	3	0	9
×				8

THERE IS A TRAIN STATION IN LONDON THAT HAS A PLATFORM 0!

Platform 0 at King's Cross station was named that way when it was opened in 2010 because – as the 12th platform – it was on the opposite side of the station to Platform 11, and right next to Platform 1. It would have been very confusing for people trying to use the trains (and me as well!) if they needed to get from Platform 11 to 12 and had to walk all that way. Platform 0 is also the longest platform at the station to accommodate longer trains.

DAY 51

Division: 4-Digit by 1-Digit with No Reminders

1)

5)2545

2)

5)2035

3)

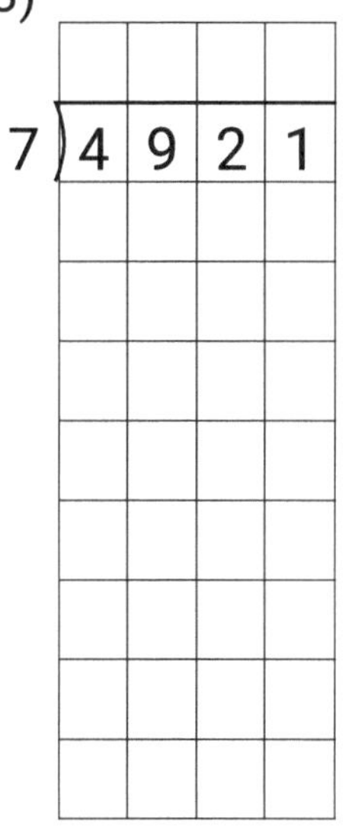

4)

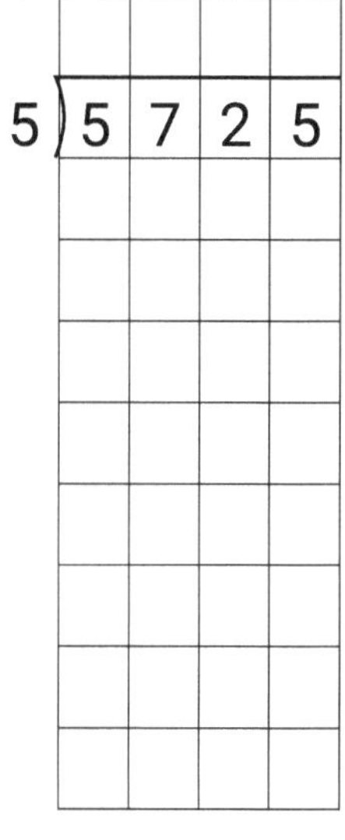

5)

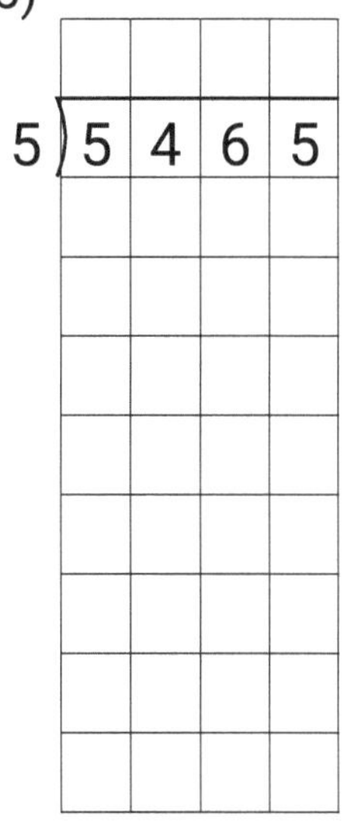

6)

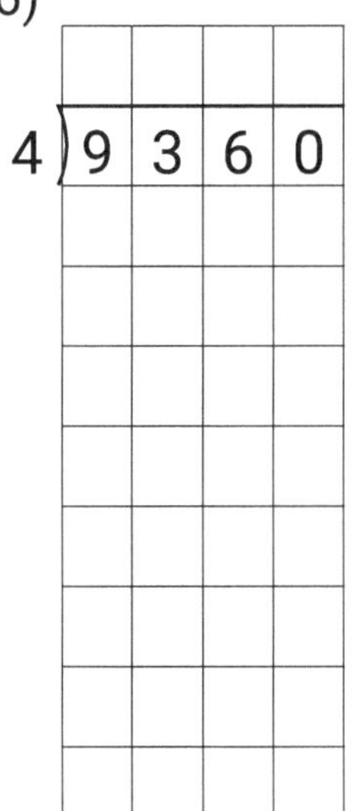

7)

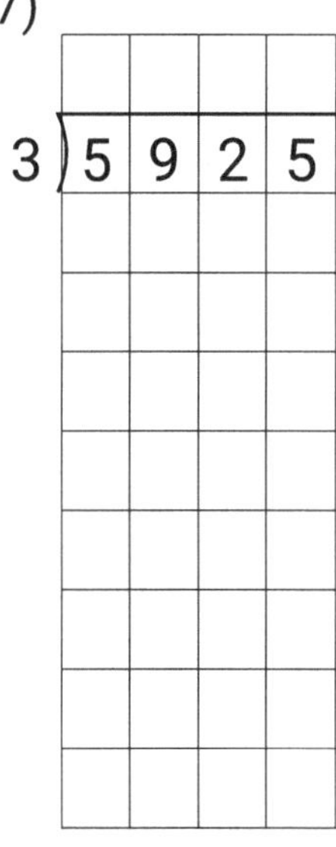

8)

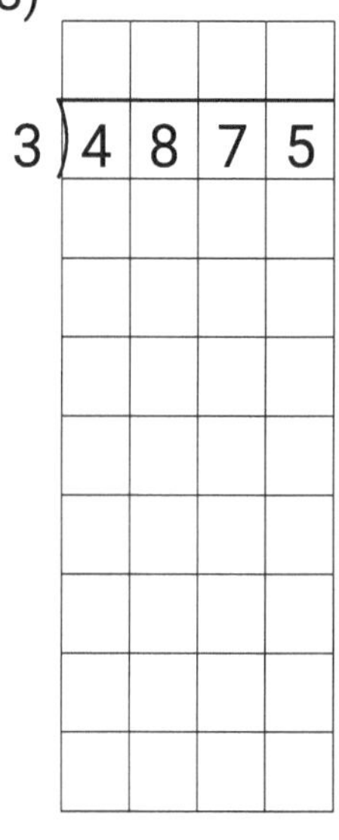

9)

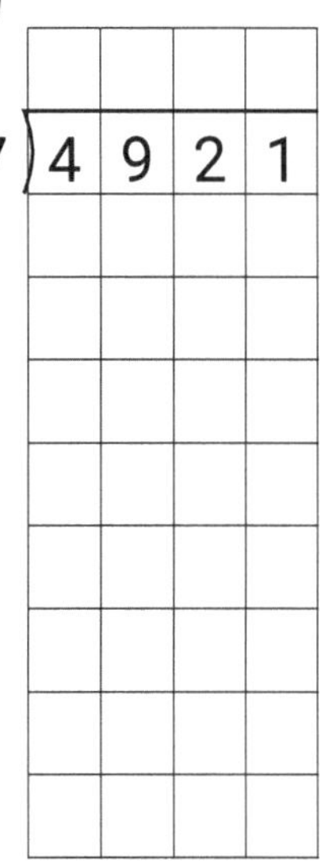

10)

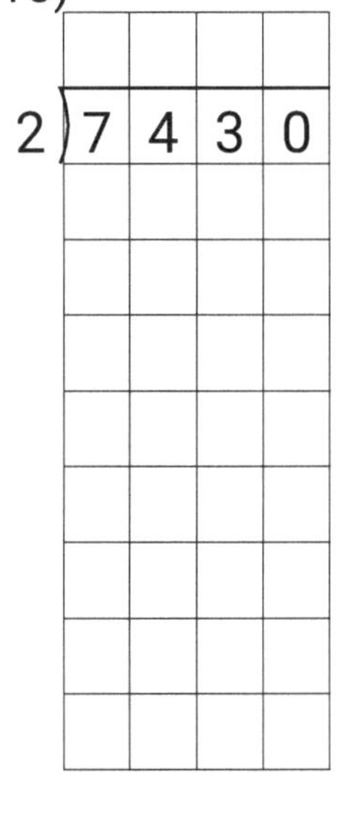

11)

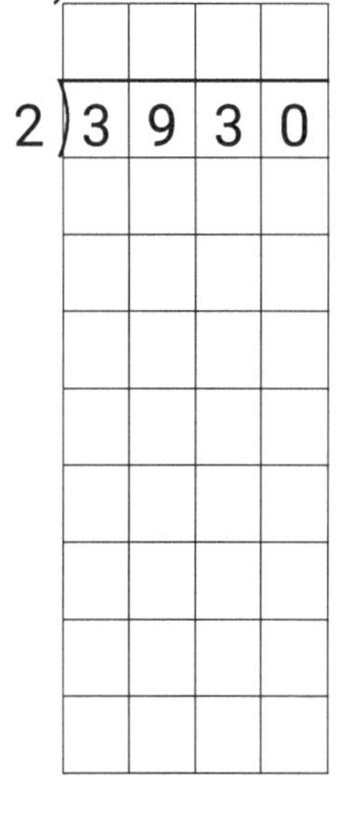

12)

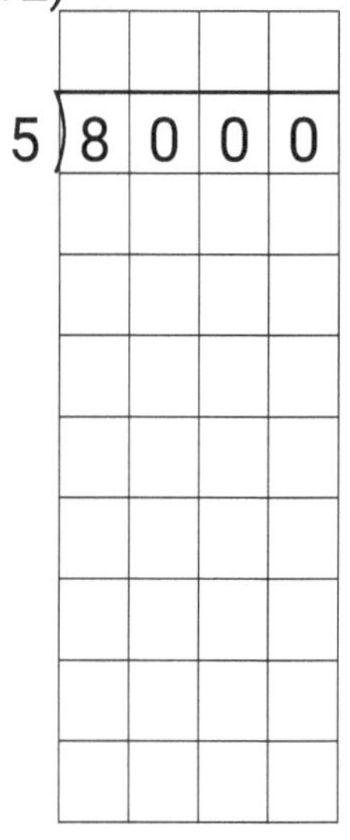

DAY 52

Division: 4-Digit by 1-Digit with No Reminders

1)

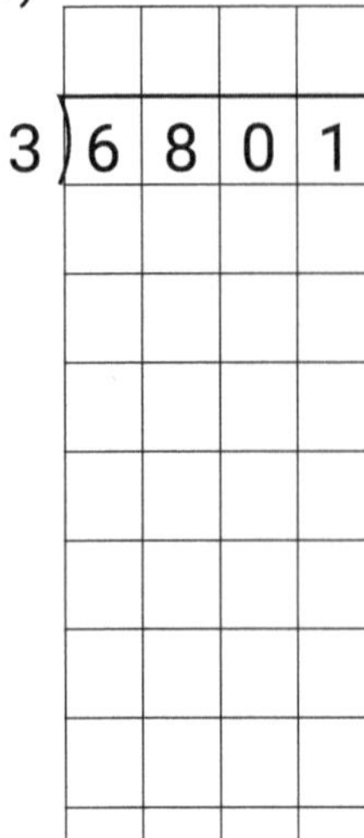

2)

2)8496

3)

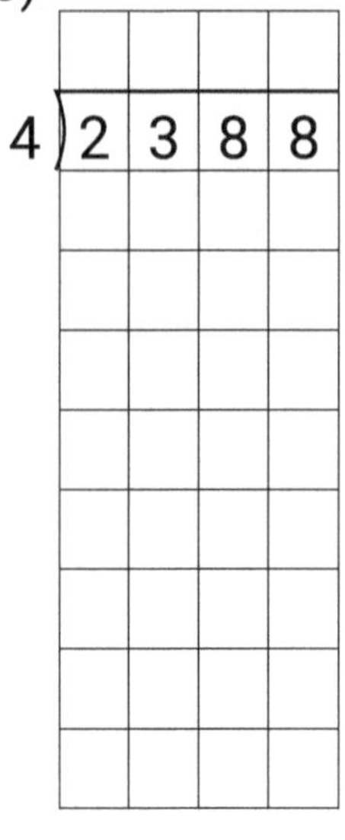

4)

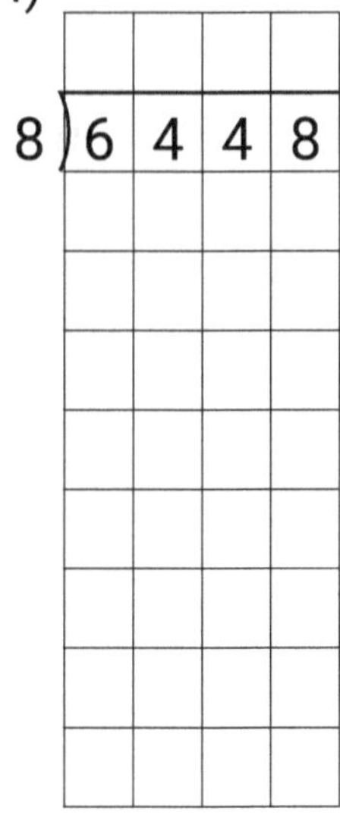

5)

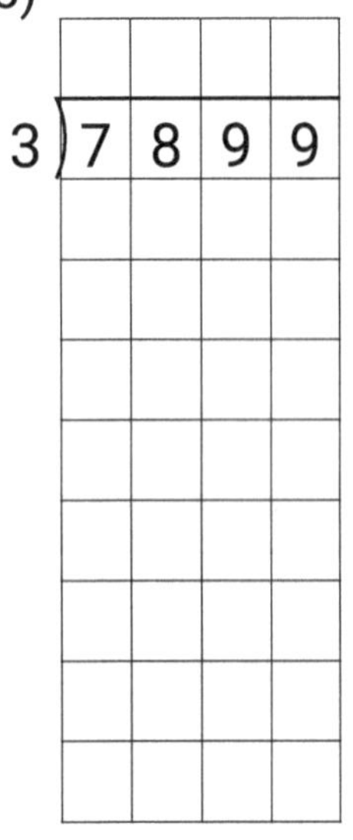

6)

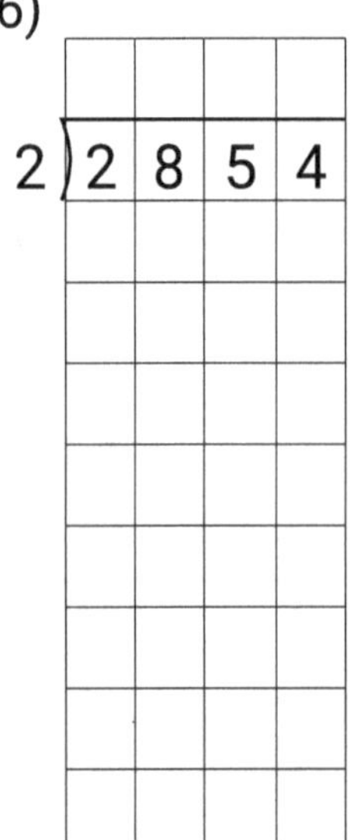

7)

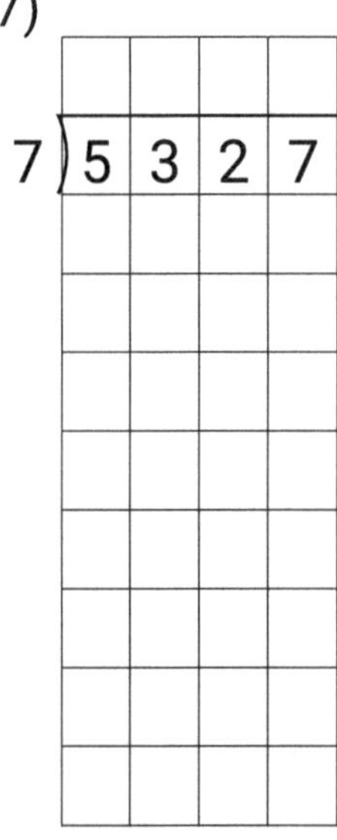

8)

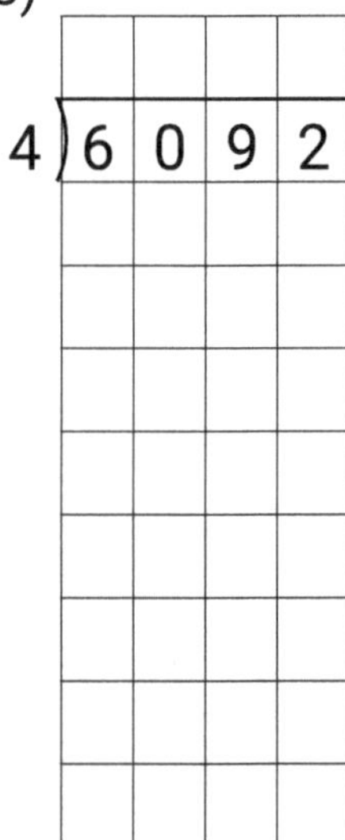

9)

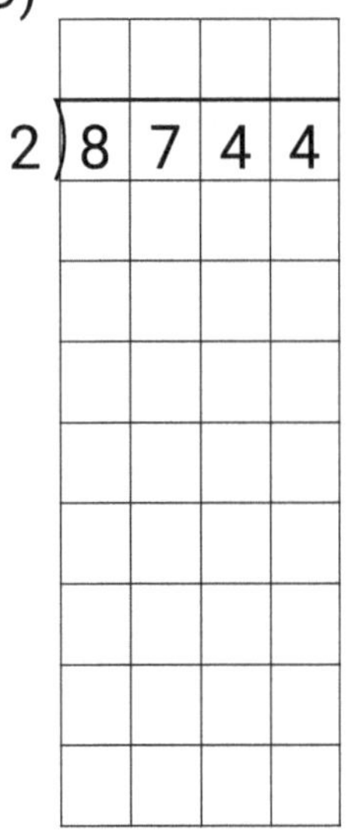

10)

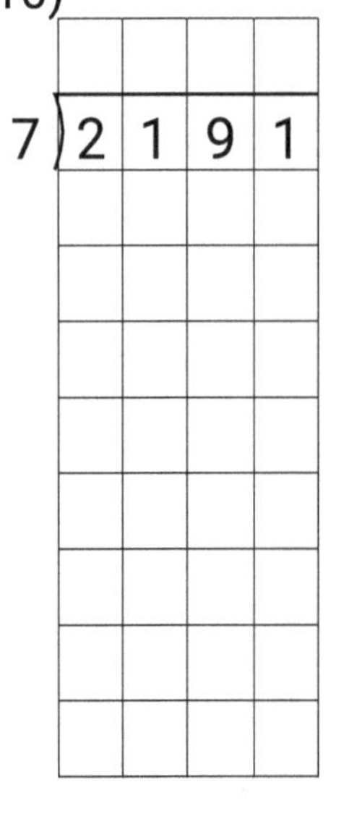

11)

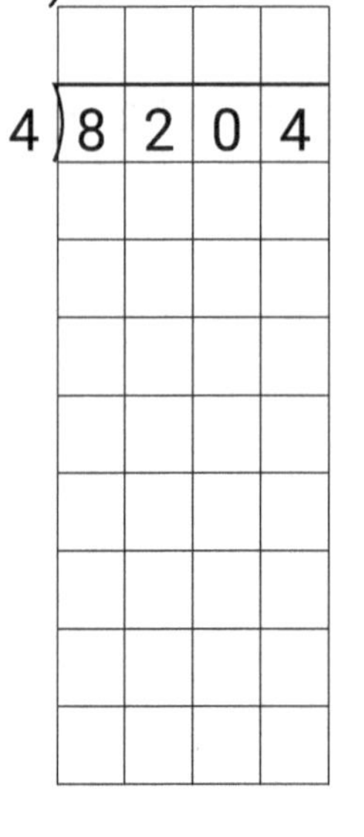

12)

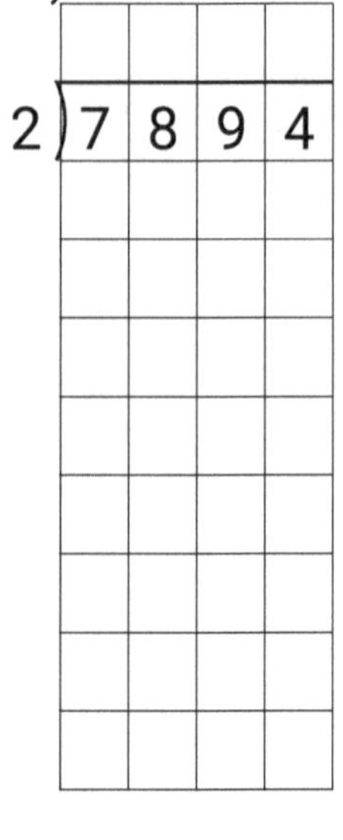

DAY 53

Division: 4-Digit by 1-Digit with No Reminders

1)

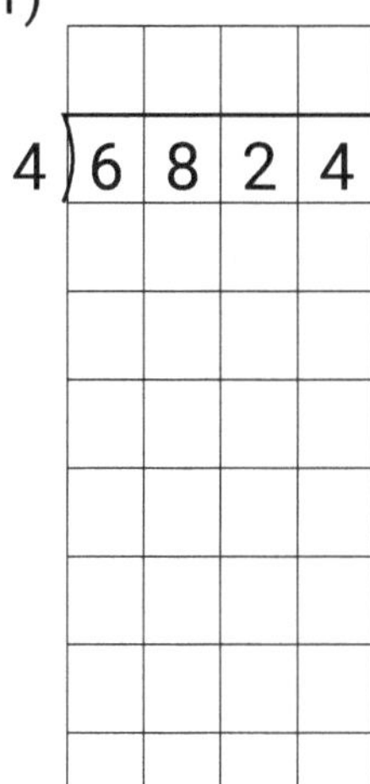

2)

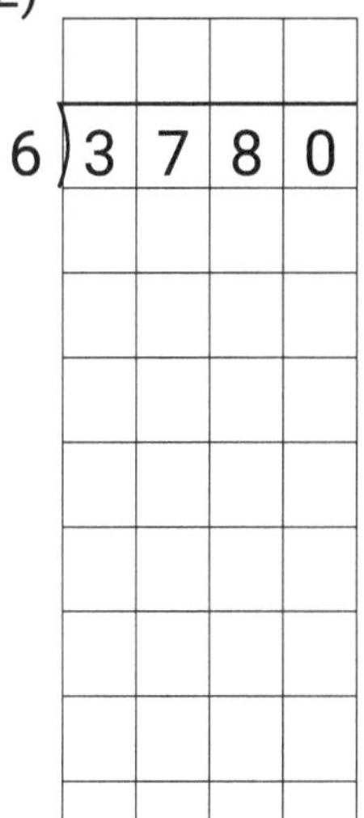

3)

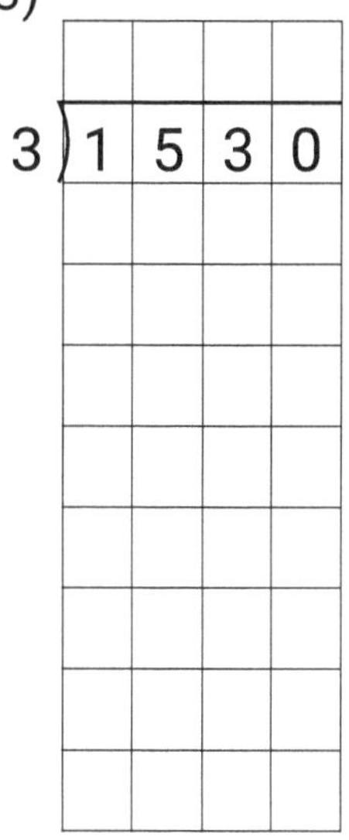

4)

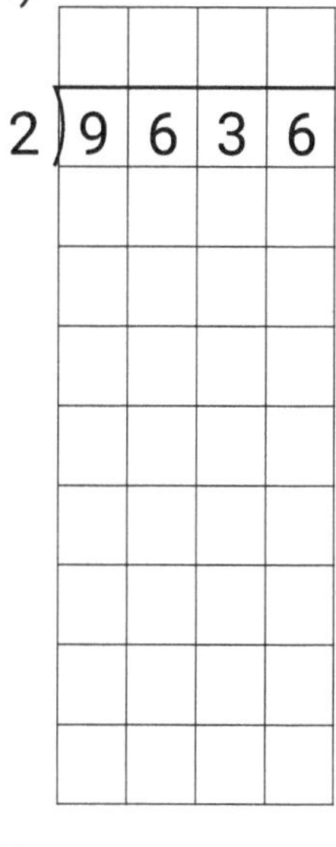

5)

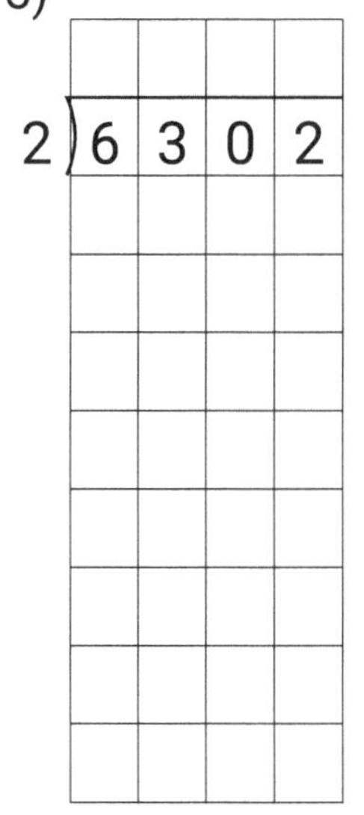

6)

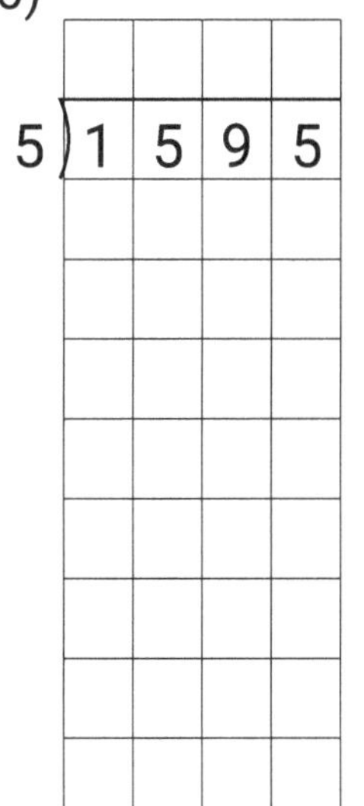

7)

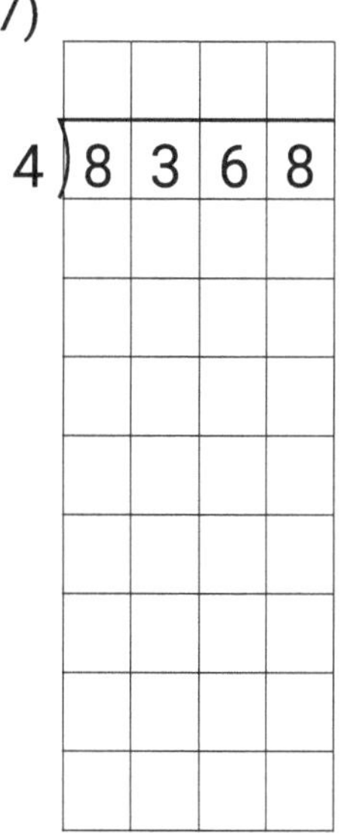

8)

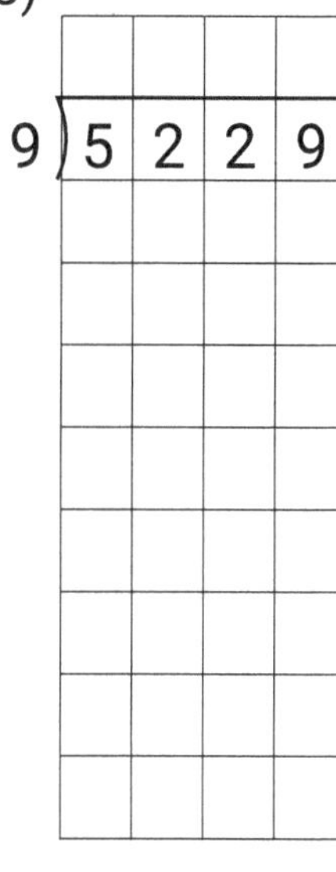

9)

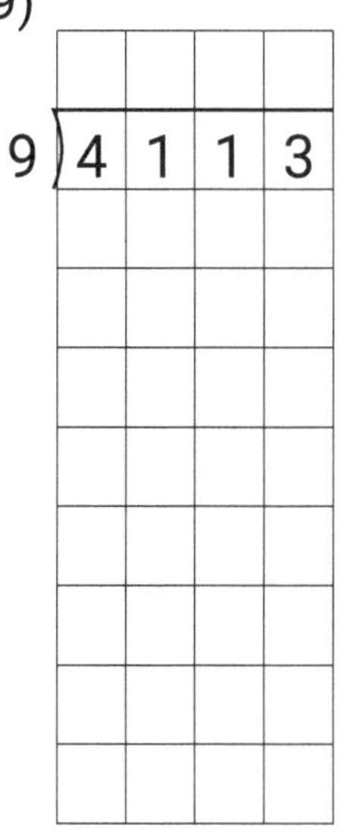

10)

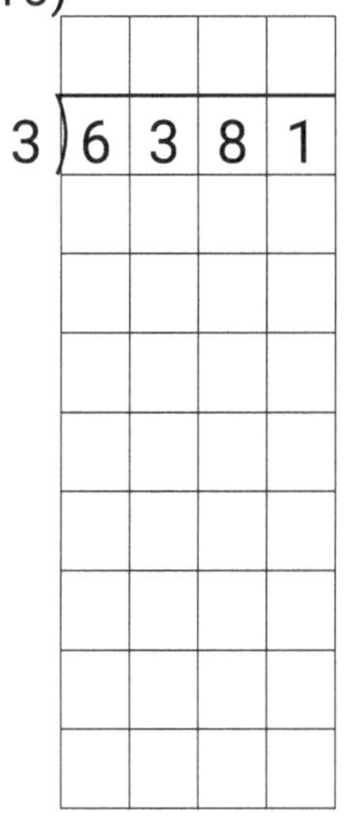

11)

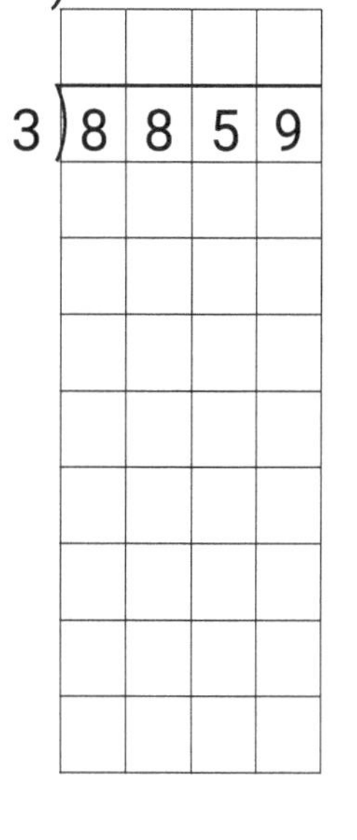

12)

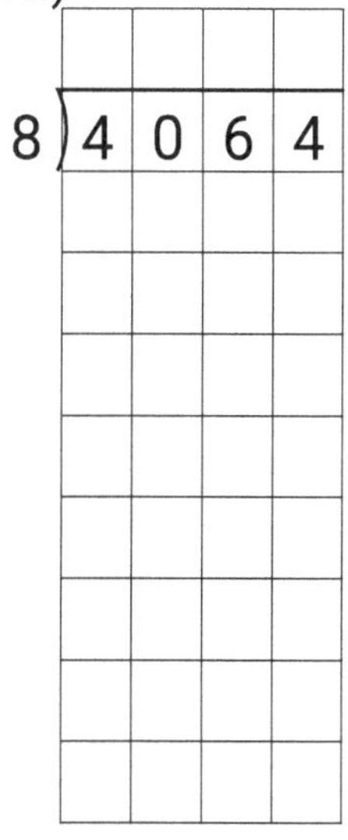

DAY 54

Division: 4-Digit by 1-Digit with No Reminders

1)

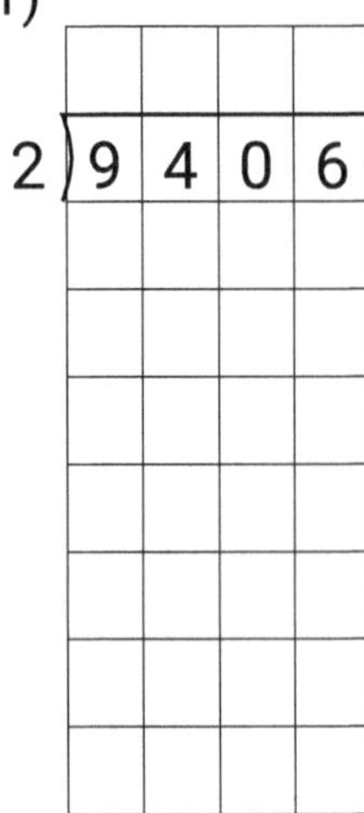

2)

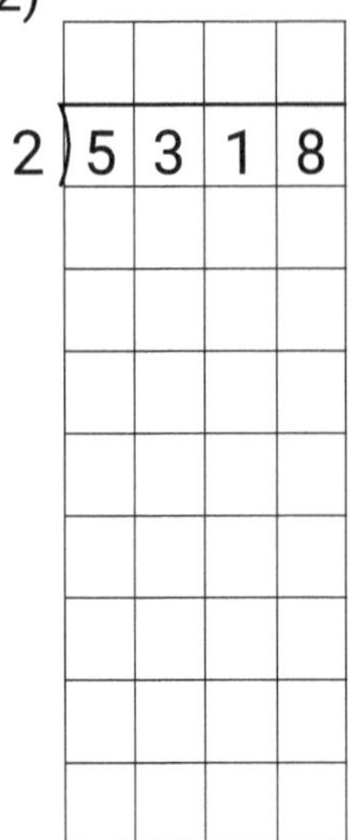

3)

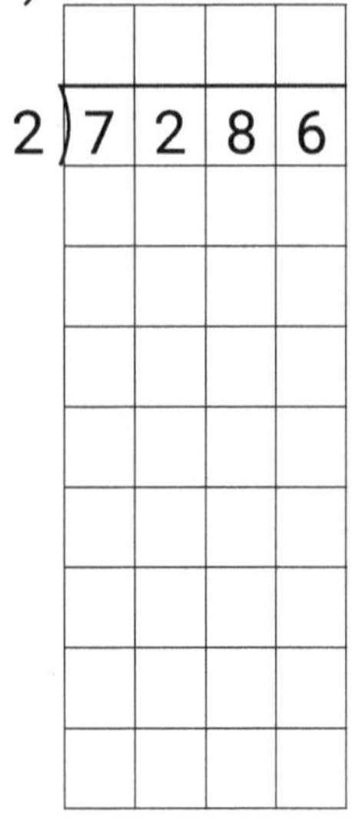

4)

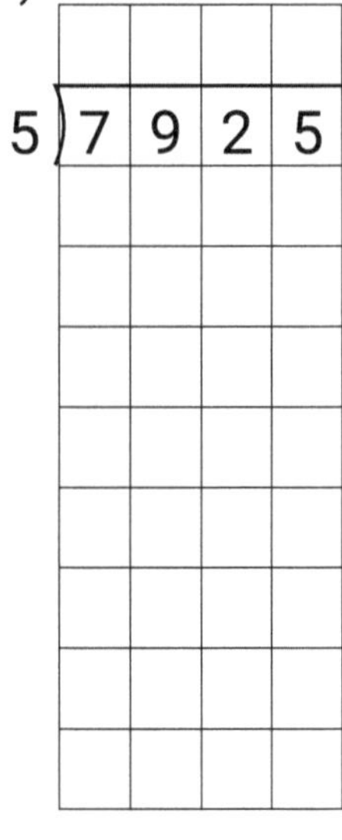

5)

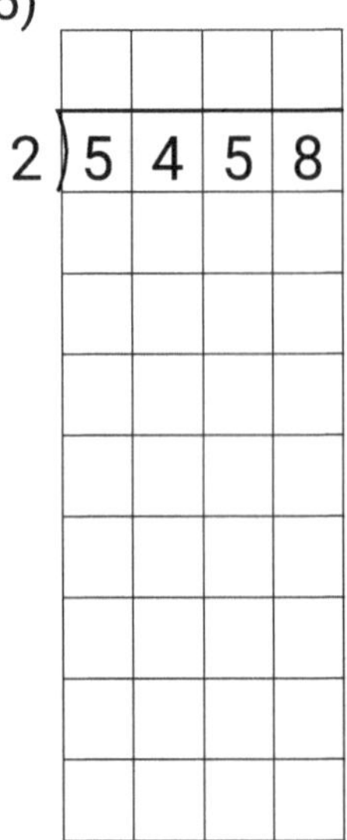

6)

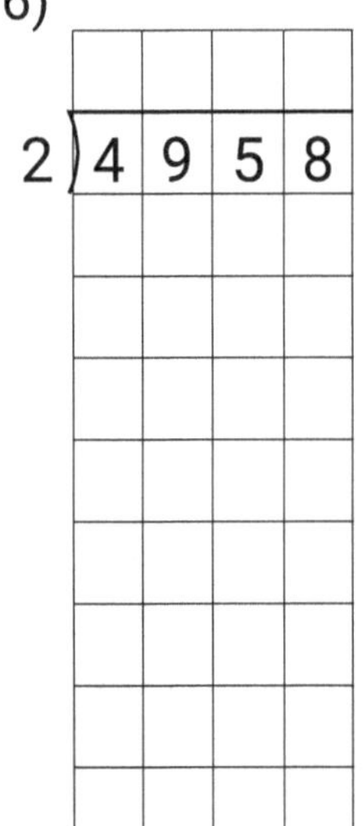

7)

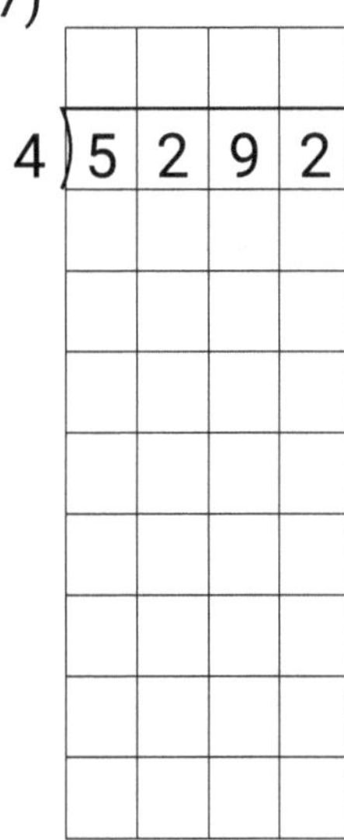

8)

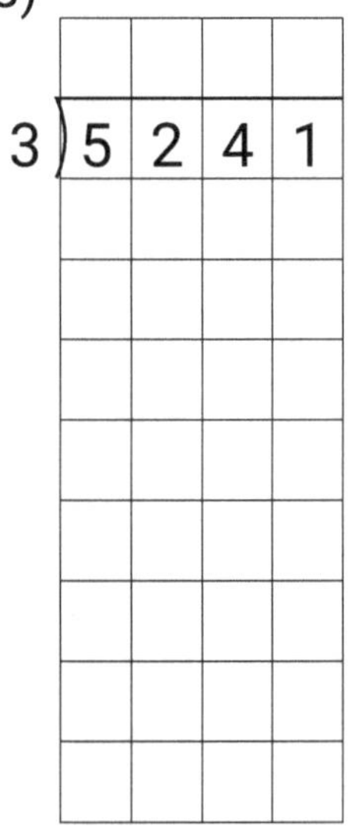

9)

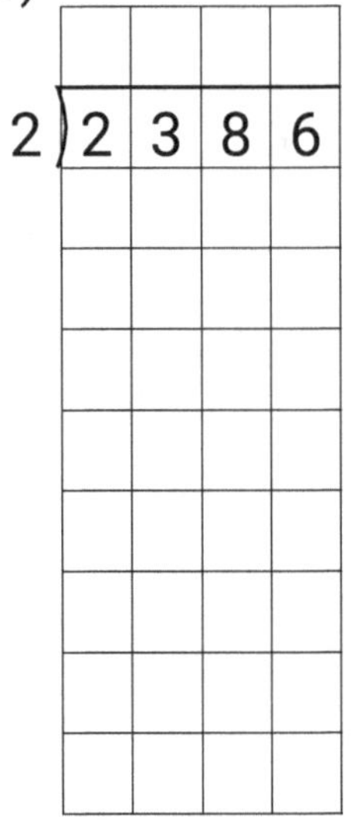

10)

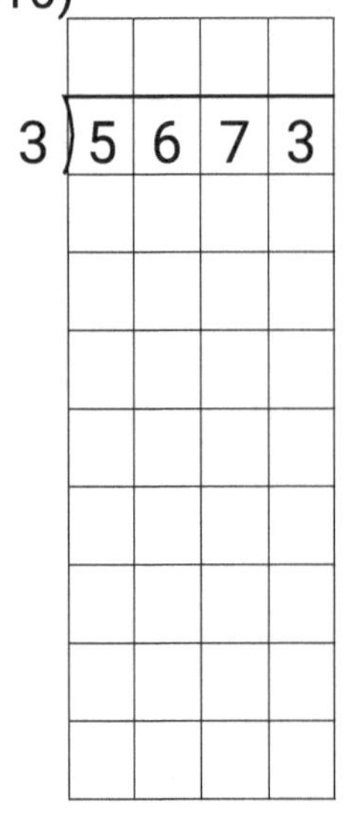

11)

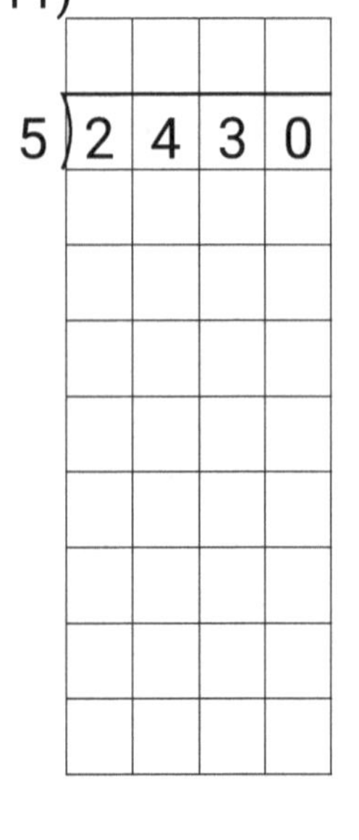

12)

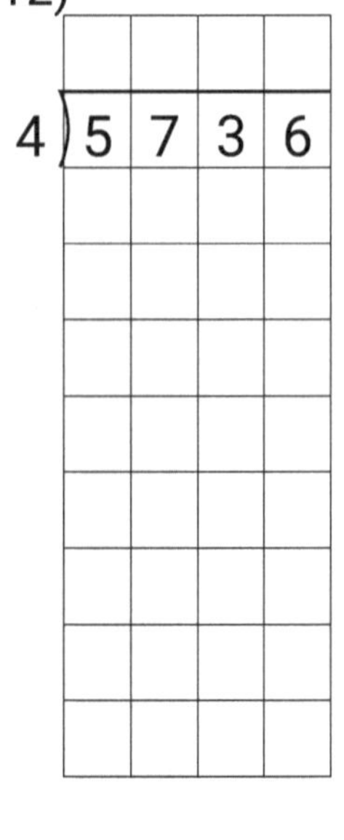

DAY 55

Division: 4-Digit by 1-Digit with No Reminders

1) $9\overline{)2007}$

2) $3\overline{)2991}$

3)

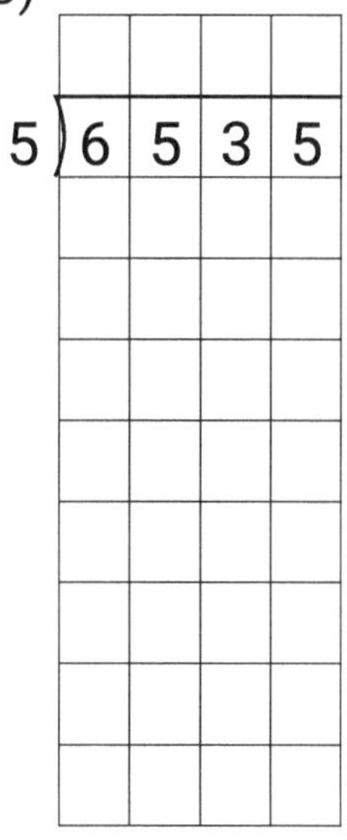

4)

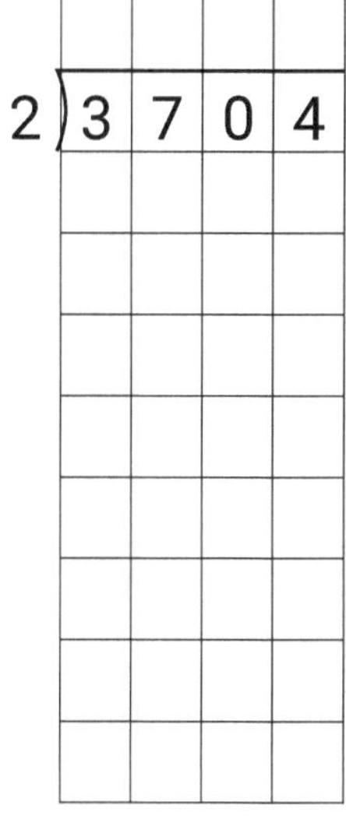

5)

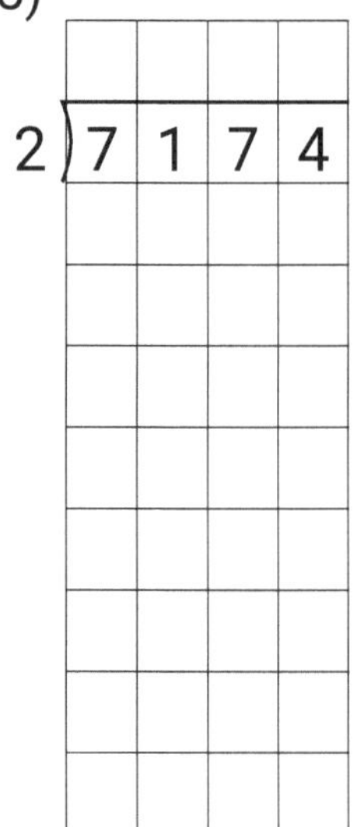

6)

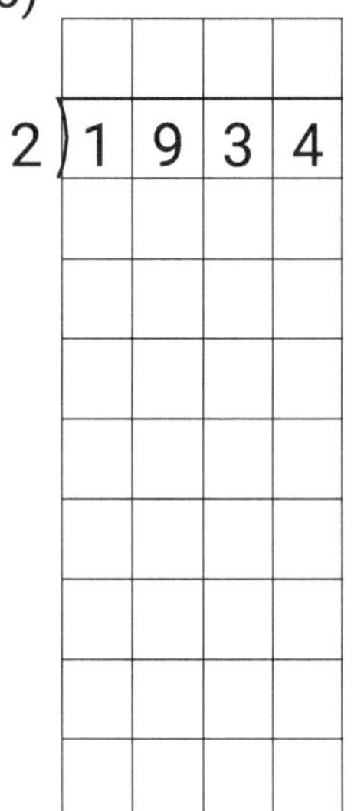

7)

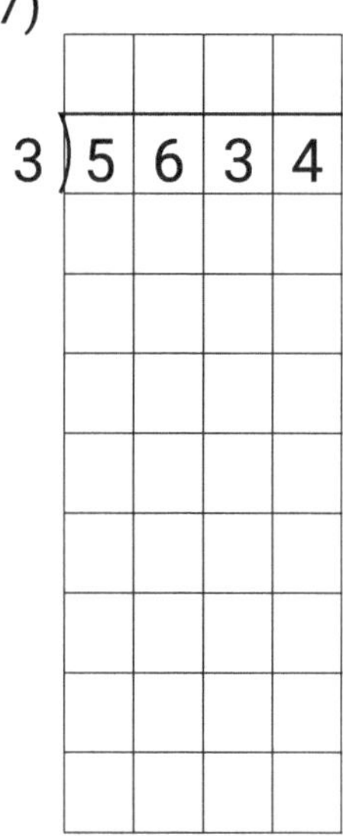

8)

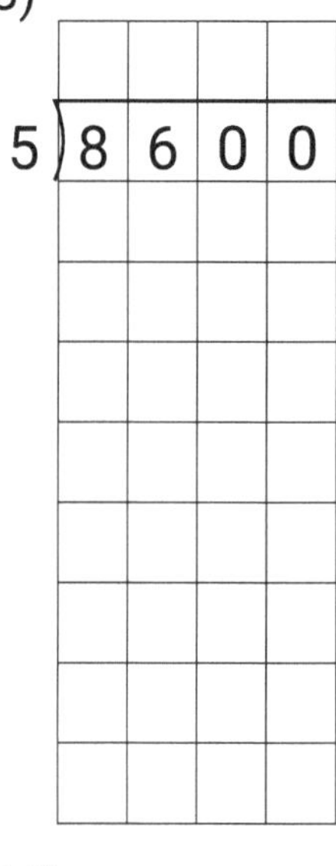

9)

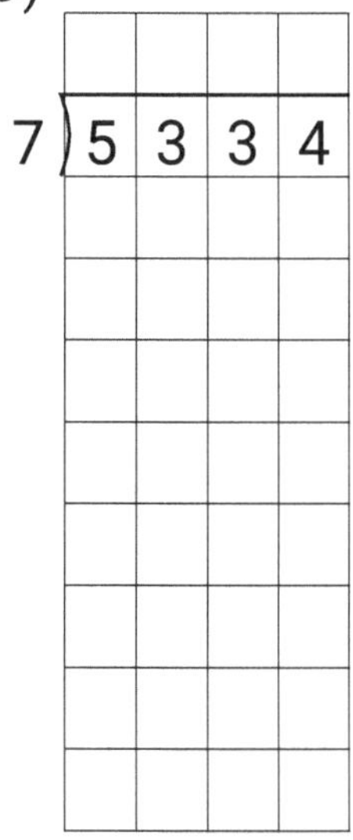

10)

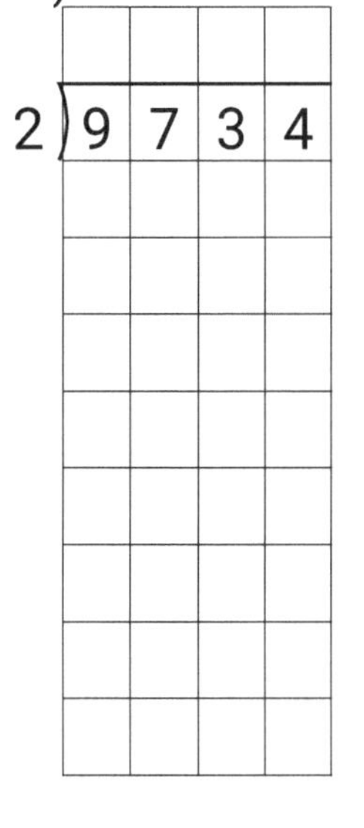

11)

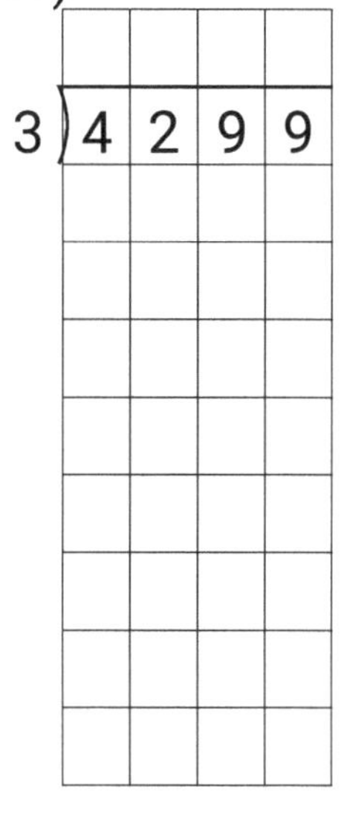

12)

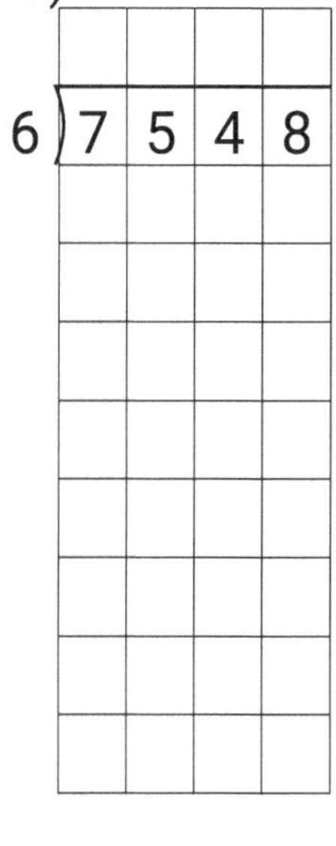

1)
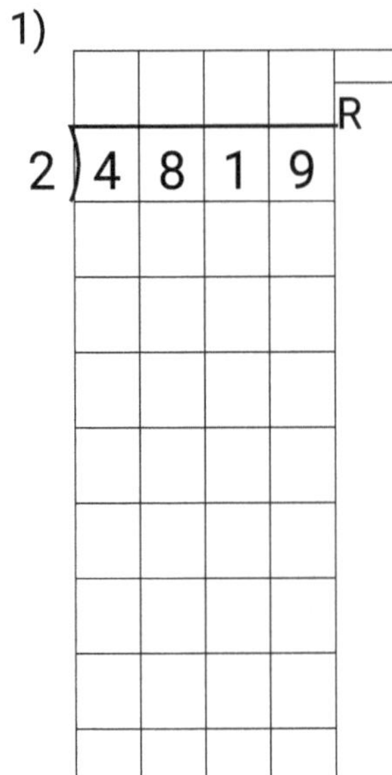

2)
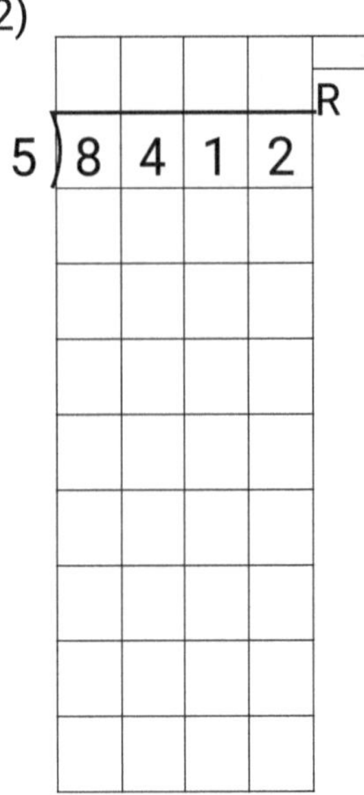

3)
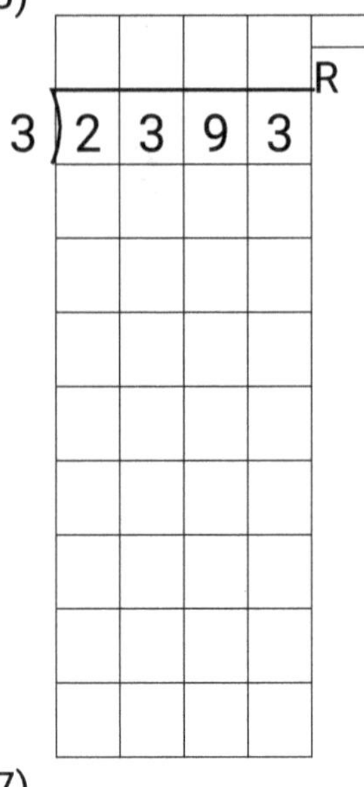

4)
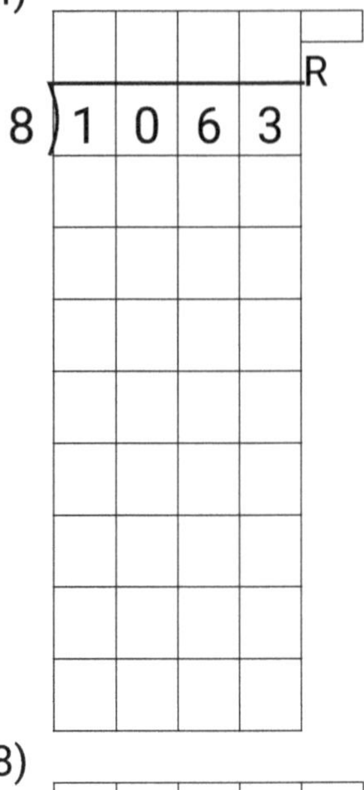

5)
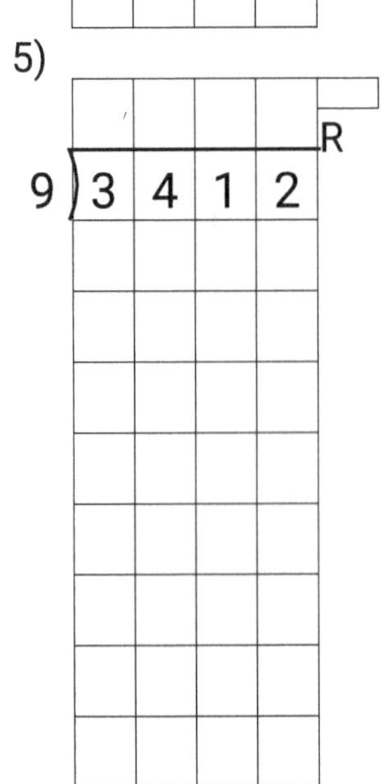

6)
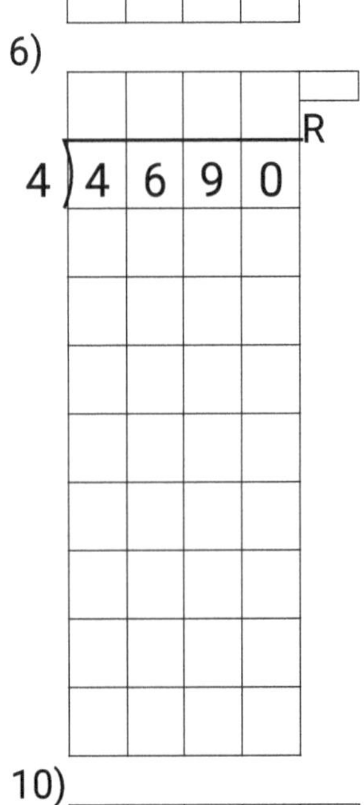

7)
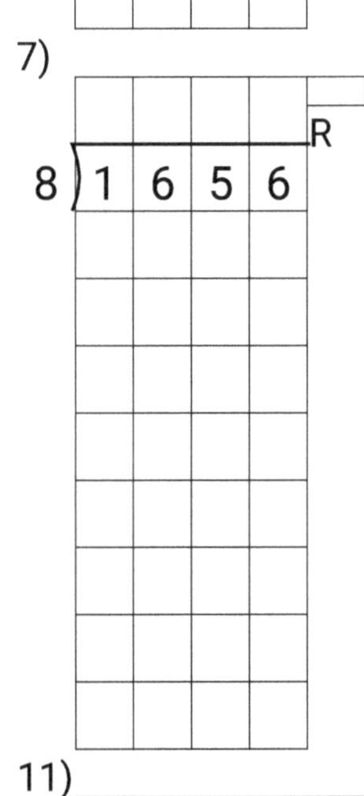

8)

R

4)8 1 0 0

9)
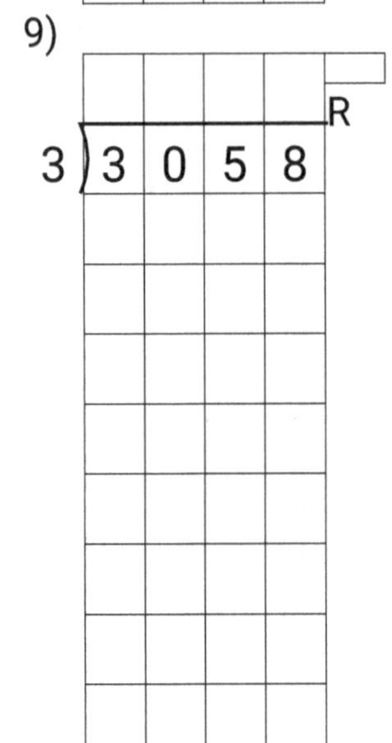

10)
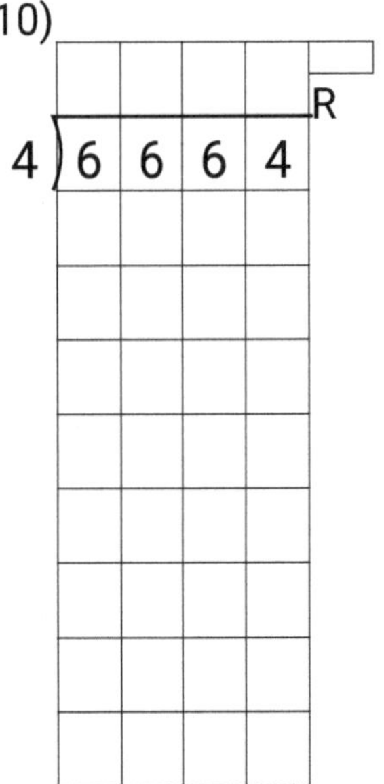

11)
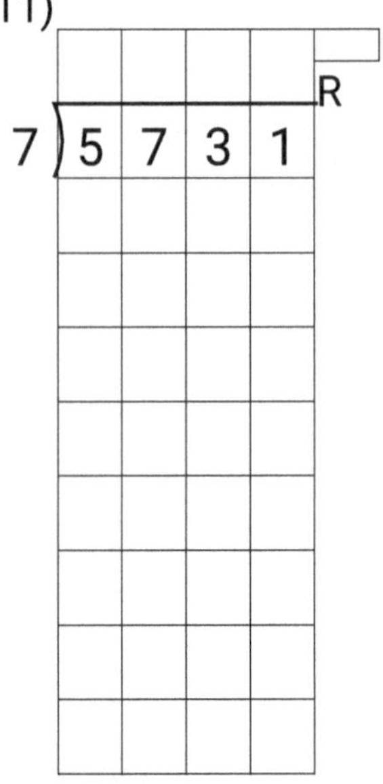

12)

R

2)3 0 7 6

DAY 57

Division: 4-Digit by 1-Digit with Reminders

1)

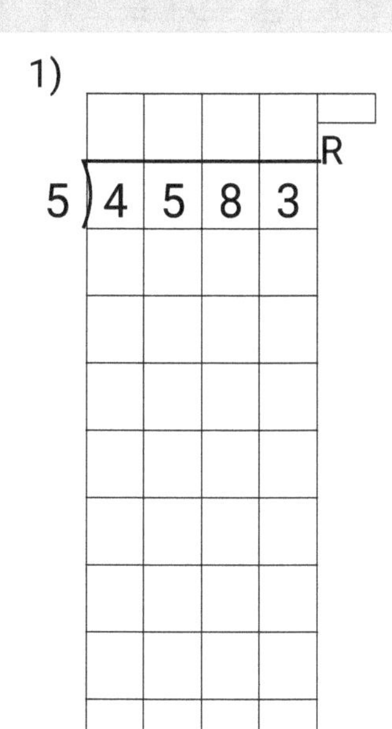

2)

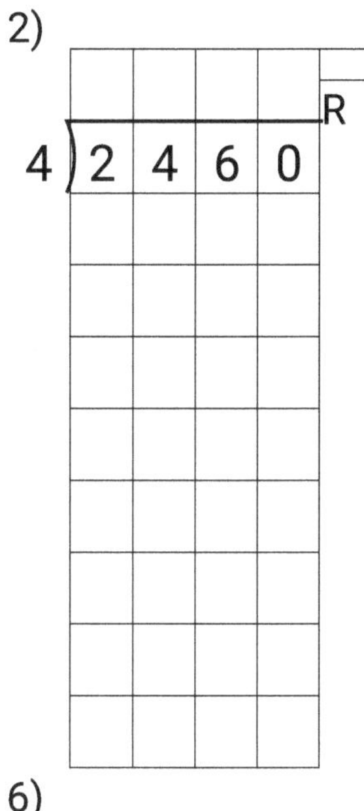

3)

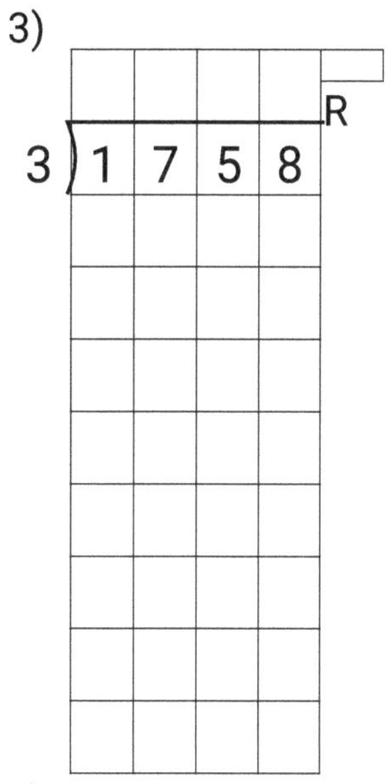

4)

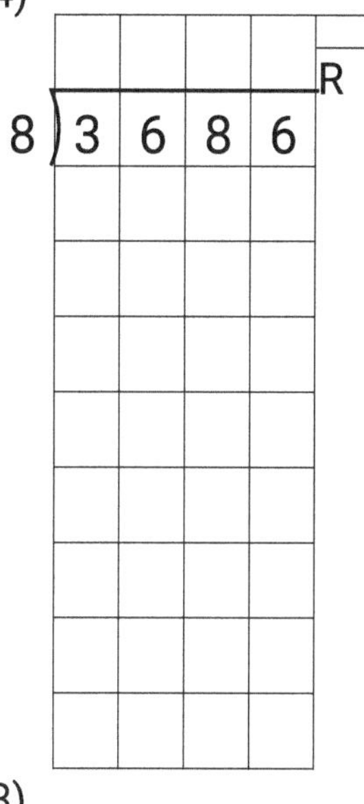

5)

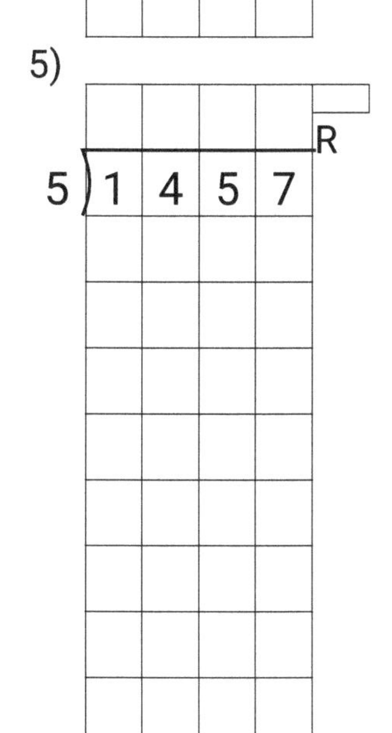

6)

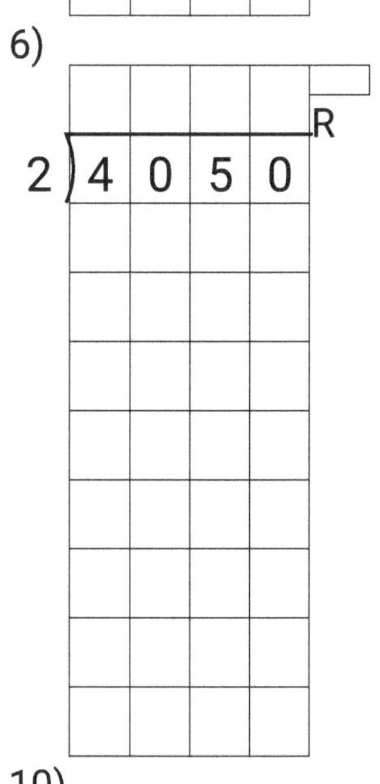

7)

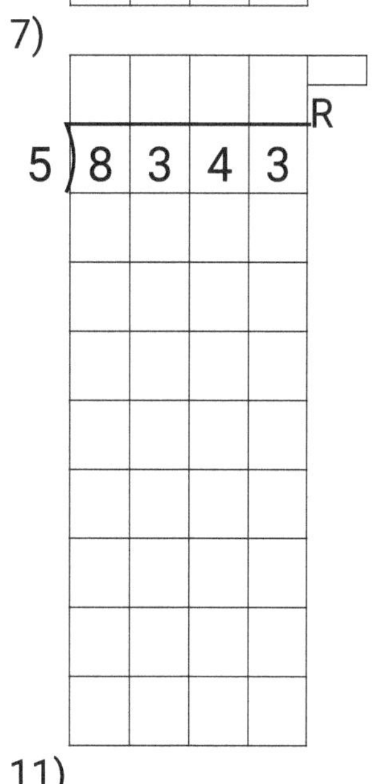

8)

R

8) 1 5 6 3

9)

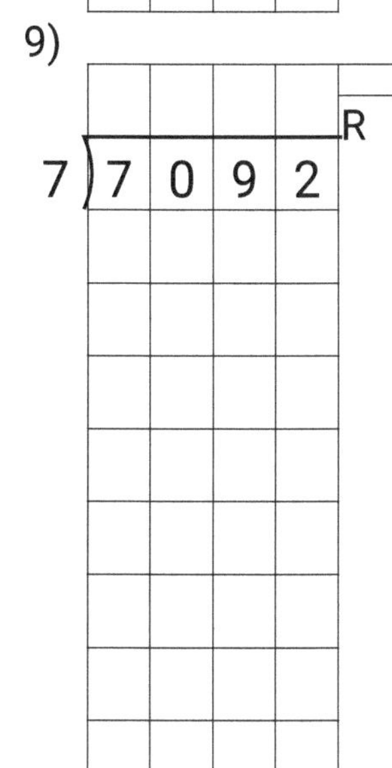

10)

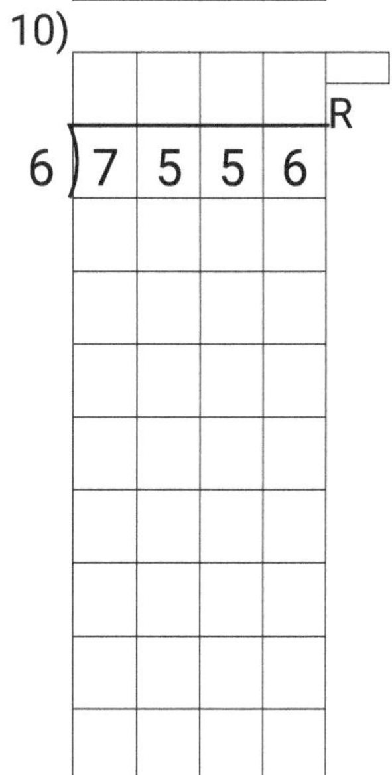

11)

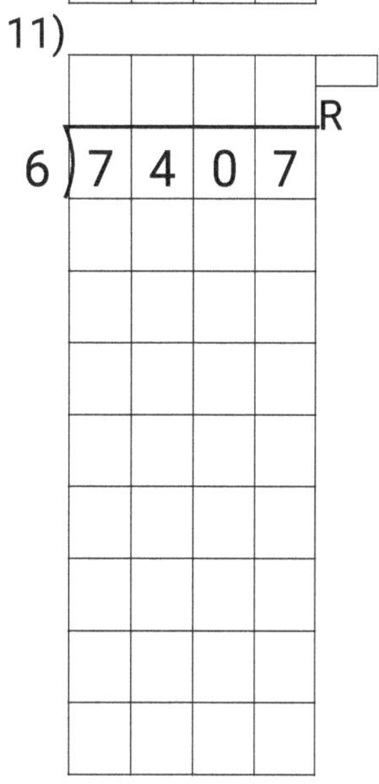

12)

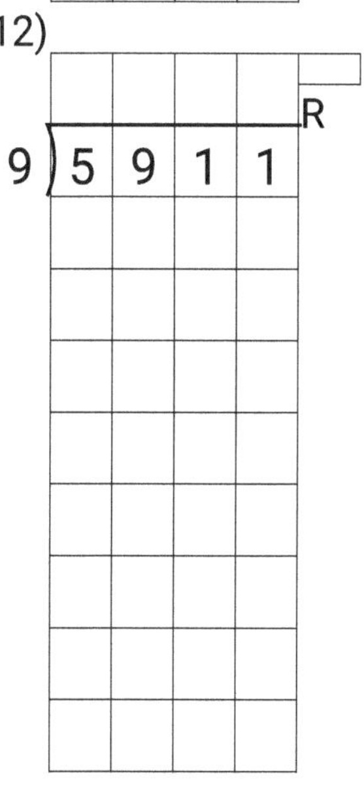

DAY 58

Division: 4-Digit by 1-Digit with Reminders

Time :

Score /12

1) 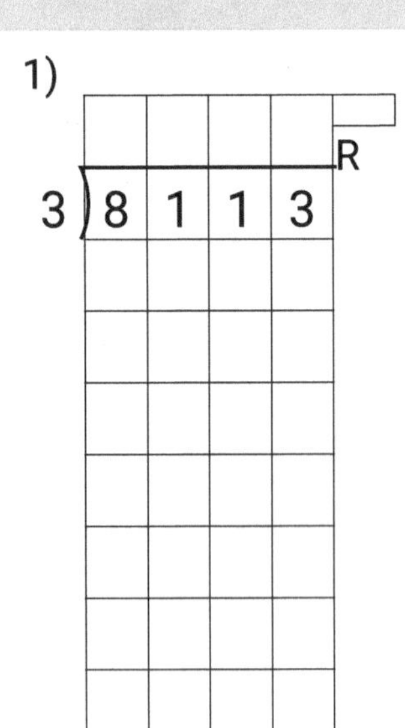

3) 8 1 1 3 R

2) 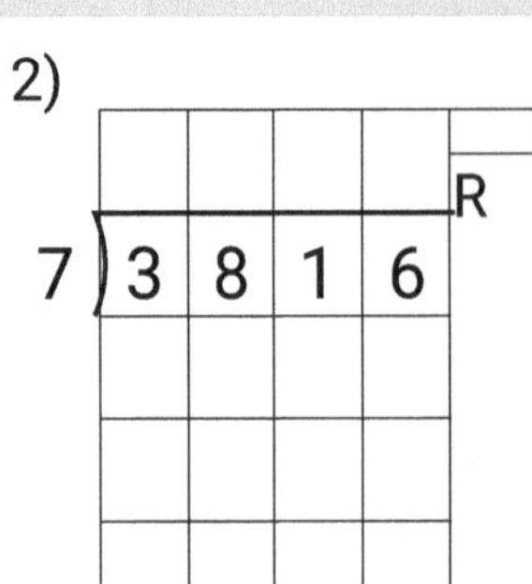

7) 3 8 1 6 R

3) 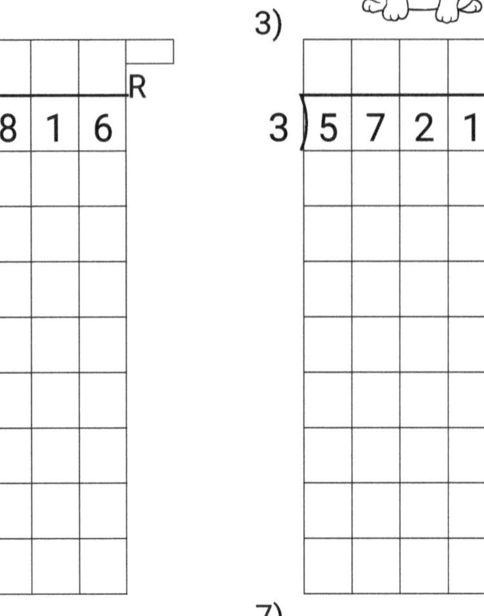

3) 5 7 2 1 R

4) 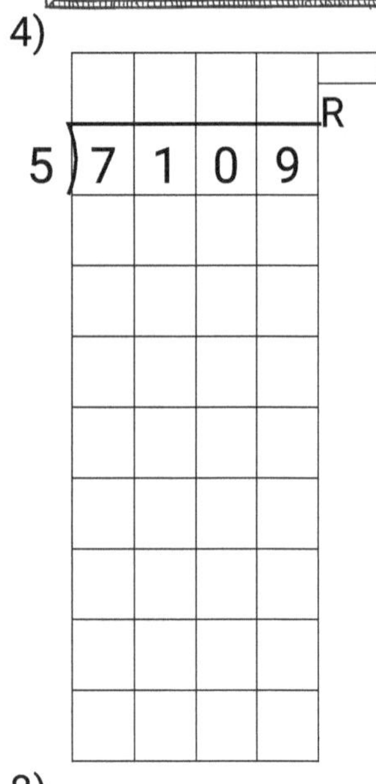

5) 7 1 0 9 R

5) 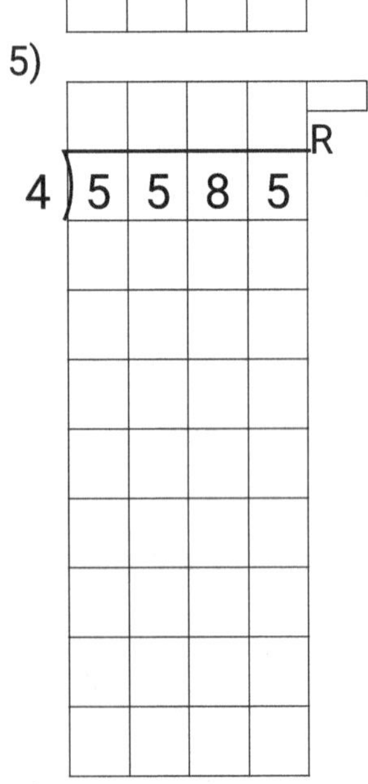

4) 5 5 8 5 R

6) 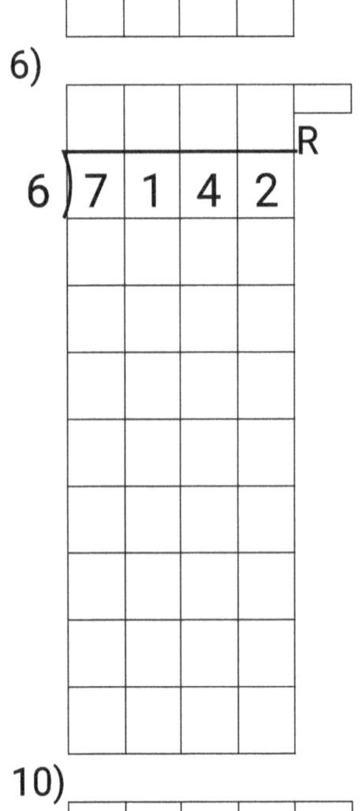

6) 7 1 4 2 R

7) 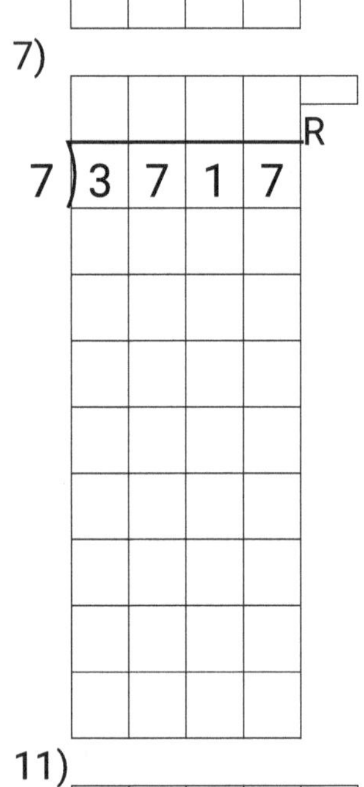

7) 3 7 1 7 R

8)

6) 4 2 8 5 R

9) 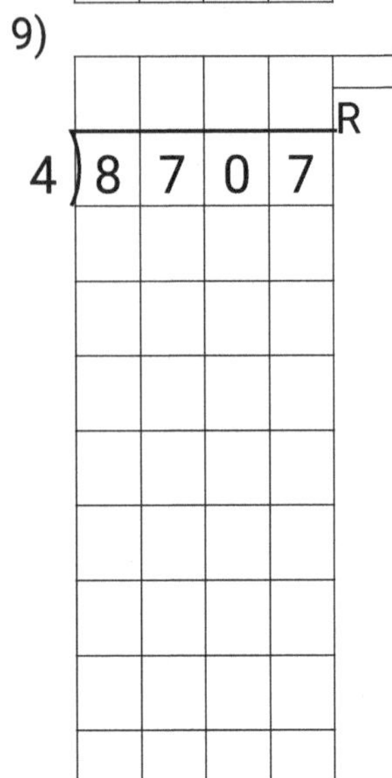

4) 8 7 0 7 R

10) 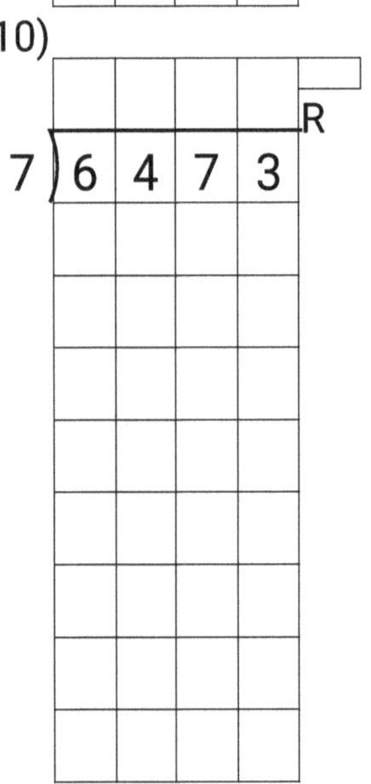

7) 6 4 7 3 R

11) 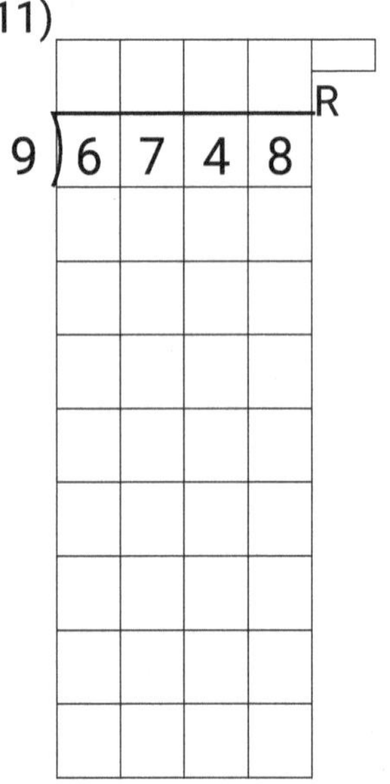

9) 6 7 4 8 R

12) 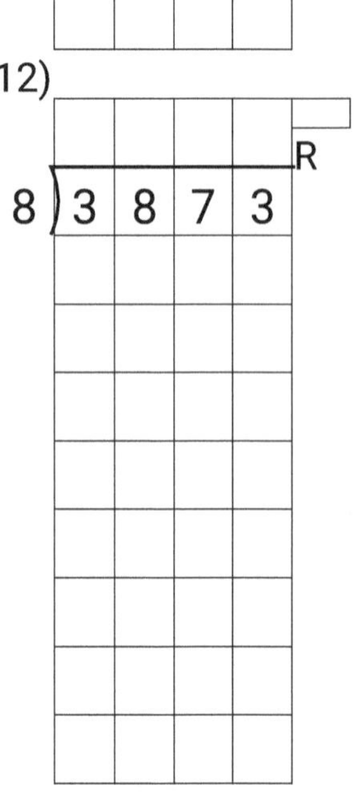

8) 3 8 7 3 R

DAY 59

Division: 4-Digit by 1-Digit with Reminders

1) 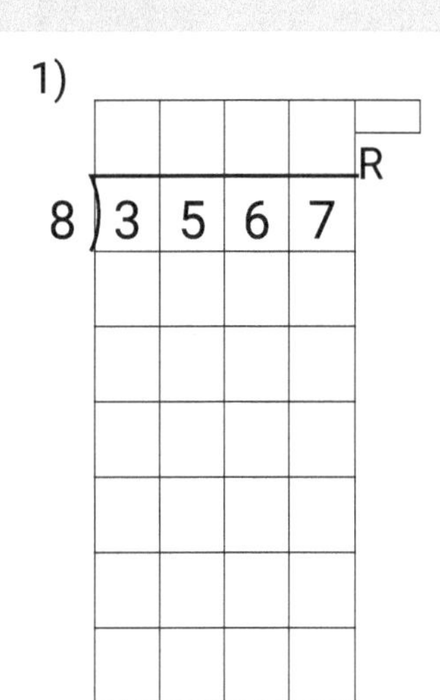

2) 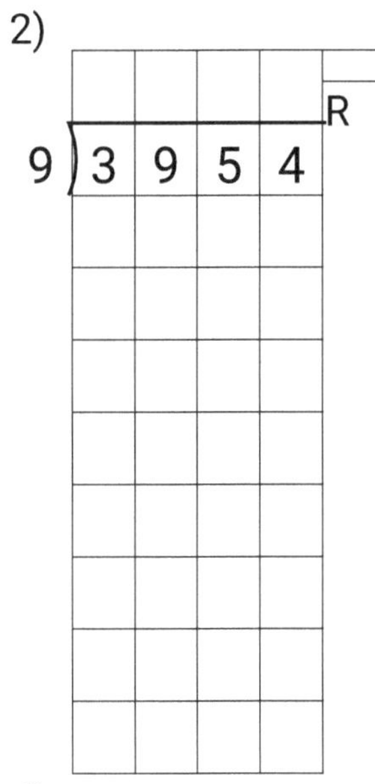

3) 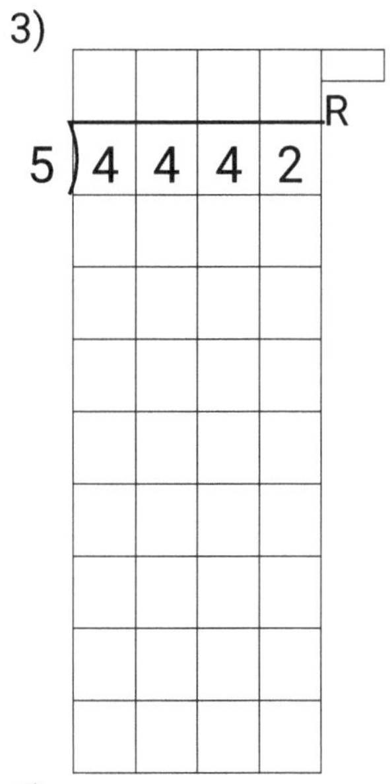

4) 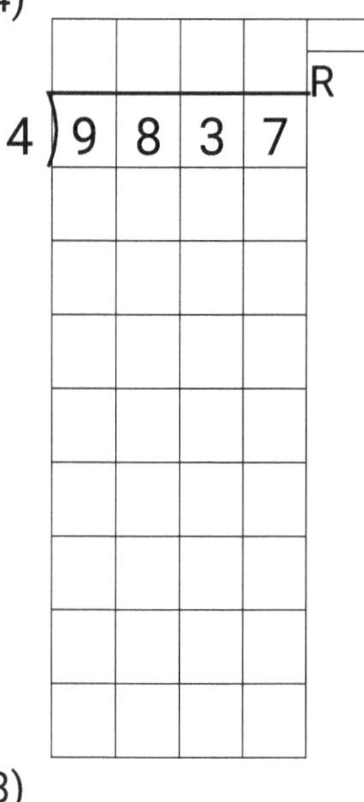

5) 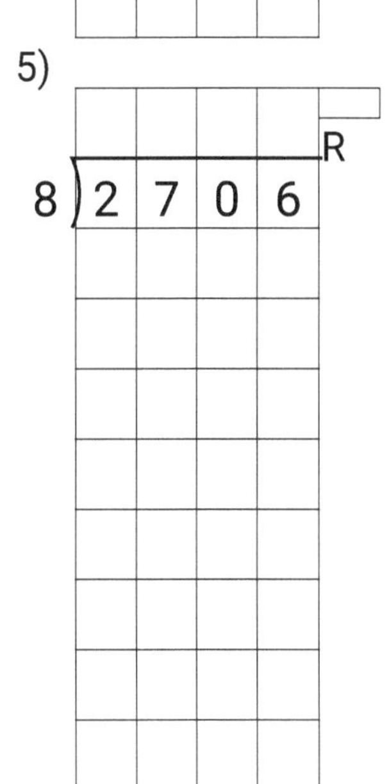

6) 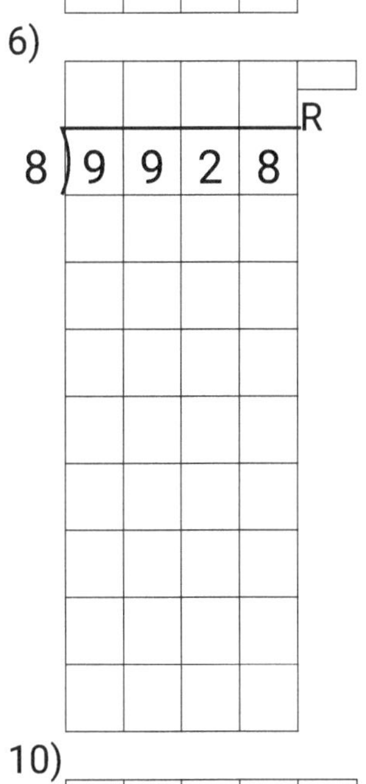

7) 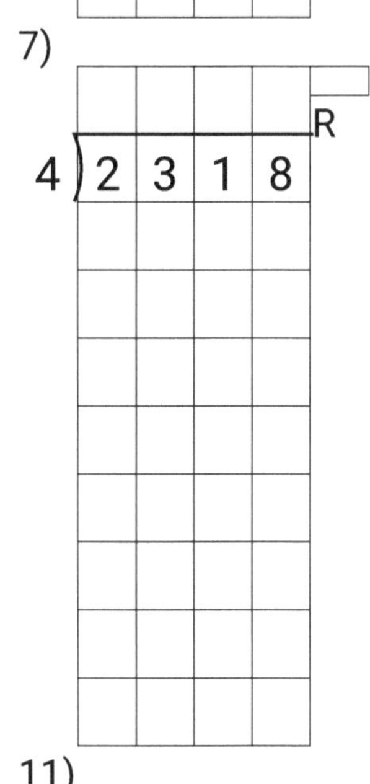

8) 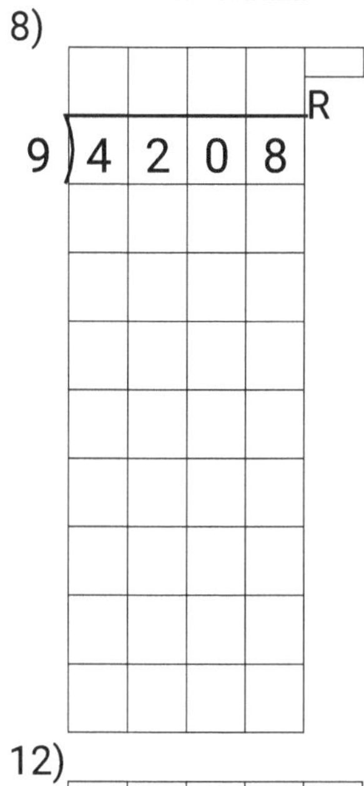

9) 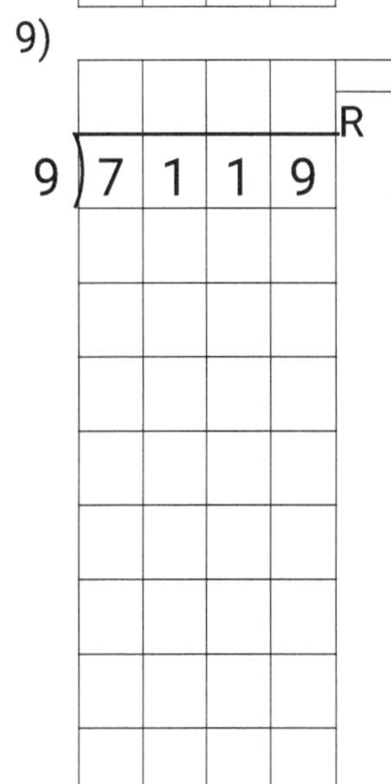

10) 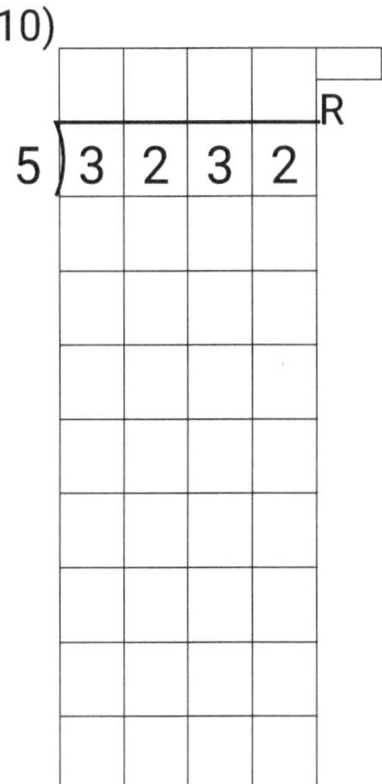

11) 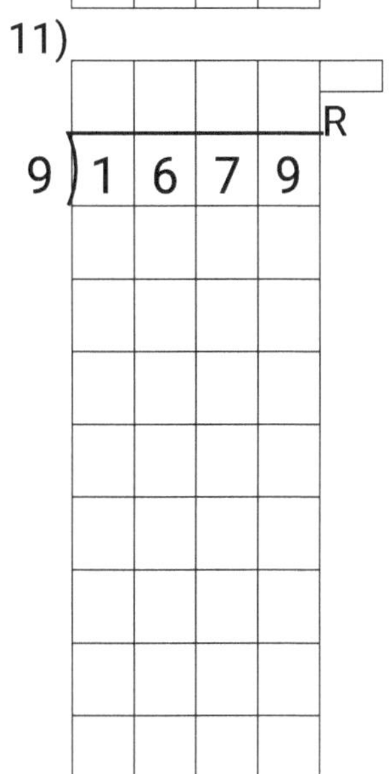

12) 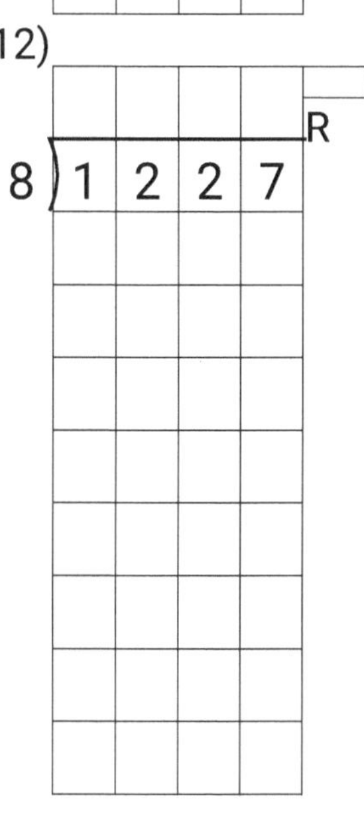

DAY 60

Division: 4-Digit by 1-Digit with Reminders

Time
:

Score
/12

1)
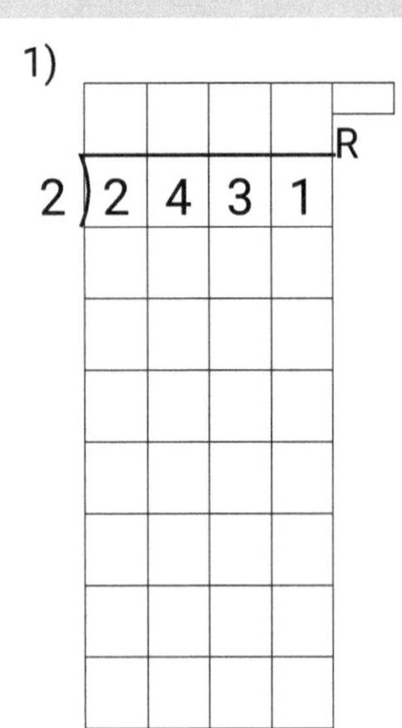

2)
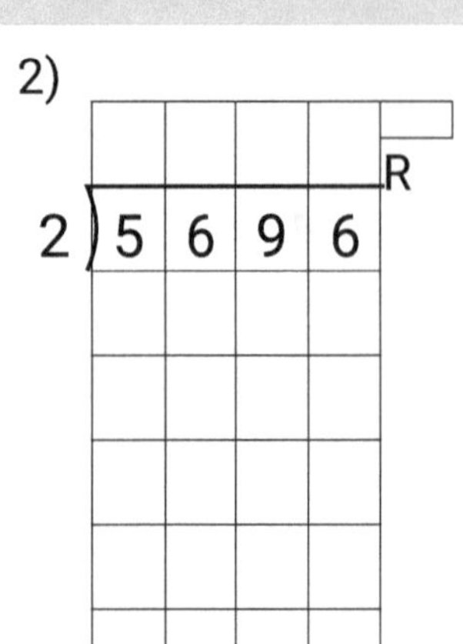

3)
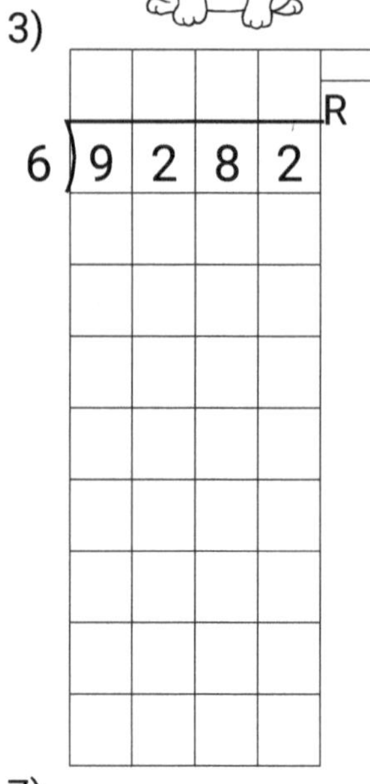

4)
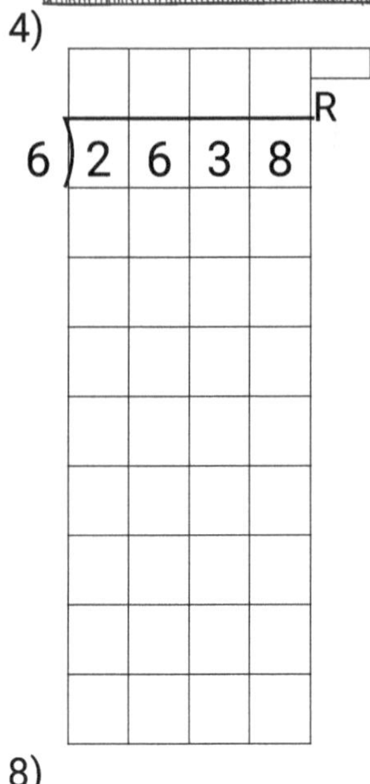

5)
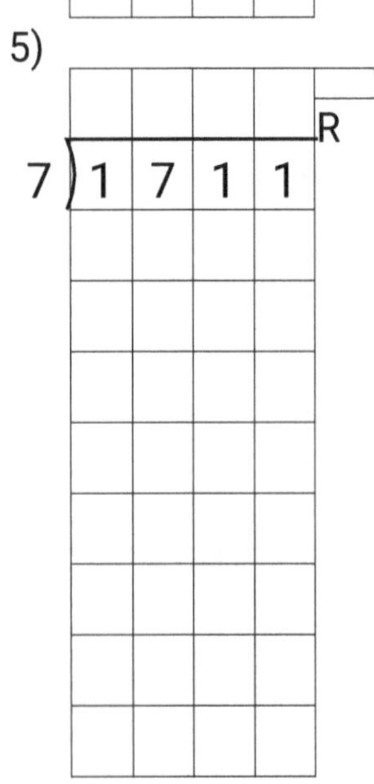

6)
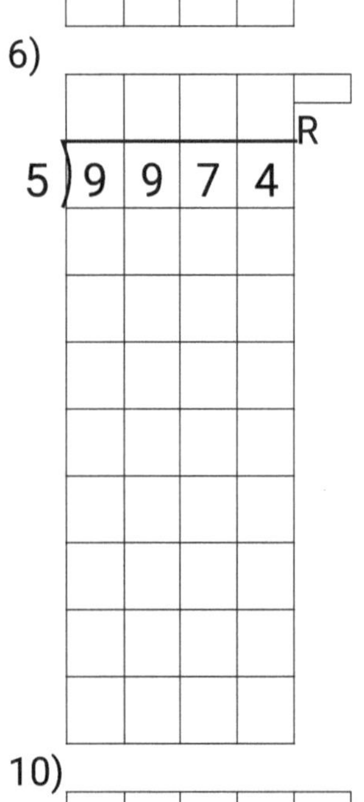

7)
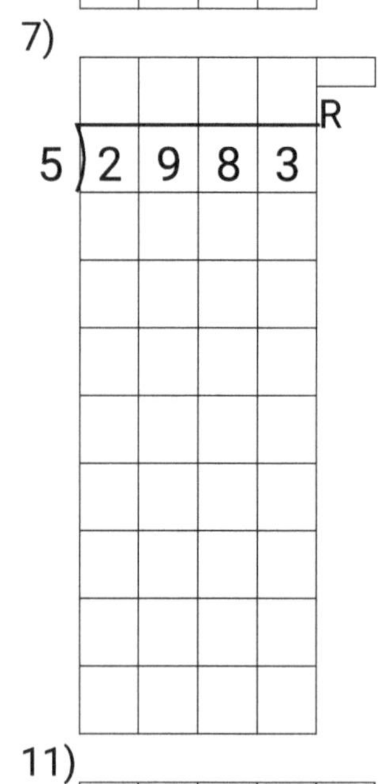

8)

R

3)1 3 9 9

9)
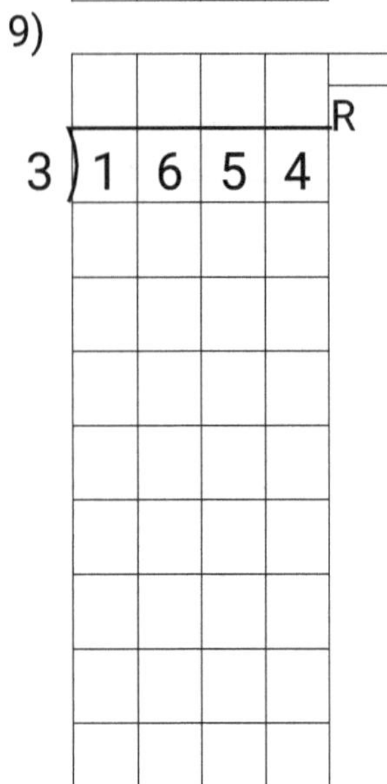

10)
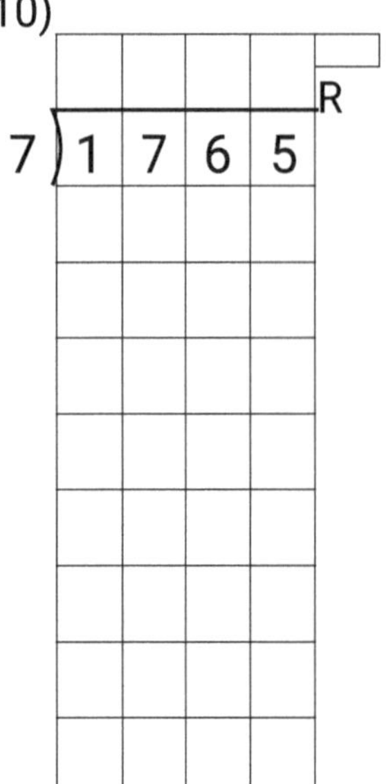

11)
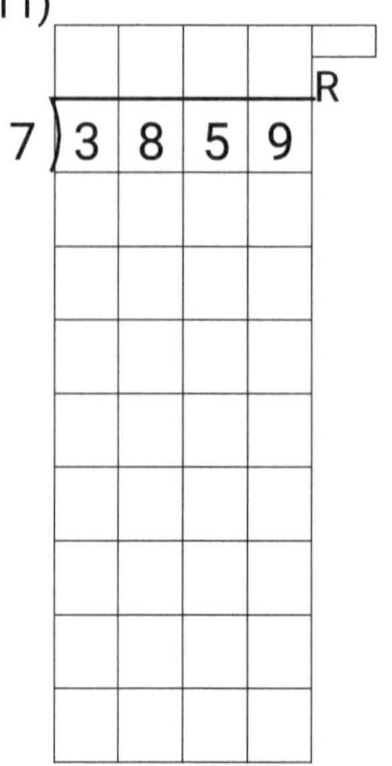

12)

R

2)3 1 1 5

MULTIPLICATION

2-DIGIT BY 2-DIGIT

Give yourself a delicious banana! You flew through that last exercise! Now it's time to get to some seriously big numbers. Let's check out multiplying two numbers together with two digits!

1)

			8	1
		×	6	7
+				

2)

			8	1
		×	6	7
		5	6	7
+				

3)

			8	1
		×	6	7
		5	6	7
+	4	8	6	

4)

			8	1
		×	6	7
		5	6	7
+	4	8	6	
	5	4	2	7

1. It's like I always say, look after the little bananas first, and the big ones take care of themselves!

2. We'll start by multiplying the ones digit of the bottom number (7) by the top number (81). Write the answer below the line: 567

3. Ready for the big bananas? Now, move on to the tens digit of the bottom number (6). Multiply it with the top number (81), but make sure to shift the result one position to the left, as you're dealing with the tens place.

4. Add the two partial answers together: 567 and 4860. This gives you the sum, which is your final result: 5427!

Give yourself a high-paw! You did awesome!

DAY 61

Multiplication: 2-Digit by 2-Digit

1)

			6	5
		×	9	2
+				

2)

			7	7
		×	8	8
+				

3)

			8	1
		×	6	8
+				

4)

			4	1
		×	8	5
+				

5)

			6	9
		×	4	9
+				

6)

			9	8
		×	3	6
+				

7)

			6	3
		×	9	0
+				

8)

			9	9
		×	9	2
+				

9)

			4	0
		×	5	3
+				

10)

			9	0
		×	7	6
+				

11)

			3	2
		×	5	8
+				

12)

			5	5
		×	8	8
+				

DAY 62

Multiplication: 2-Digit by 2-Digit

1)

			5	6
		×	7	9
+				

2)

			8	8
		×	9	0
+				

3)

			5	0
		×	6	5
+				

4)

			9	2
		×	5	3
+				

5)

			8	9
		×	8	1
+				

6)

			6	8
		×	6	1
+				

7)

			8	9
		×	4	7
+				

8)

			6	5
		×	3	9
+				

9)

			8	3
		×	5	0
+				

10)

			5	1
		×	7	4
+				

11)

			8	1
		×	3	4
+				

12)

			3	0
		×	6	7
+				

DAY 63

Multiplication: 2-Digit by 2-Digit

1)

			4	8
		×	5	7
+				

2)

			4	7
		×	7	8
+				

3)

			5	8
		×	3	9
+				

4)

			3	8
		×	8	8
+				

5)

			8	1
		×	6	4
+				

6)

			8	9
		×	6	1
+				

7)

			5	8
		×	4	7
+				

8)

			6	6
		×	5	6
+				

9)

			8	8
		×	7	2
+				

10)

			4	2
		×	7	1
+				

11)

			8	8
		×	4	4
+				

12)

			9	0
		×	7	7
+				

DAY 64

Multiplication: 2-Digit by 2-Digit

1)

			7	3
		×	9	9
+				

2)

			5	5
		×	9	9
+				

3)

			4	5
		×	8	8
+				

4)

			4	6
		×	5	5
+				

5)

			7	9
		×	3	2
+				

6)

			8	4
		×	7	3
+				

7)

			5	5
		×	7	1
+				

8)

			4	4
		×	3	7
+				

9)

			3	2
		×	3	0
+				

10)

			6	3
		×	3	7
+				

11)

			5	9
		×	9	7
+				

12)

			4	0
		×	3	8
+				

DAY 65

Multiplication: 2-Digit by 2-Digit

1) $\begin{array}{r} 57 \\ \times\ 70 \\ \hline \\ + \\ \hline \end{array}$

2) $\begin{array}{r} 41 \\ \times\ 41 \\ \hline \\ + \\ \hline \end{array}$

3) $\begin{array}{r} 68 \\ \times\ 92 \\ \hline \\ + \\ \hline \end{array}$

4) $\begin{array}{r} 97 \\ \times\ 97 \\ \hline \\ + \\ \hline \end{array}$

5) $\begin{array}{r} 78 \\ \times\ 55 \\ \hline \\ + \\ \hline \end{array}$

6) $\begin{array}{r} 42 \\ \times\ 70 \\ \hline \\ + \\ \hline \end{array}$

7) $\begin{array}{r} 84 \\ \times\ 95 \\ \hline \\ + \\ \hline \end{array}$

8) $\begin{array}{r} 65 \\ \times\ 96 \\ \hline \\ + \\ \hline \end{array}$

9) $\begin{array}{r} 34 \\ \times\ 48 \\ \hline \\ + \\ \hline \end{array}$

10) $\begin{array}{r} 46 \\ \times\ 60 \\ \hline \\ + \\ \hline \end{array}$

11) $\begin{array}{r} 32 \\ \times\ 69 \\ \hline \\ + \\ \hline \end{array}$

12) $\begin{array}{r} 78 \\ \times\ 45 \\ \hline \\ + \\ \hline \end{array}$

DAY 66

Multiplication: 2-Digit by 2-Digit

1) 42 × 54 =

2) 57 × 81 =

3) 50 × 47 =

4) 50 × 39 =

5) 71 × 76 =

6) 92 × 90 =

7) 73 × 90 =

8) 54 × 56 =

9) 94 × 82 =

10) 88 × 67 =

11) 79 × 55 =

12) 81 × 41 =

DAY 67

Multiplication: 2-Digit by 2-Digit

1) 71 × 63

2) 44 × 31

3) 79 × 46

4) 82 × 59

5) 84 × 32

6) 92 × 33

7) 69 × 86

8) 80 × 50

9) 75 × 30

10) 30 × 60

11) 89 × 65

12) 32 × 55

DAY 68

Multiplication: 2-Digit by 2-Digit

Time :

Score /12

1)
$$\begin{array}{r} 57 \\ \times\ 53 \\ \hline \end{array}$$

2)
$$\begin{array}{r} 91 \\ \times\ 46 \\ \hline \end{array}$$

3)
$$\begin{array}{r} 69 \\ \times\ 84 \\ \hline \end{array}$$

4)
$$\begin{array}{r} 68 \\ \times\ 69 \\ \hline \end{array}$$

5)
$$\begin{array}{r} 47 \\ \times\ 79 \\ \hline \end{array}$$

6)
$$\begin{array}{r} 82 \\ \times\ 32 \\ \hline \end{array}$$

7)
$$\begin{array}{r} 30 \\ \times\ 73 \\ \hline \end{array}$$

8)
$$\begin{array}{r} 99 \\ \times\ 35 \\ \hline \end{array}$$

9)
$$\begin{array}{r} 49 \\ \times\ 73 \\ \hline \end{array}$$

10)
$$\begin{array}{r} 49 \\ \times\ 39 \\ \hline \end{array}$$

11)
$$\begin{array}{r} 69 \\ \times\ 85 \\ \hline \end{array}$$

12)
$$\begin{array}{r} 70 \\ \times\ 87 \\ \hline \end{array}$$

DAY 69

Multiplication: 2-Digit by 2-Digit

Time :

Score /12

1) 34 × 31

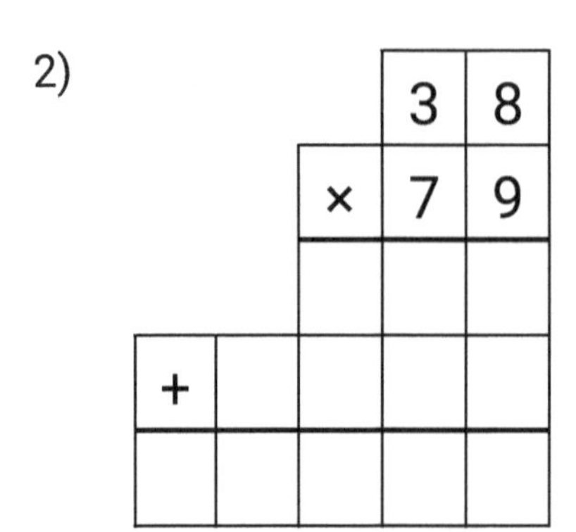

3) 32 × 70

4) 72 × 69

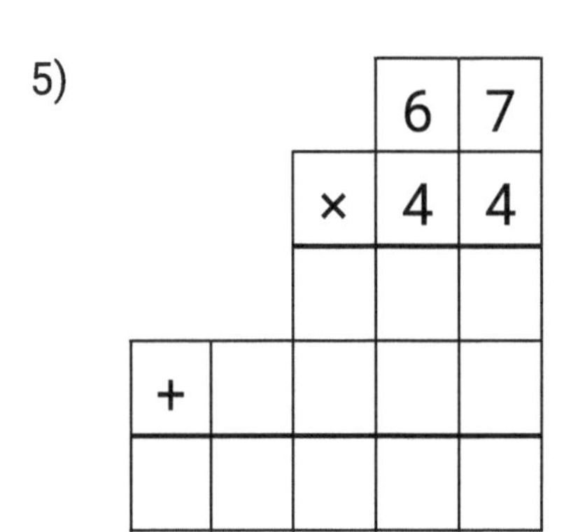

6) 53 × 63

7) 95 × 74

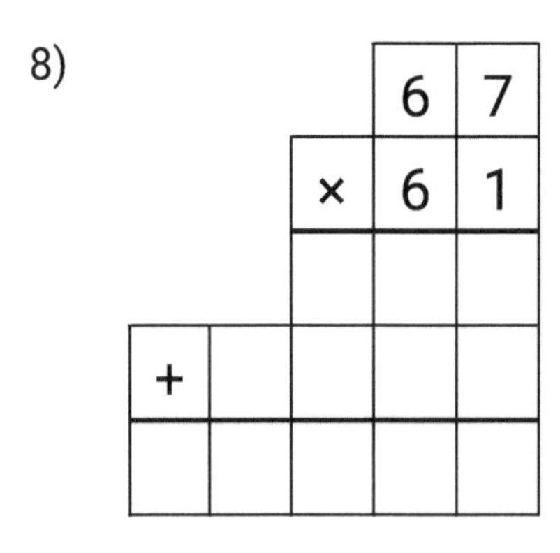

9) 38 × 65

10) 39 × 74

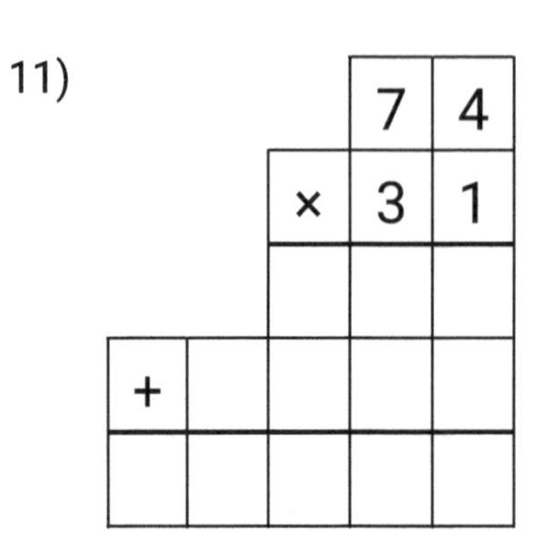

12) 44 × 86

DAY 70

Multiplication: 2-Digit by 2-Digit

Time :

Score /12

1) 83×61

2) 44×97

3) 54×82

4) 48×68

5) 39×39

6) 66×88

7) 35×86

8) 42×61

9) 85×92

10) 69×93

11) 66×56

12) 63×39

THE NINE CHAPTERS ON THE MATHEMATICAL ART

Division has been around for quite some time, with an early record of it being The Nine Chapters on the Mathematical Art which was written by multiple Chinese scholars from the 10th to the 2nd centuries BC. In it, there are methods described for solving nine different types of mathematical problems ranging from areas to currency to more complex algebra and other theories. It is considered to be one of the earliest surviving mathematical texts in China and has been reproduced and translated into multiple languages throughout history.

DAY 71

Multiplication: 3-Digit by 2-Digit

Time :

Score / 12

1) 668×19

2) 652×33

3) 595×67

4) 821×96

5) 303×51

6) 682×25

7) 909×41

8) 237×71

9) 819×84

10) 447×39

11) 162×11

12) 291×21

DAY 72

Multiplication: 3-Digit by 2-Digit

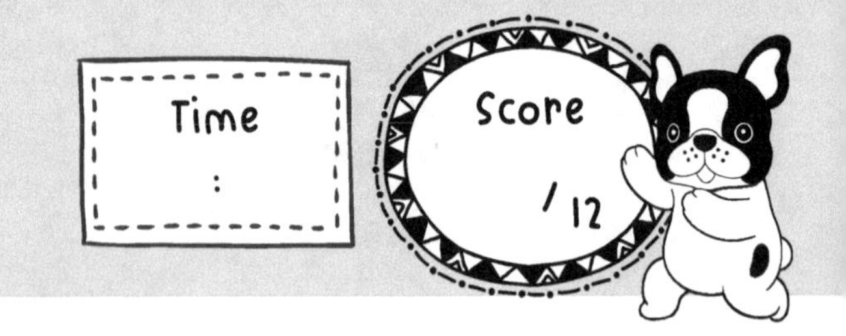

1)

			7	5	9
		×		1	4
+					

2)

			9	8	6
		×		9	7
+					

3)

			3	7	6
		×		8	3
+					

4)

			9	1	7
		×		2	8
+					

5)

			2	3	2
		×		7	8
+					

6)

			8	9	4
		×		8	7
+					

7)

			4	3	0
		×		8	9
+					

8)

			6	7	1
		×		6	9
+					

9)

		1	2	0
	×		2	2
+				

10)

			3	3	3
		×		7	6
+					

11)

		1	0	6
	×		1	1
+				

12)

			1	6	2
		×		3	7
+					

DAY 73

Multiplication: 3-Digit by 2-Digit

1) 596 × 33

2) 412 × 36

3) 826 × 17

4) 799 × 45

5) 471 × 37

6) 103 × 25

7) 708 × 57

8) 809 × 18

9) 210 × 74

10) 259 × 82

11) 303 × 59

12) 139 × 24

DAY 74

Multiplication: 3-Digit by 2-Digit

Time :

Score / 12

1) 726 × 10 =

2) 801 × 96 =

3) 423 × 13 =

4) 228 × 88 =

5) 333 × 94 =

6) 594 × 22 =

7) 287 × 11 =

8) 500 × 45 =

9) 449 × 44 =

10) 526 × 21 =

11) 658 × 31 =

12) 586 × 73 =

DAY 75

Multiplication: 3-Digit by 2-Digit

1)

			3	7	0
		×		4	6
+					

2)

			8	6	2
		×		3	4
+					

3)

			3	7	3
		×		7	8
+					

4)

			9	7	4
		×		6	3
+					

5)

			4	6	1
		×		4	8
+					

6)

			9	0	2
		×		9	0
+					

7)

			2	6	1
		×		5	8
+					

8)

			5	8	3
		×		4	3
+					

9)

			9	3	8
		×		1	5
+					

10)

			3	5	0
		×		4	3
+					

11)

			2	9	6
		×		7	0
+					

12)

			6	6	4
		×		7	8
+					

DAY 76

Multiplication: 3-Digit by 2-Digit

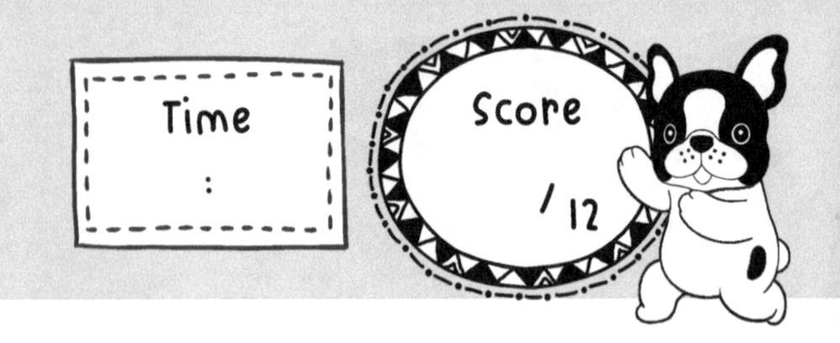

1)

			3	6	2
		×		5	6
+					

2)

			9	6	0
		×		1	1
+					

3)

			6	8	1
		×		4	5
+					

4)

			6	5	0
		×		2	7
+					

5)

			7	6	7
		×		3	4
+					

6)

			5	2	0
		×		4	4
+					

7)

			8	0	2
		×		6	4
+					

8)

			7	6	8
		×		7	3
+					

9)

			1	2	7
		×		3	3
+					

10)

			4	4	6
		×		8	9
+					

11)

			1	6	4
		×		9	7
+					

12)

			2	2	5
		×		4	2
+					

DAY 77

Multiplication: 3-Digit by 2-Digit

1)

			3	7	7
		×		9	8
+					

2)

			4	8	7
		×		4	2
+					

3)

			7	2	5
		×		1	1
+					

4)

			4	7	1
		×		6	6
+					

5)

			2	6	6
		×		3	7
+					

6)

			3	4	6
		×		1	2
+					

7)

			8	0	8
		×		7	7
+					

8)

			1	0	7
		×		2	2
+					

9)

			2	8	3
		×		4	5
+					

10)

			5	2	3
		×		8	6
+					

11)

			2	1	5
		×		4	2
+					

12)

			3	3	5
		×		2	9
+					

DAY 78

Multiplication: 3-Digit by 2-Digit

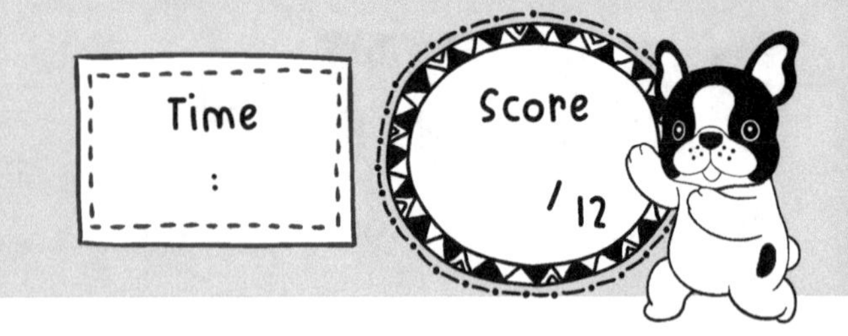

1) 544 × 63

2) 835 × 99

3) 154 × 33

4) 630 × 25

5) 397 × 34

6) 414 × 54

7) 848 × 13

8) 280 × 77

9) 360 × 85

10) 847 × 77

11) 361 × 76

12) 604 × 10

DAY 79

Multiplication: 3-Digit by 2-Digit

1)

			2	2	9
		×		2	6
+					

2)

			1	0	2
		×		5	8
+					

3)

			6	7	4
		×		4	9
+					

4)

			2	0	5
		×		8	8
+					

5)

			6	5	9
		×		6	8
+					

6)

			8	6	8
		×		5	9
+					

7)

			4	8	6
		×		4	2
+					

8)

			2	7	7
		×		8	8
+					

9)

			3	4	5
		×		5	0
+					

10)

			9	2	5
		×		2	6
+					

11)

			1	6	5
		×		7	2
+					

12)

			2	4	0
		×		9	9
+					

DAY 80

Multiplication: 3-Digit by 2-Digit

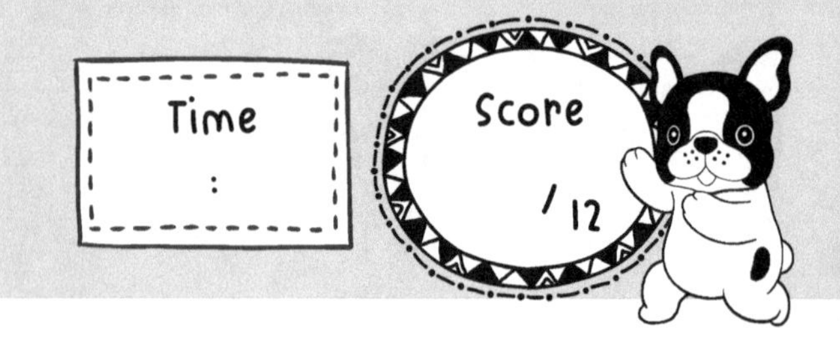

1) 396 × 30 =

2) 524 × 29 =

3) 691 × 21 =

4) 810 × 98 =

5) 105 × 56 =

6) 341 × 33 =

7) 315 × 56 =

8) 406 × 27 =

9) 677 × 15 =

10) 392 × 69 =

11) 747 × 79 =

12) 180 × 66 =

DIVISION

WITH DOUBLE DIGIT DIVISOR

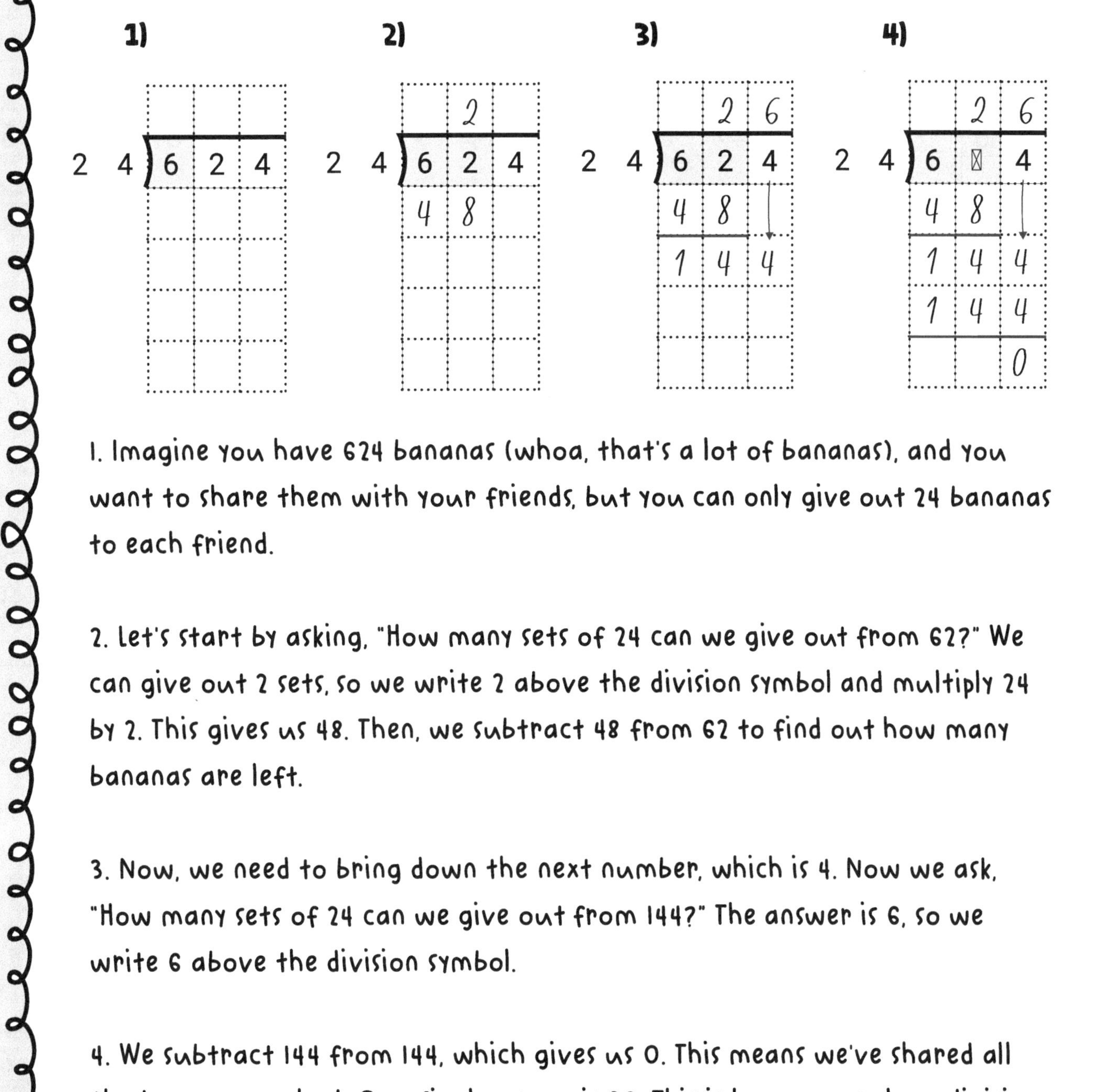

1. Imagine you have 624 bananas (whoa, that's a lot of bananas), and you want to share them with your friends, but you can only give out 24 bananas to each friend.

2. Let's start by asking, "How many sets of 24 can we give out from 62?" We can give out 2 sets, so we write 2 above the division symbol and multiply 24 by 2. This gives us 48. Then, we subtract 48 from 62 to find out how many bananas are left.

3. Now, we need to bring down the next number, which is 4. Now we ask, "How many sets of 24 can we give out from 144?" The answer is 6, so we write 6 above the division symbol.

4. We subtract 144 from 144, which gives us 0. This means we've shared all the bananas we had. Our final answer is 26. This is how we use long division to share bananas among Frenchies... I mean friends!

Wow! You've mastered long division! You're a mathematical legend!

DAY 81

Division: 3-Digit by 2-Digit with No Reminders

1) $88\overline{)176}$

2) $51\overline{)714}$

3) $30\overline{)600}$

4) $79\overline{)395}$

5) $52\overline{)416}$

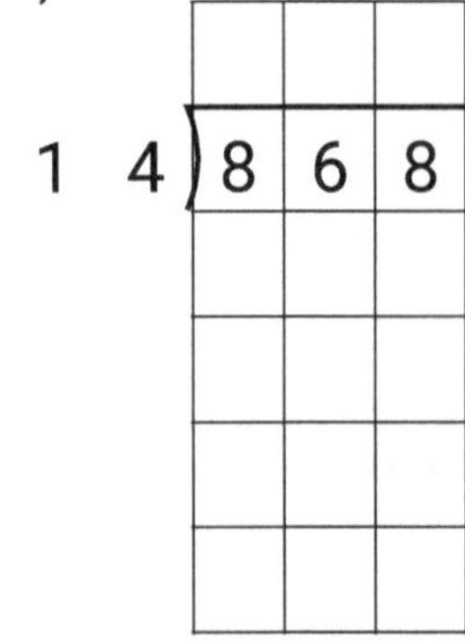

7) $25\overline{)775}$

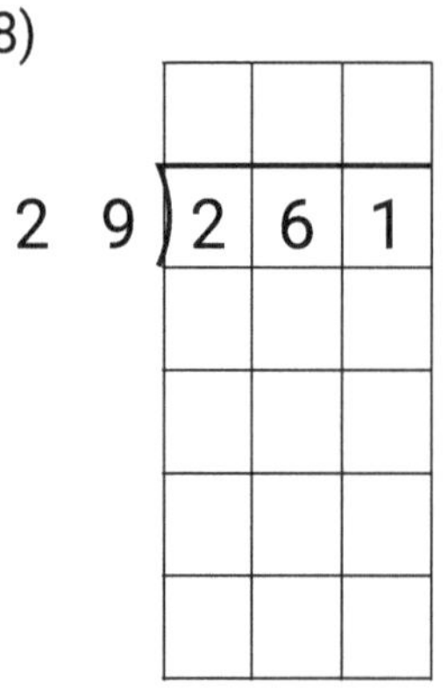

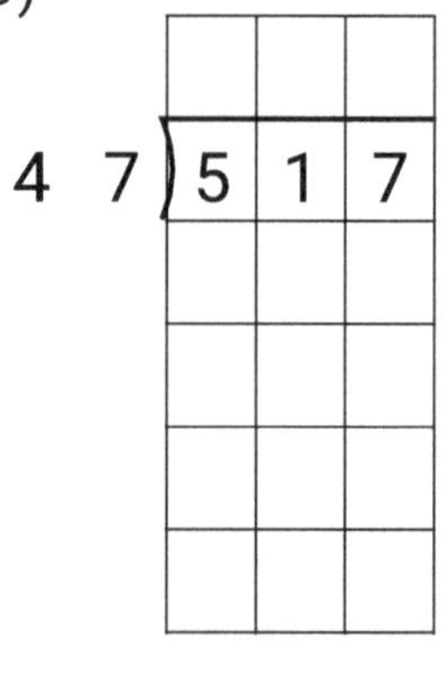

10) $53\overline{)318}$

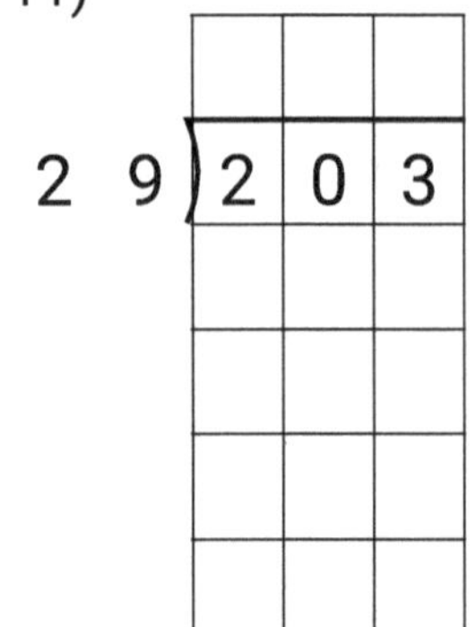

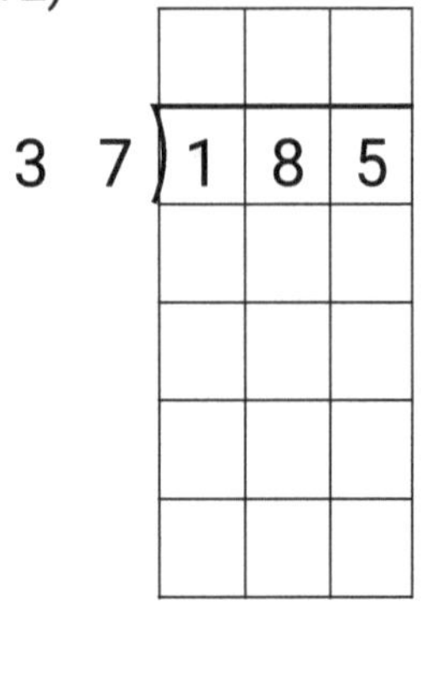

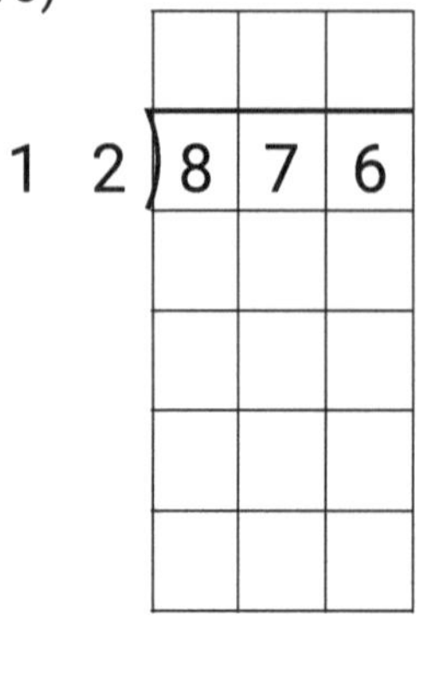

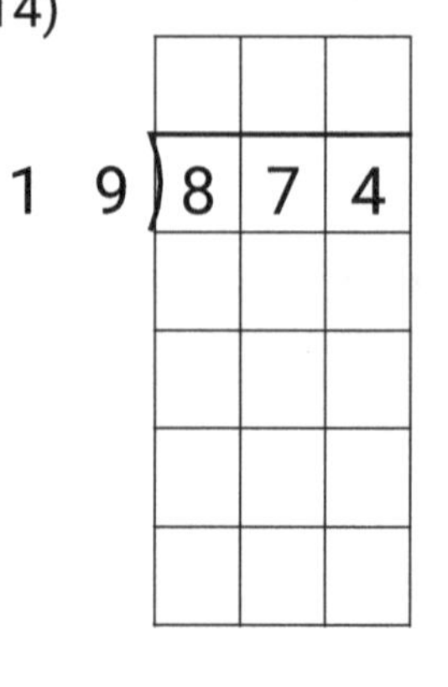

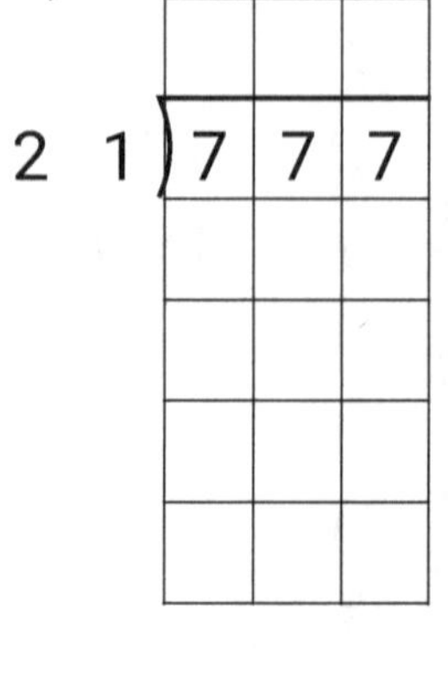

DAY 82

Division: 3-Digit by 2-Digit with No Reminders

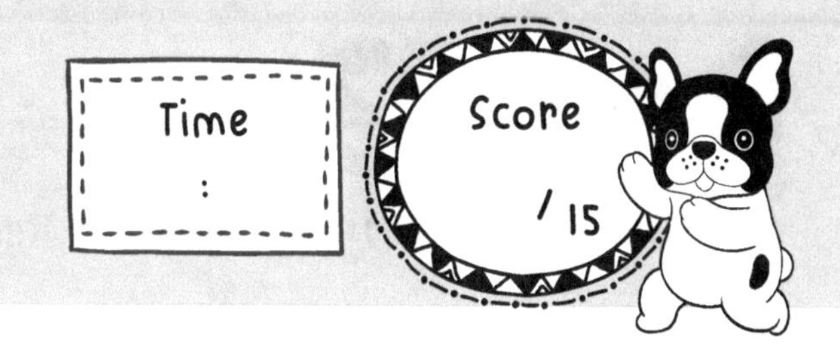

1) $35 \overline{)385}$

2) $97 \overline{)582}$

3) $15 \overline{)525}$

4) $25 \overline{)875}$

5) $25 \overline{)100}$

6) $74 \overline{)222}$

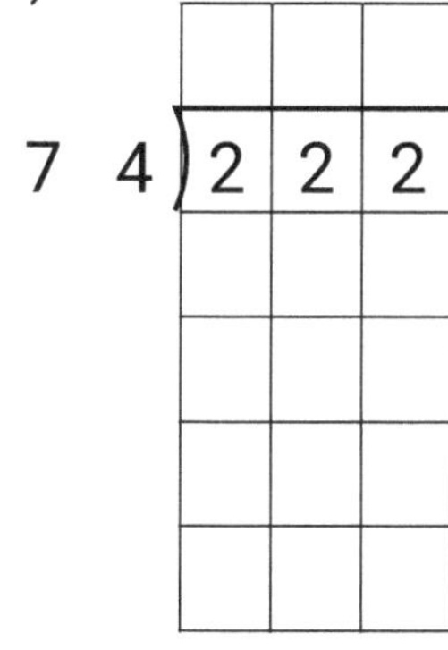

7) $61 \overline{)244}$

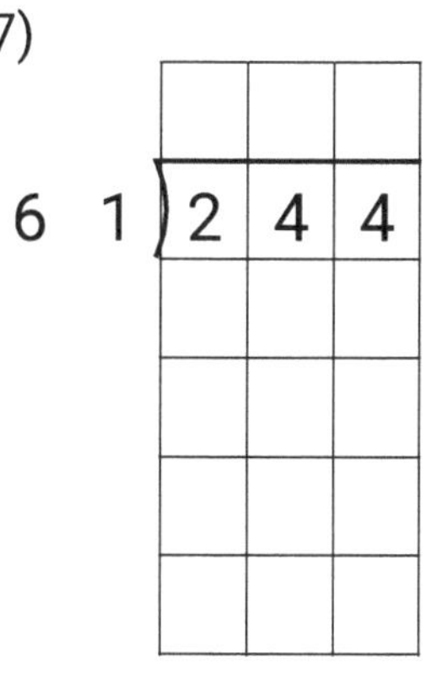

8) $66 \overline{)198}$

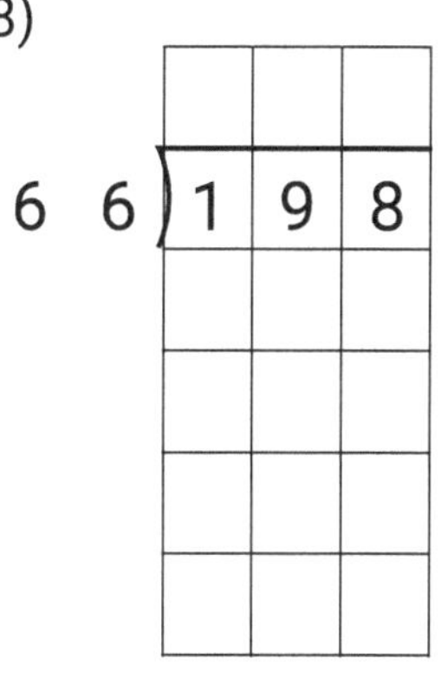

9) $39 \overline{)429}$

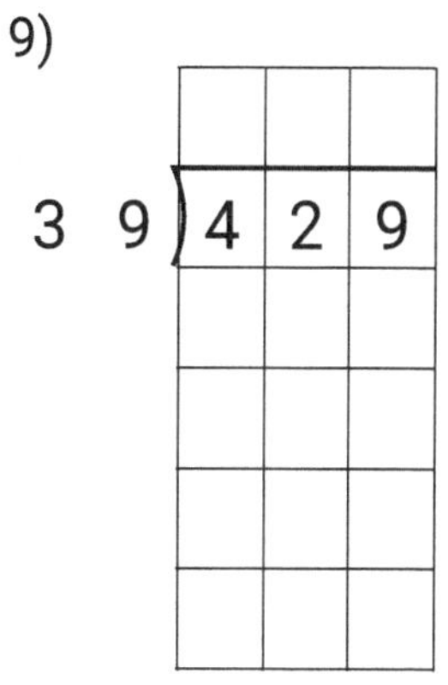

10) $17 \overline{)255}$

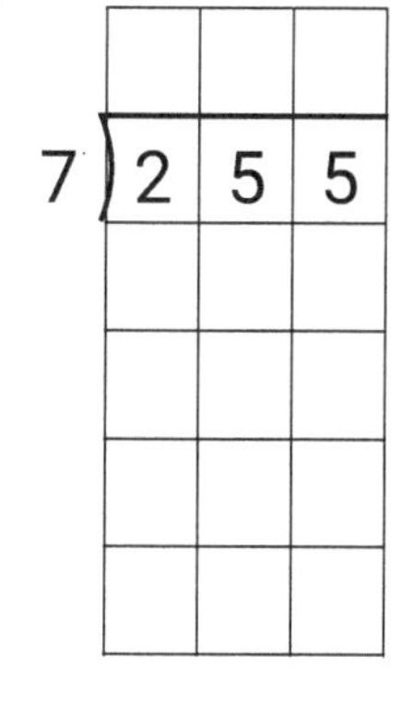

11) $47 \overline{)235}$

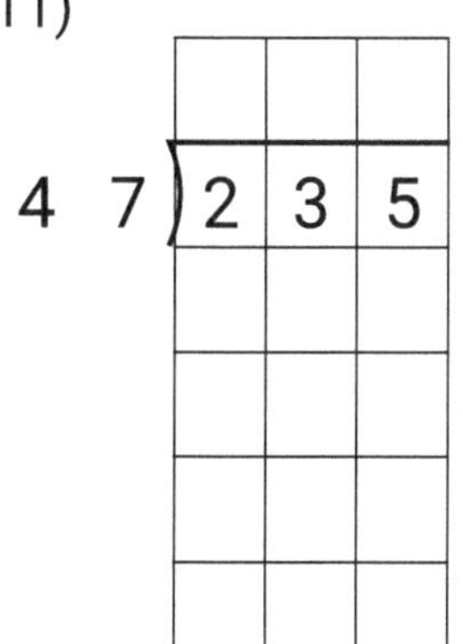

12) $26 \overline{)728}$

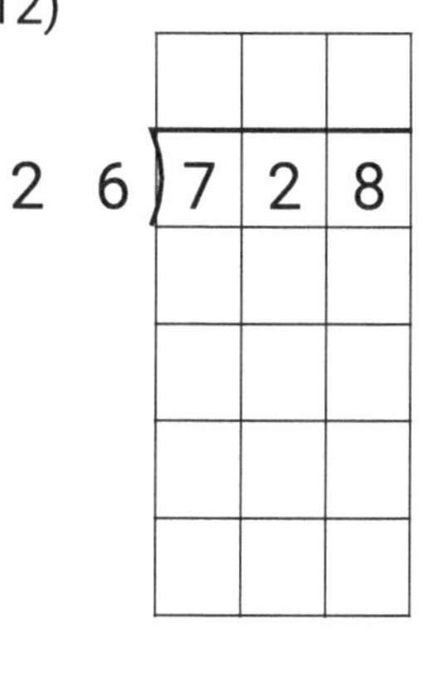

13) $61 \overline{)122}$

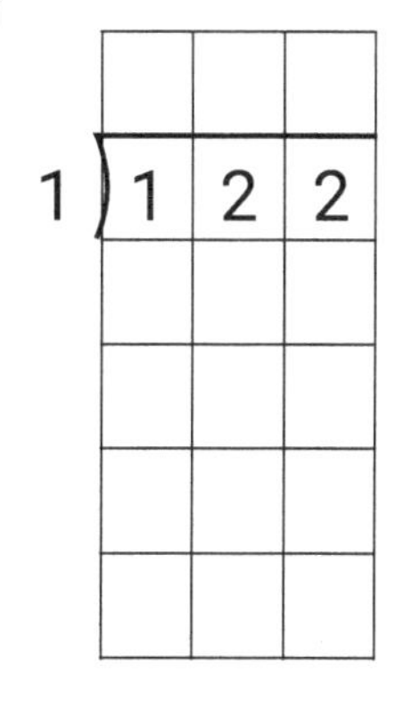

14) $34 \overline{)170}$

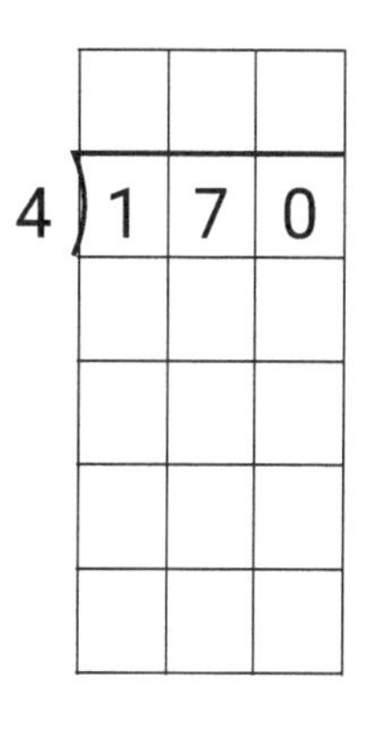

15) $14 \overline{)602}$

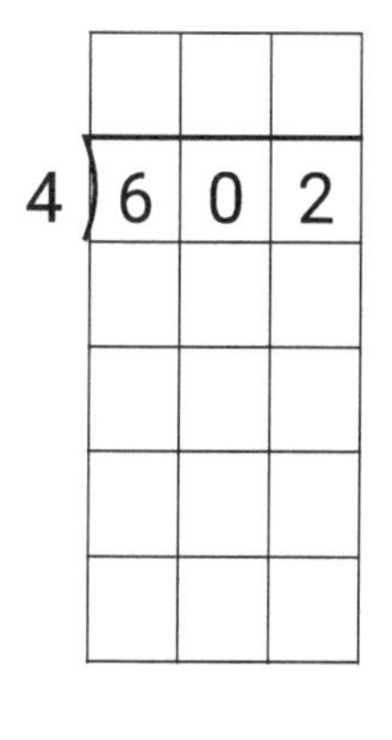

DAY 83

Division: 3-Digit by 2-Digit with No Reminders

1) 35) 805

2)
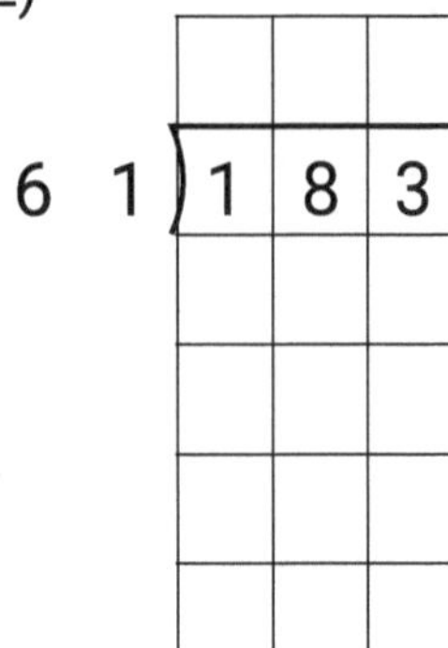
61) 183

3)
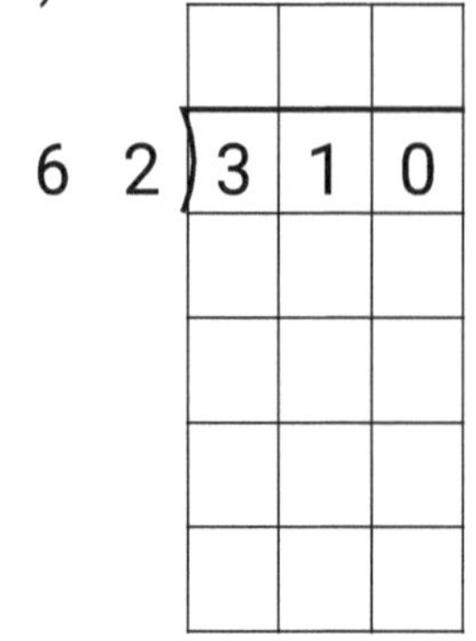
62) 310

4)
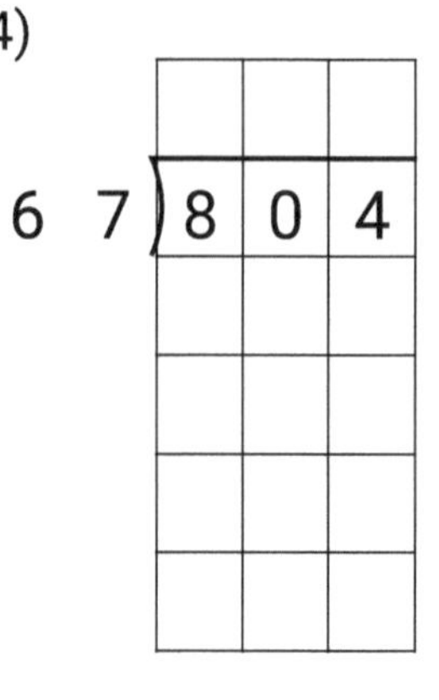
67) 804

5)
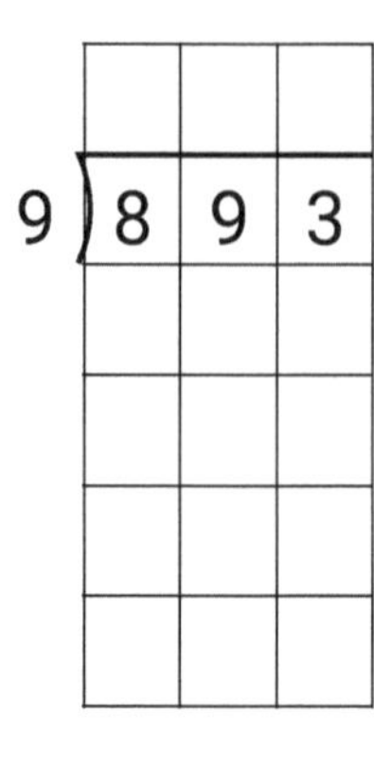
19) 893

6)
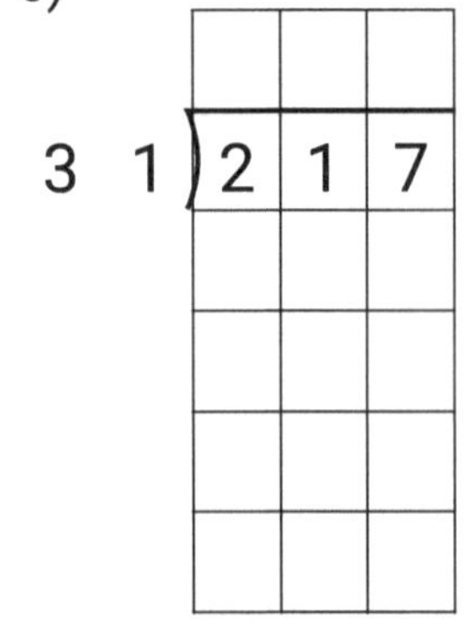
31) 217

7)
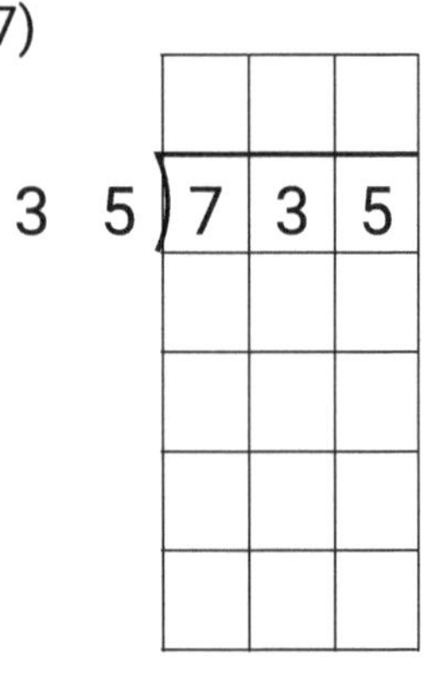
35) 735

8)
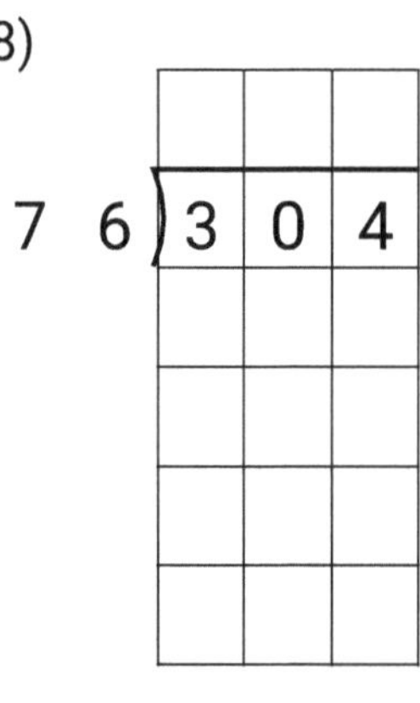
76) 304

9)
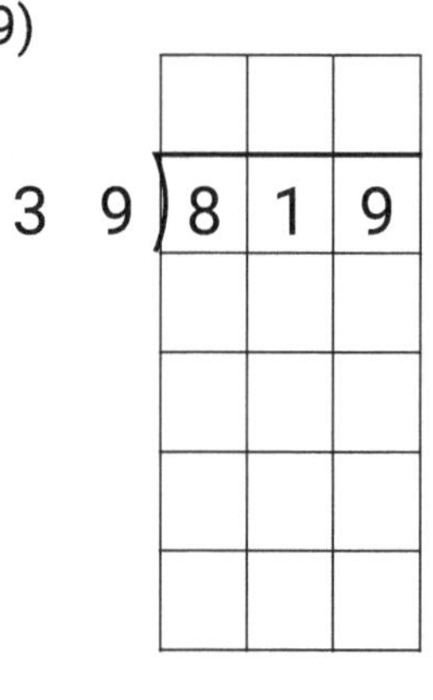
39) 819

10)
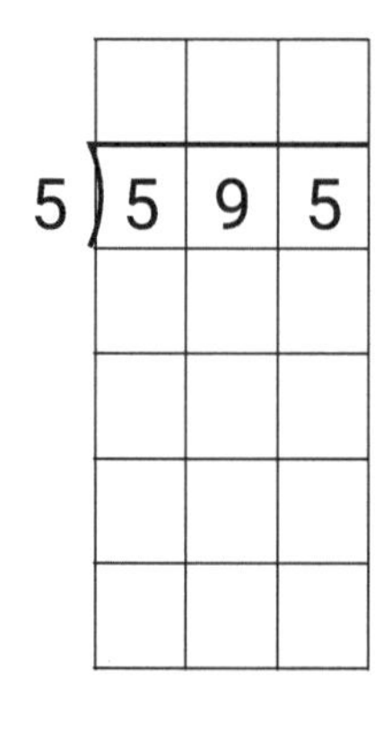
35) 595

11)
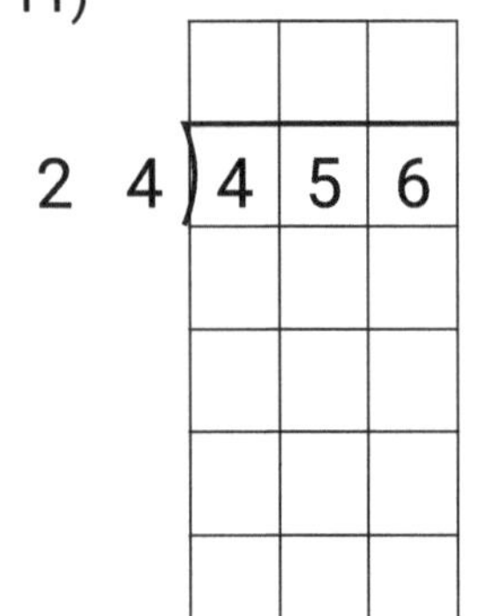
24) 456

12)
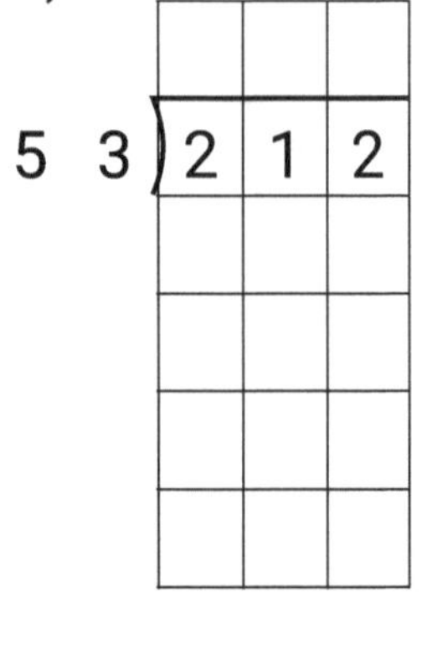
53) 212

13)
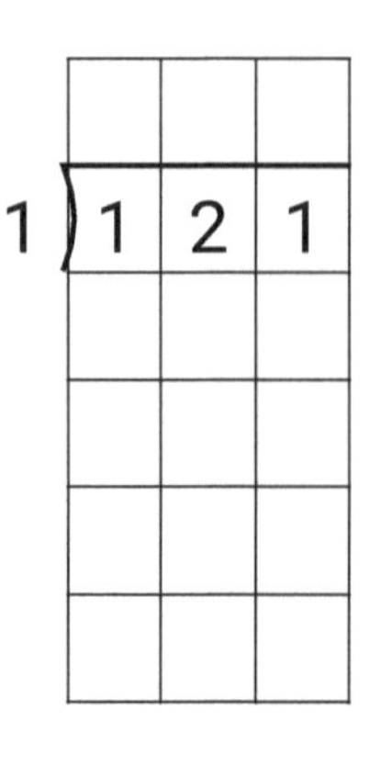
11) 121

14)
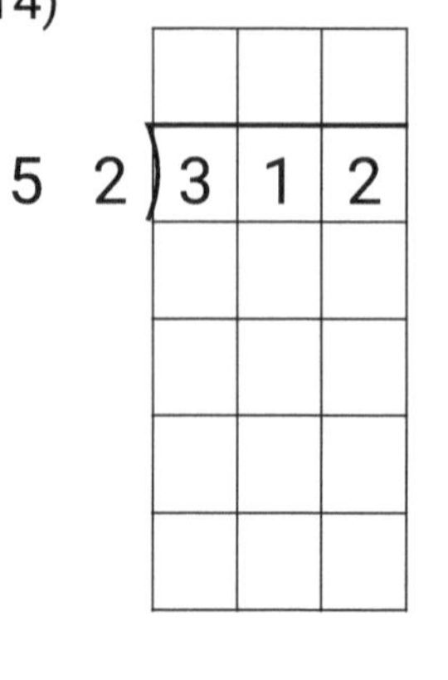
52) 312

15)
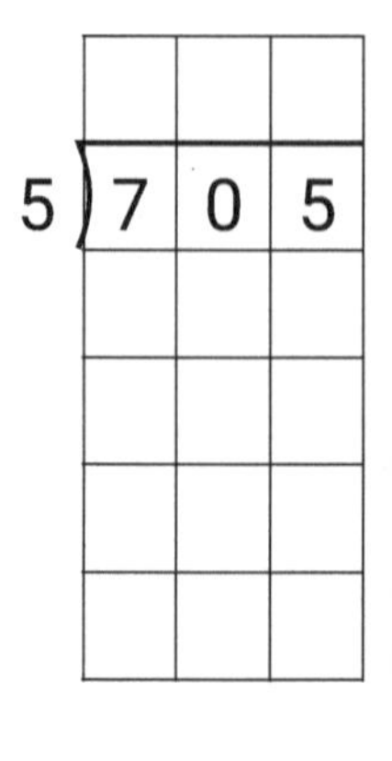
15) 705

DAY 84

Division: 3-Digit by 2-Digit with No Reminders

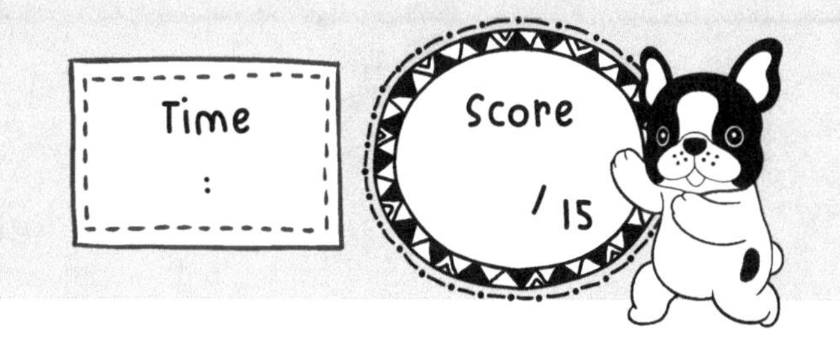

1) 23) 207

2) 52) 884

3) 46) 276

4) 11) 605

5) 61) 549

6)

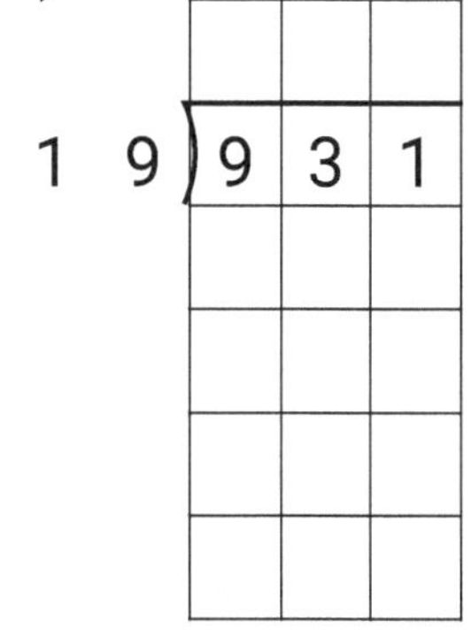

7)

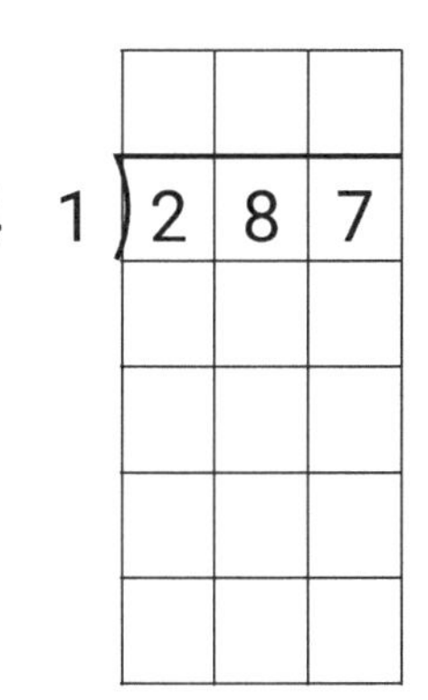

8)

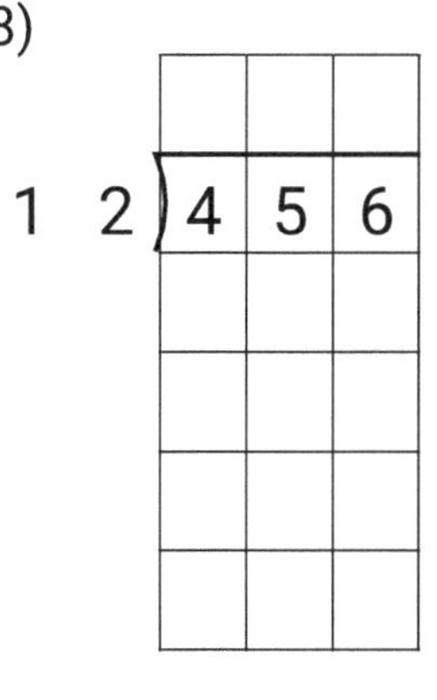

9)

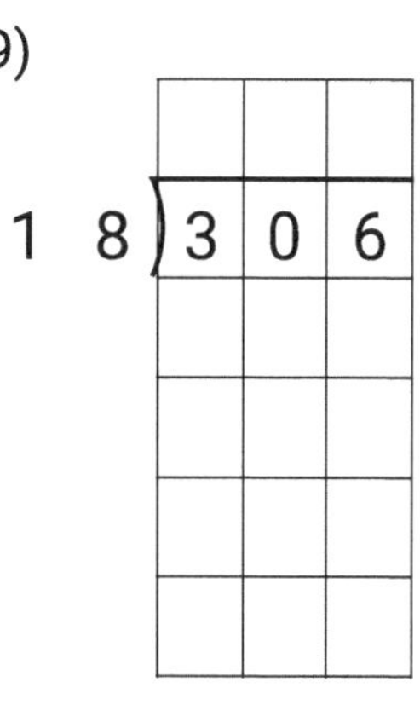

10)

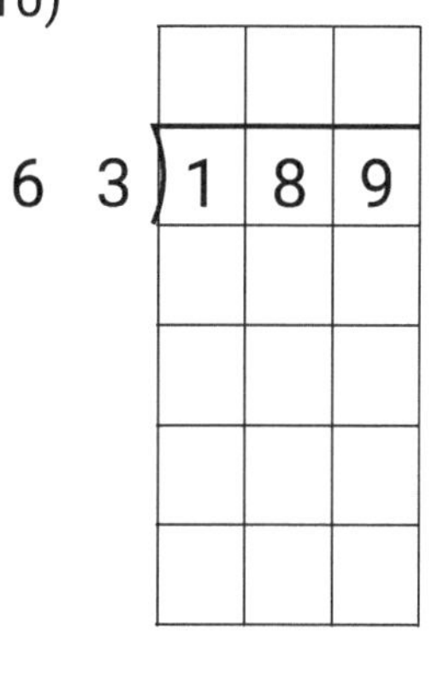

11)

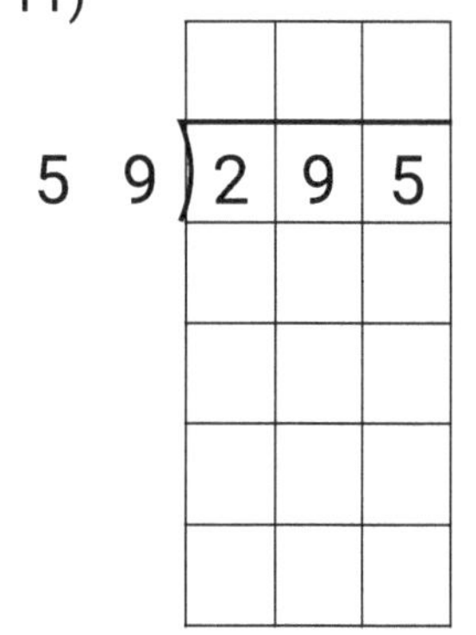

12)

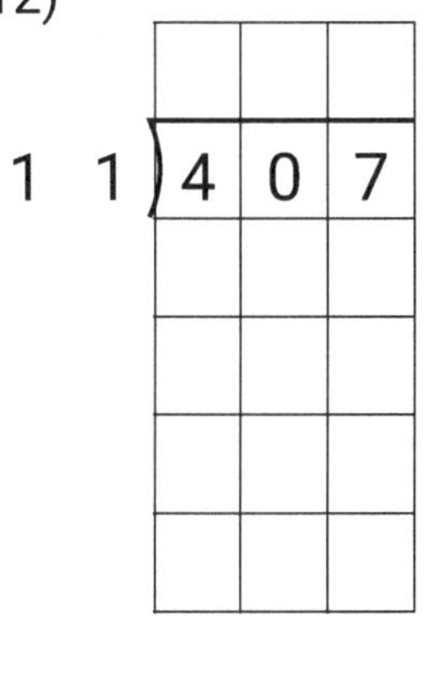

13)

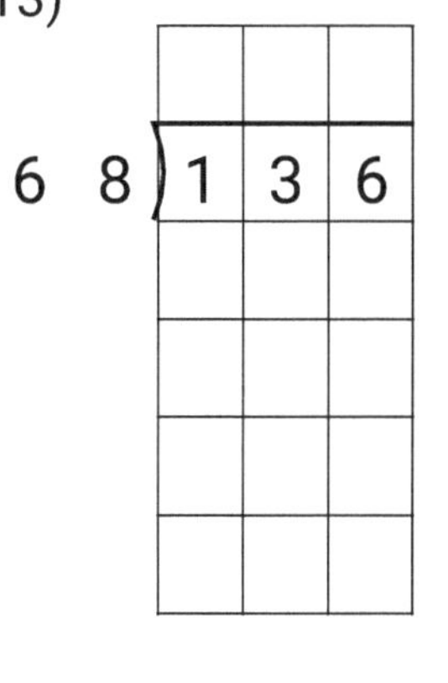

14)

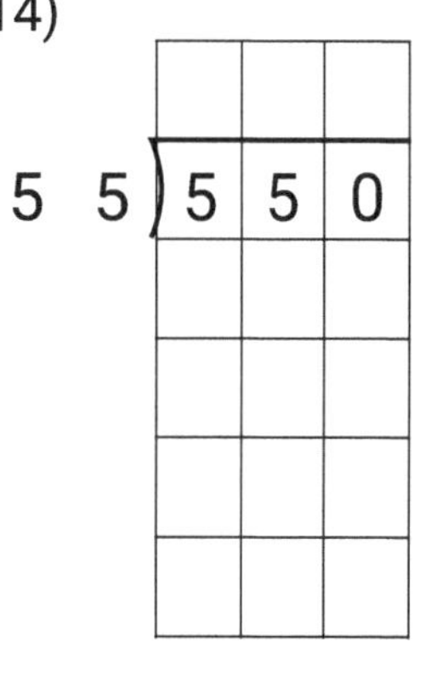

15)

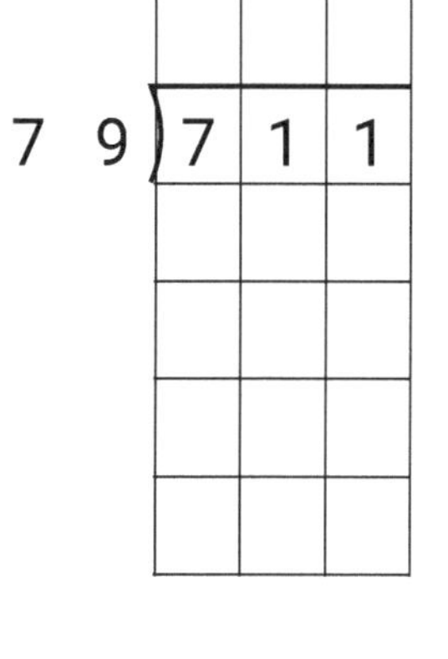

DAY 85

Division: 3-Digit by 2-Digit with No Reminders

1)

21)609

2)

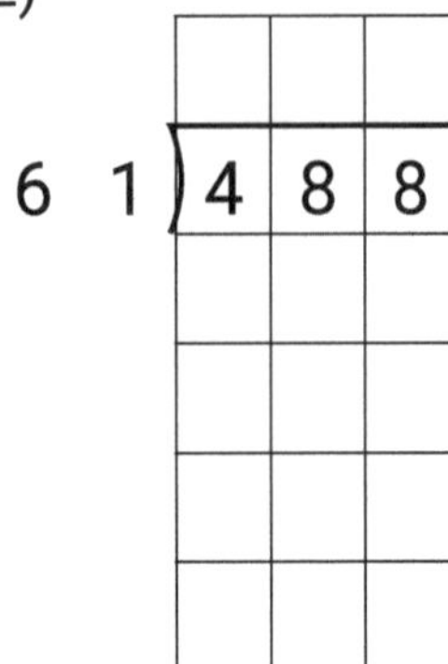

3)

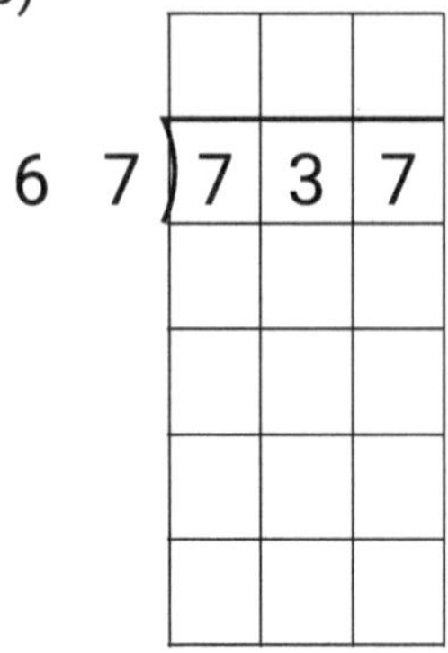

4)

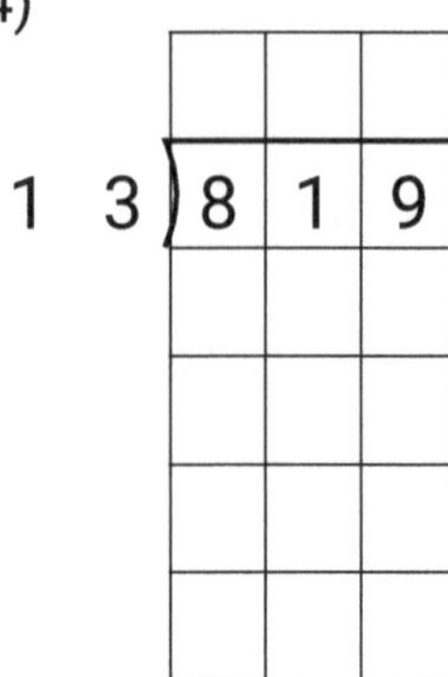

5)

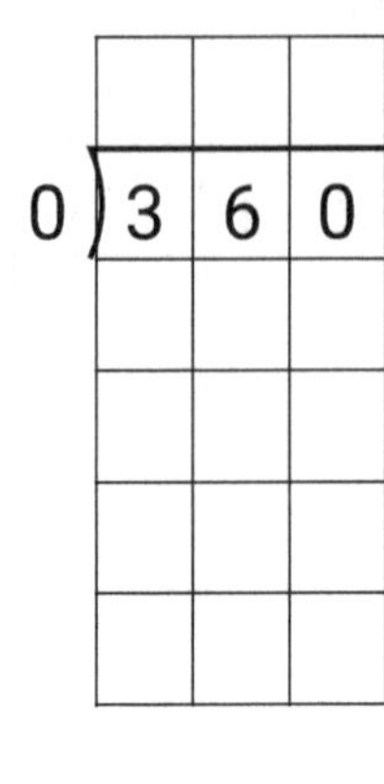

6)

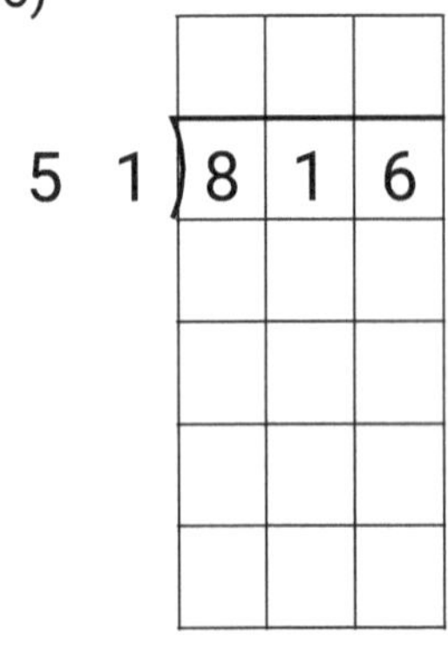

7)

24)336

8)

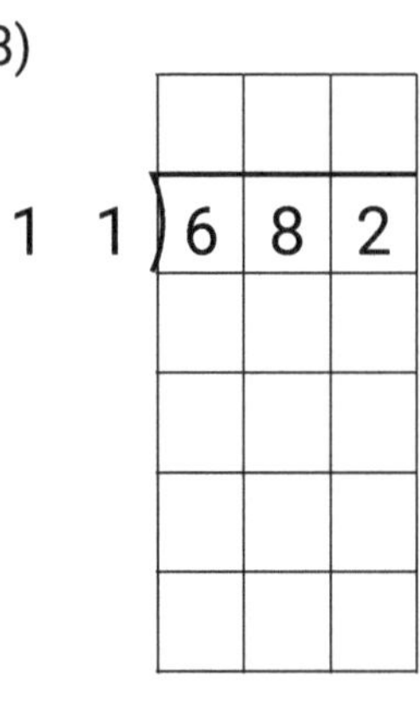

9)

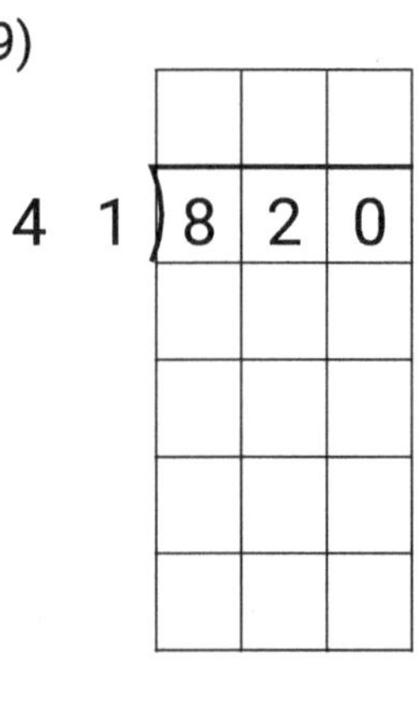

10)

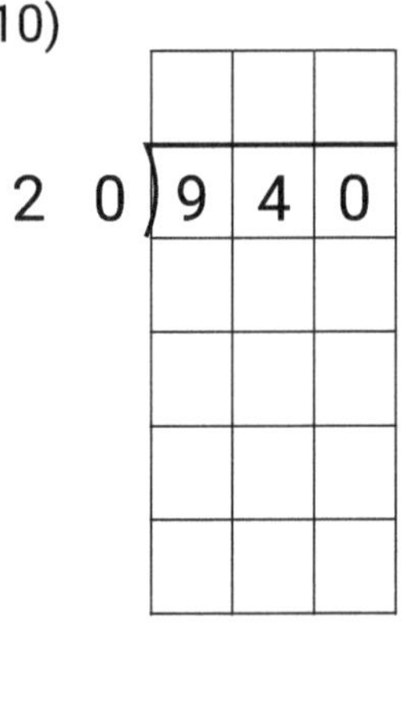

11)

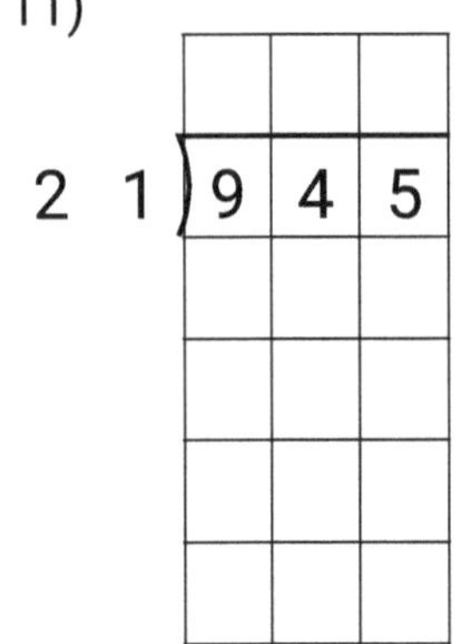

12)

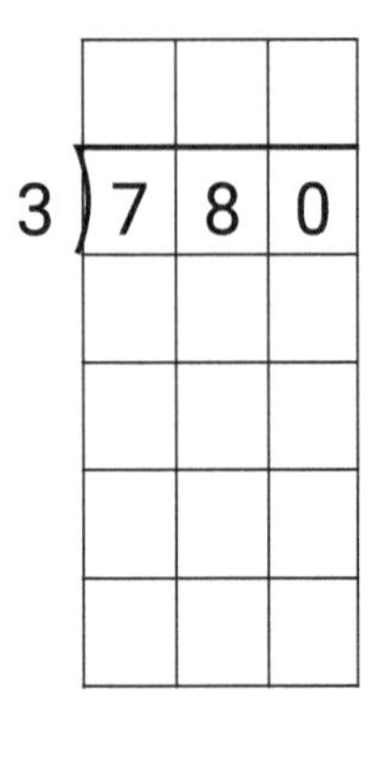

13)

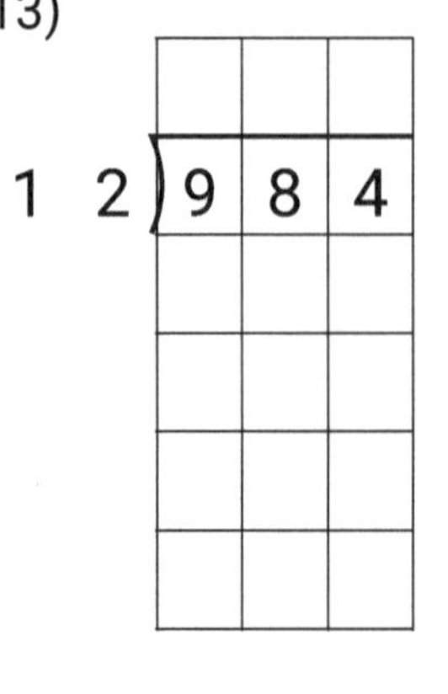

14)

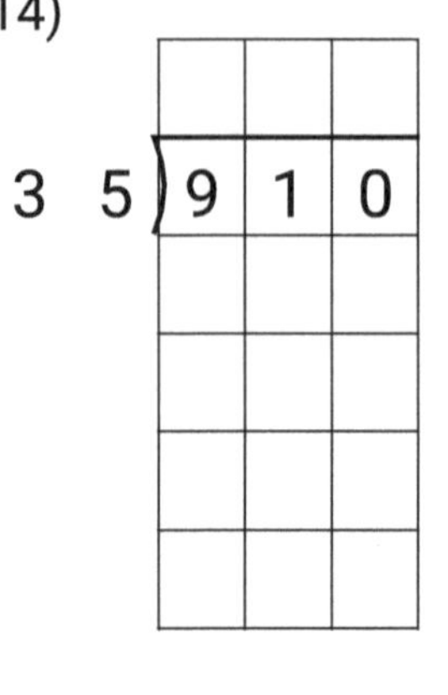

15)

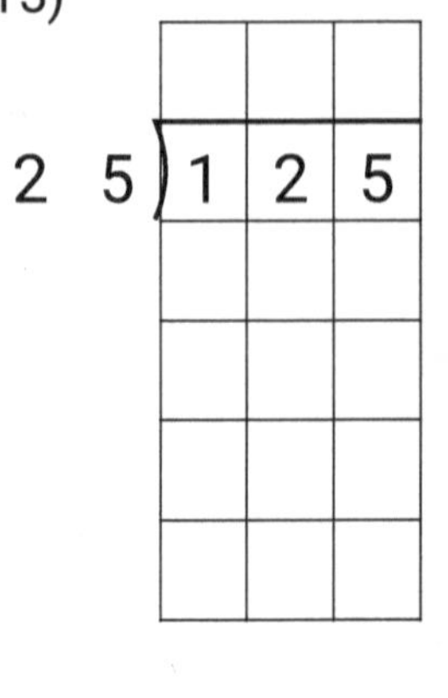

DAY 86

Division: 3-Digit by 2-Digit with Reminders

1) 39) 567 R

2) 10) 873 R

3)
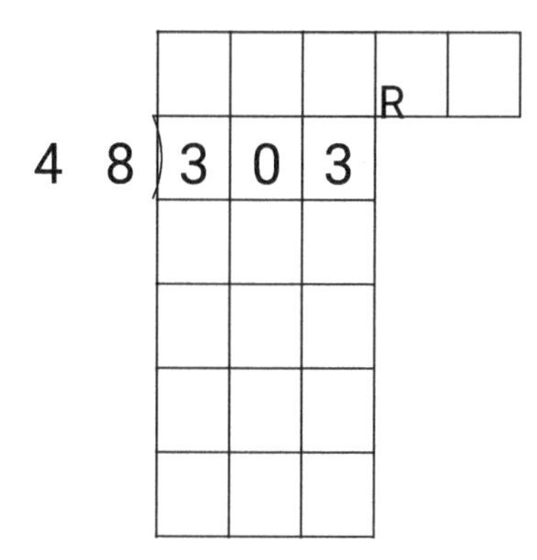

4)
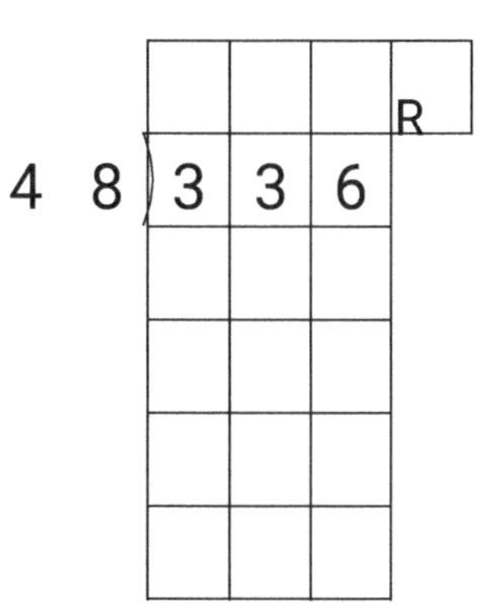

5)
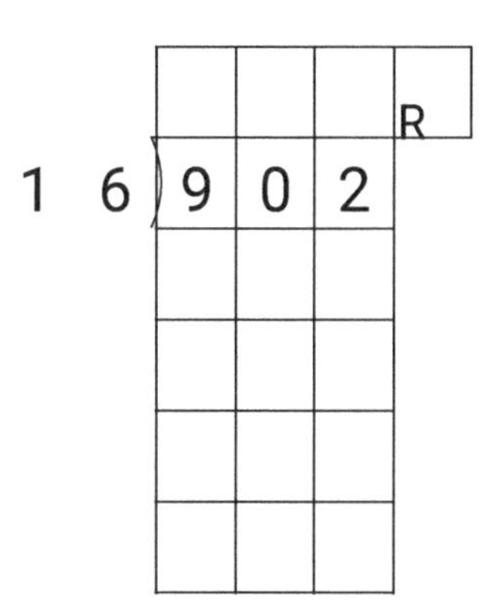

6)
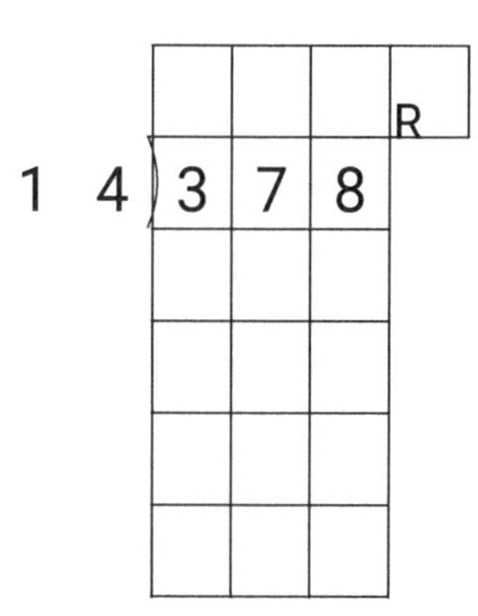

7) 11) 638 R

8)
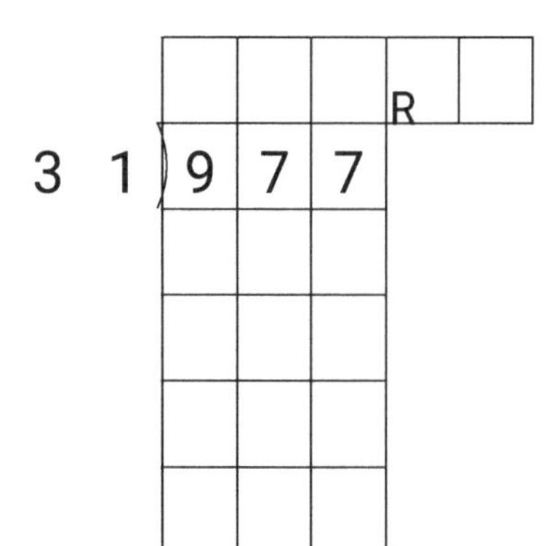

9)
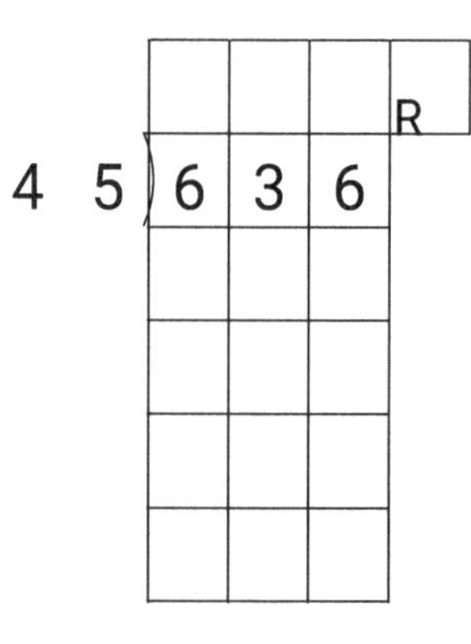

10)
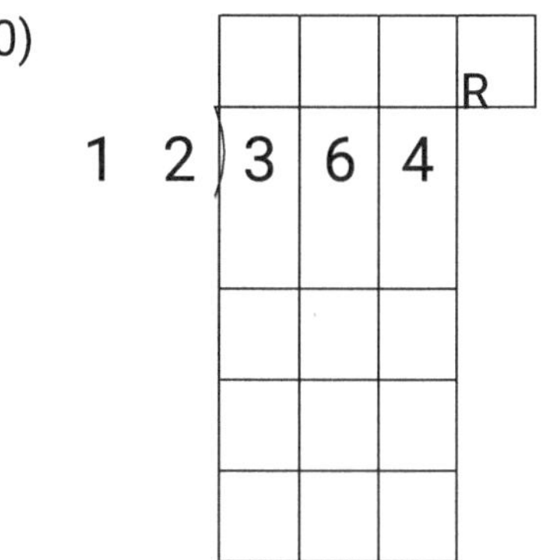

11)
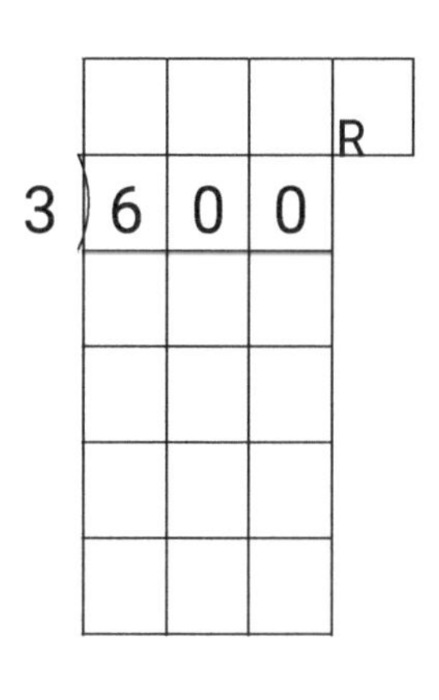

12)
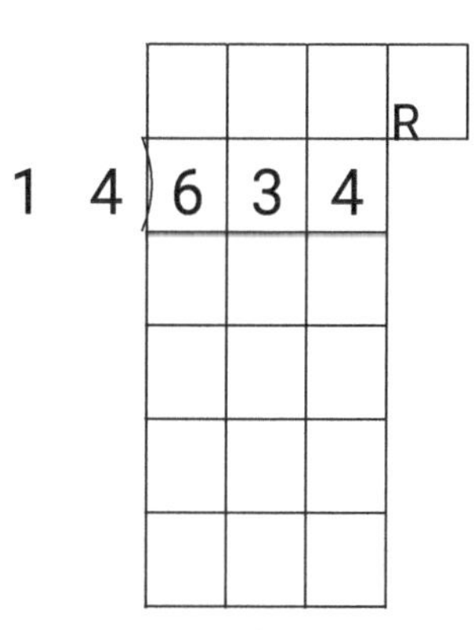

DAY 87

Division: 3-Digit by 2-Digit with Reminders

1) 13) 451 R

2) 24) 791 R

3) 31) 846 R

4) 29) 147 R

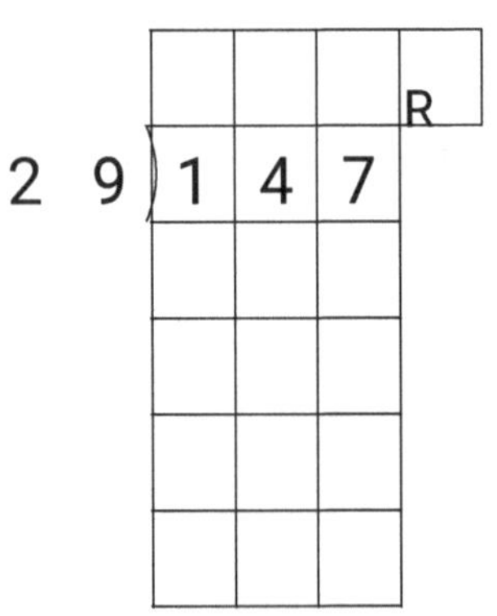

5) 30) 303 R

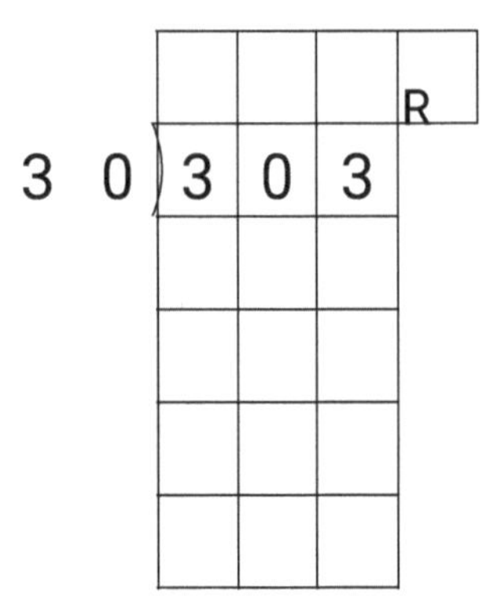

6) 32) 939 R

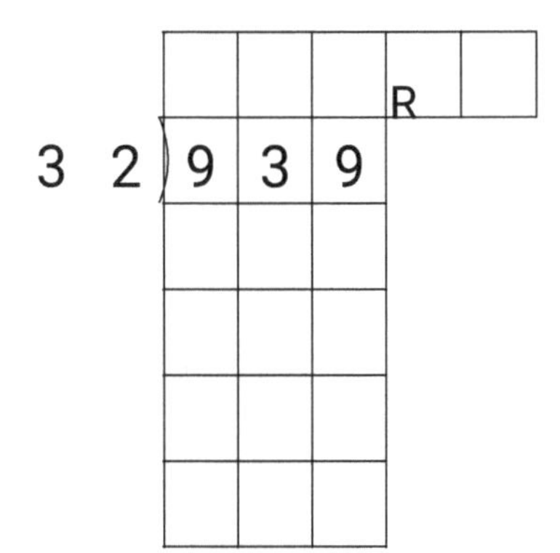

7) 35) 497 R

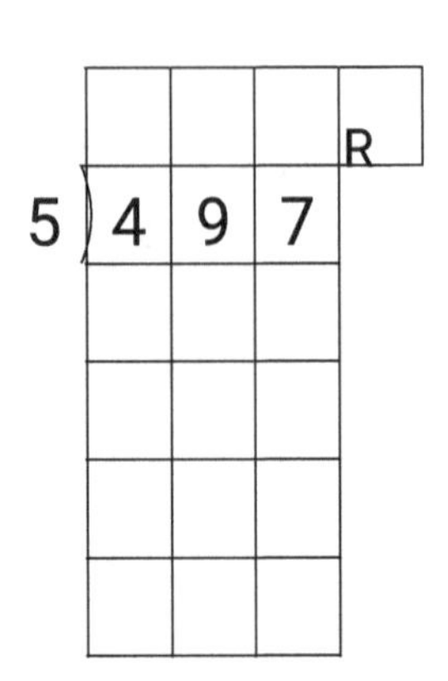

8) 13) 902 R

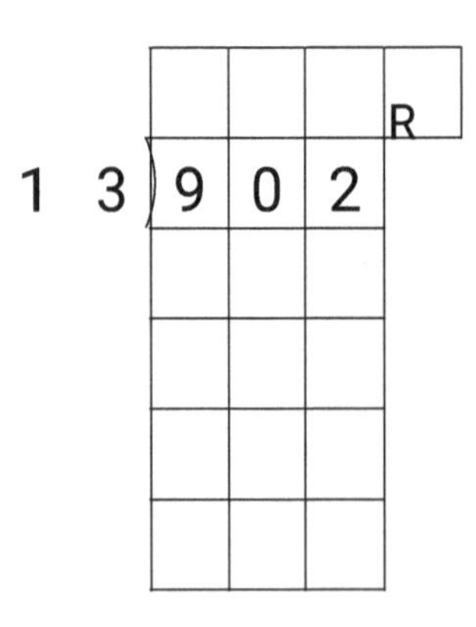

9) 38) 928 R

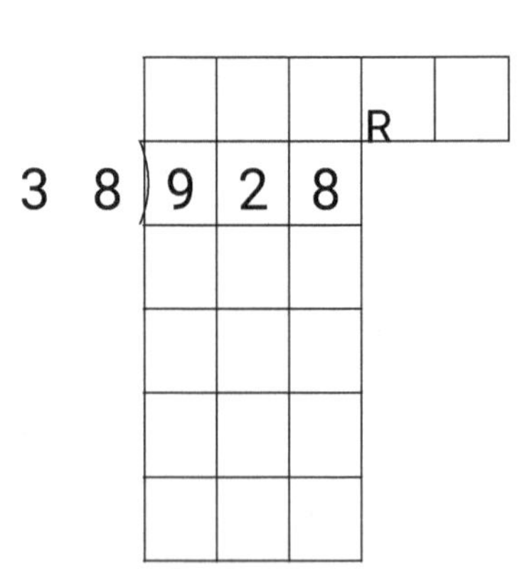

10) 47) 413 R

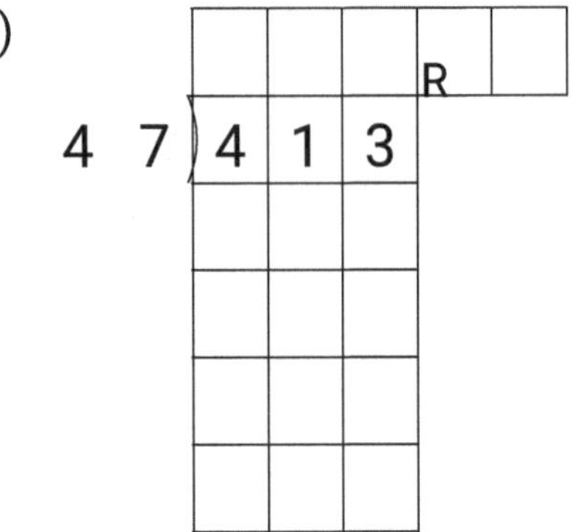

11) 36) 304 R

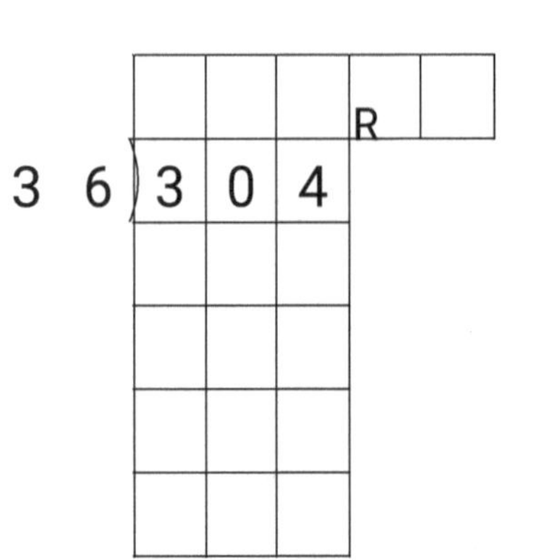

12) 15) 344 R

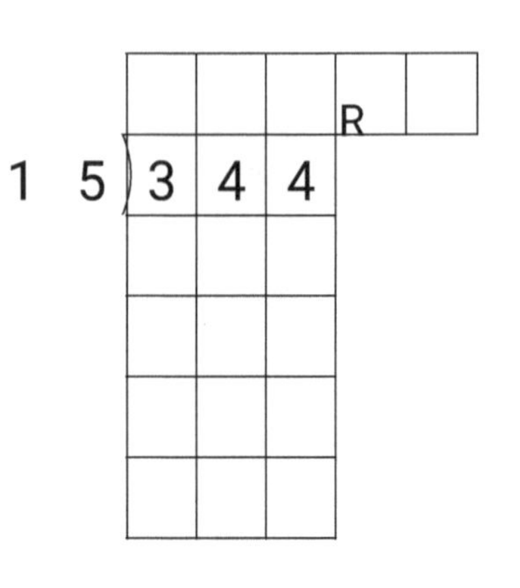

DAY 88

Division: 3-Digit by 2-Digit with Reminders

1) 23) 219 R

2) 33) 815 R

3) 45) 433 R

4)

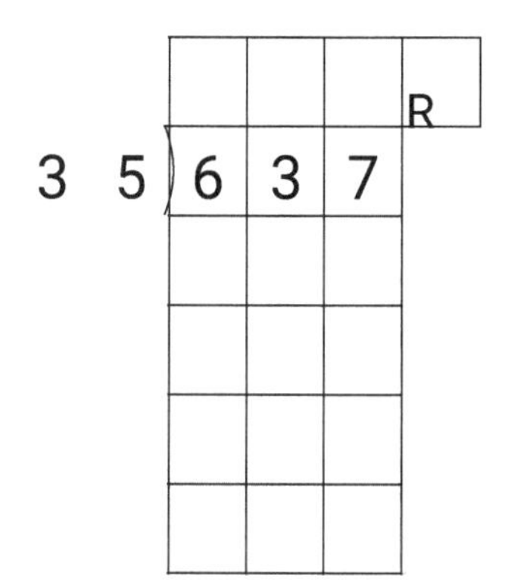

5)

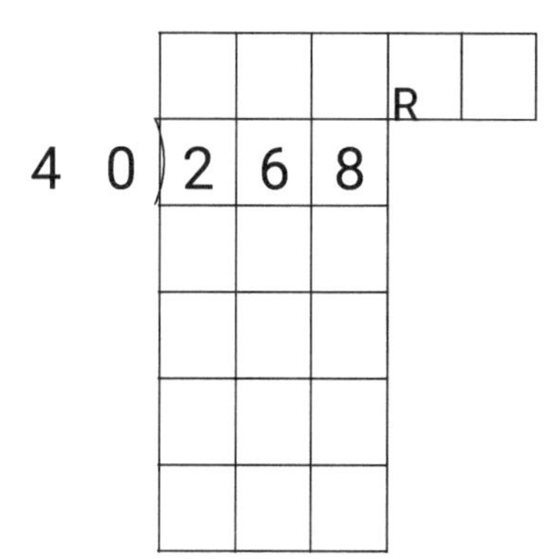

6)

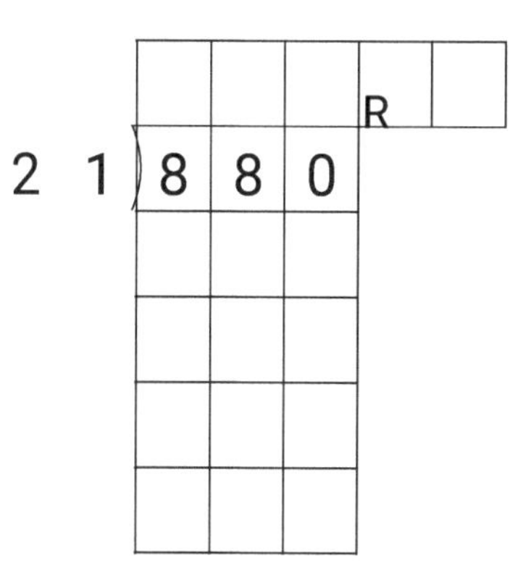

7)

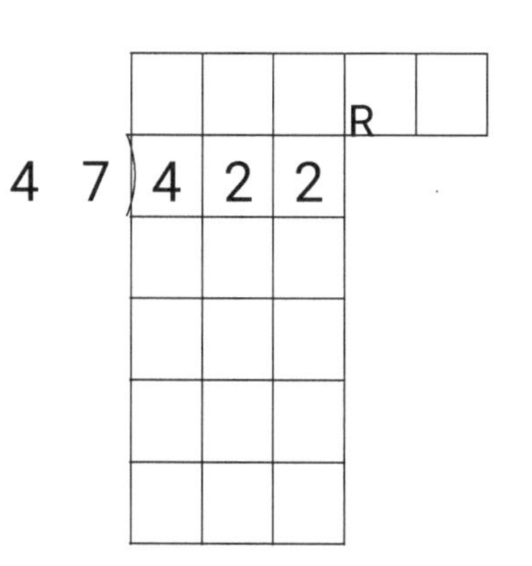

8)

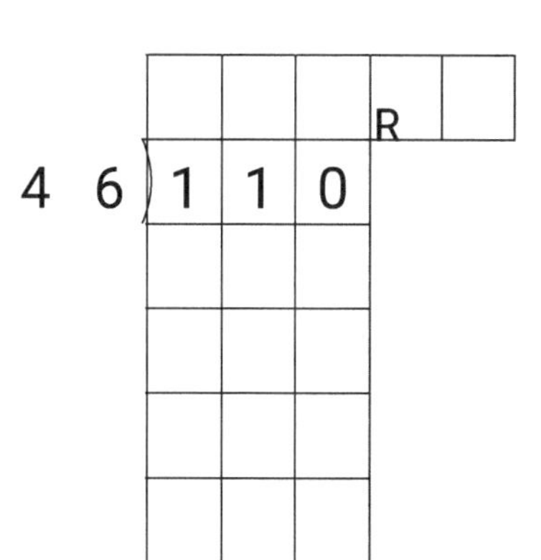

9)

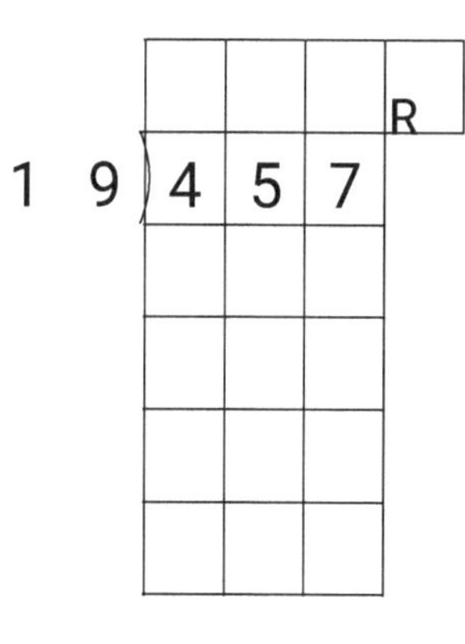

10) 16) 352 R

11)

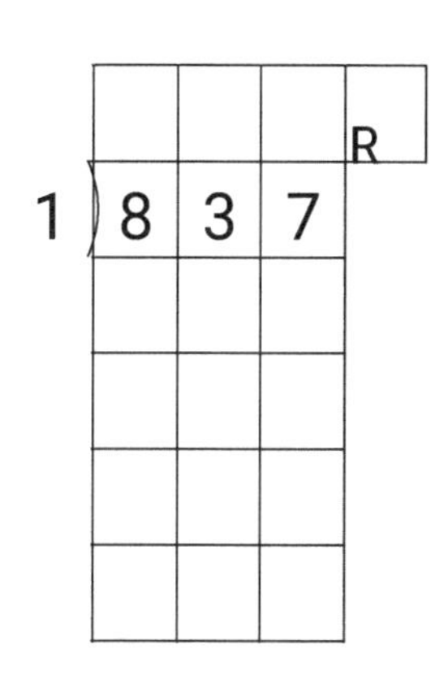

12)

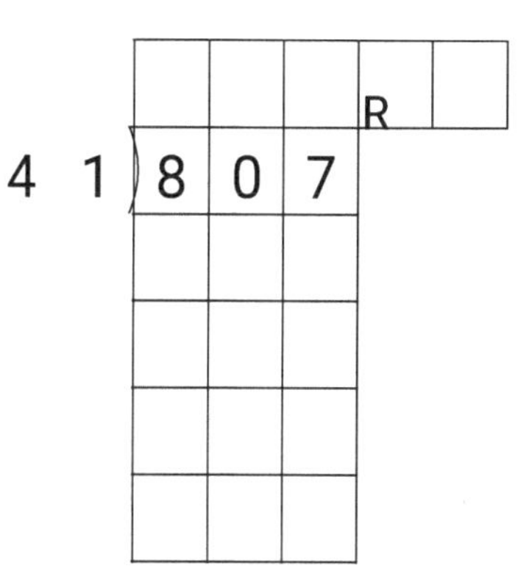

DAY 89

Division: 3-Digit by 2-Digit with Reminders

1) 48)497 R

2) 26)857 R

3) 16)288 R

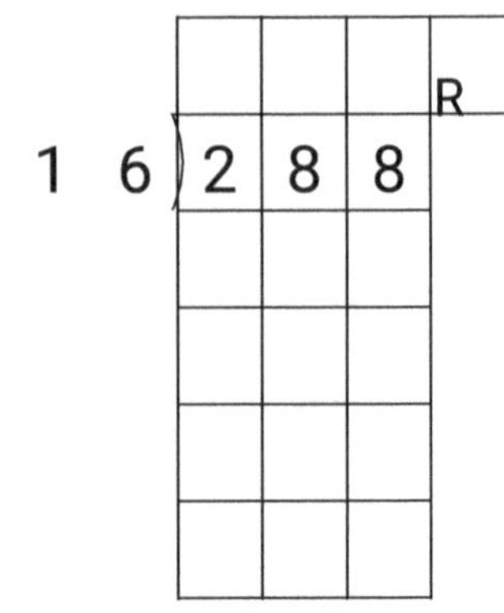

4) 38)690 R

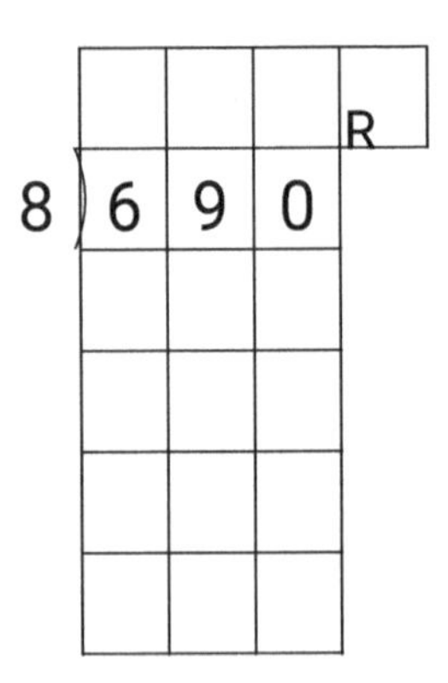

5) 34)875 R

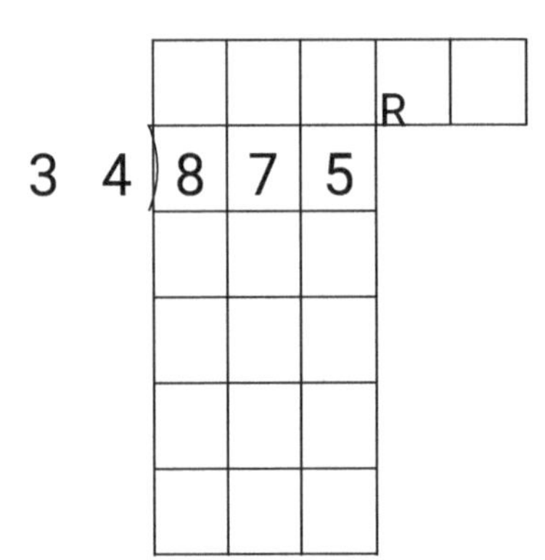

6) 32)178 R

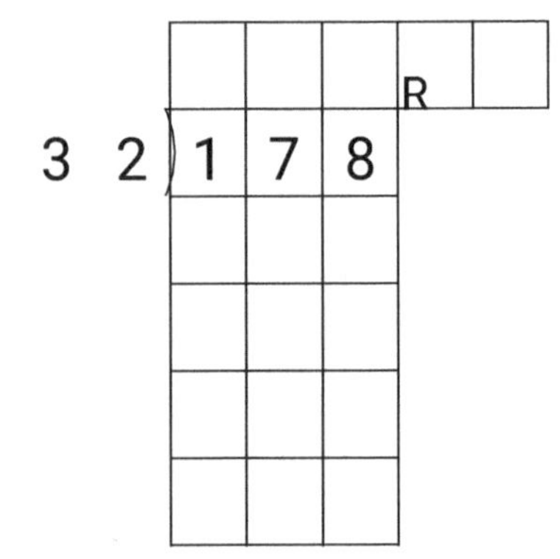

7) 23)407 R

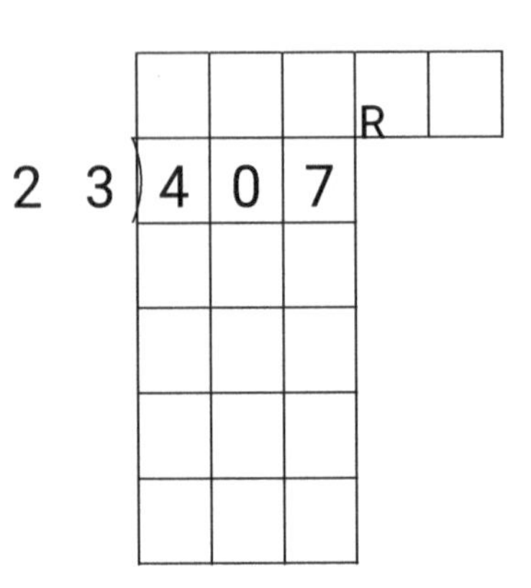

8) 22)375 R

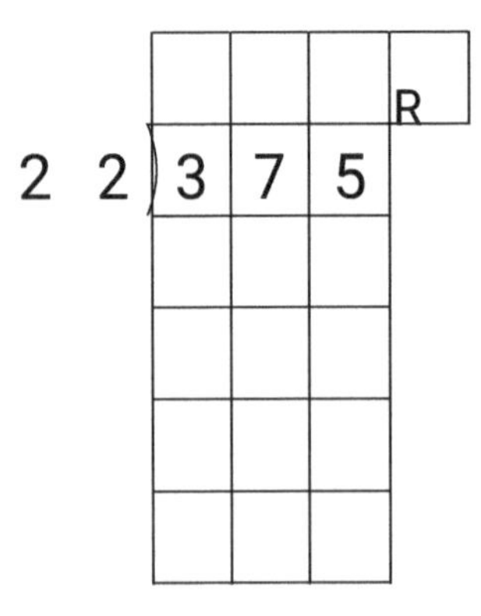

9) 39)248 R

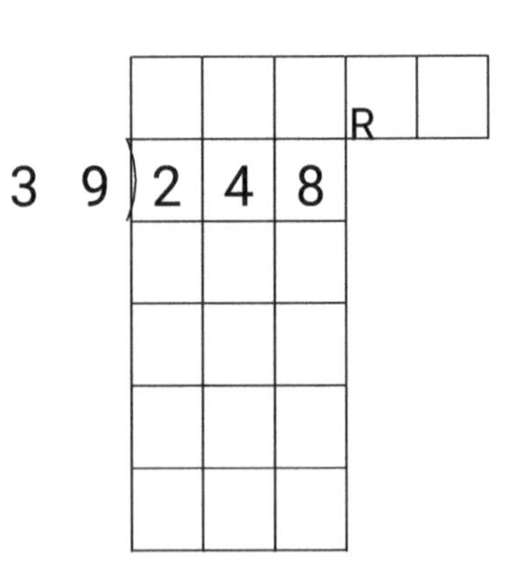

10) 16)865 R

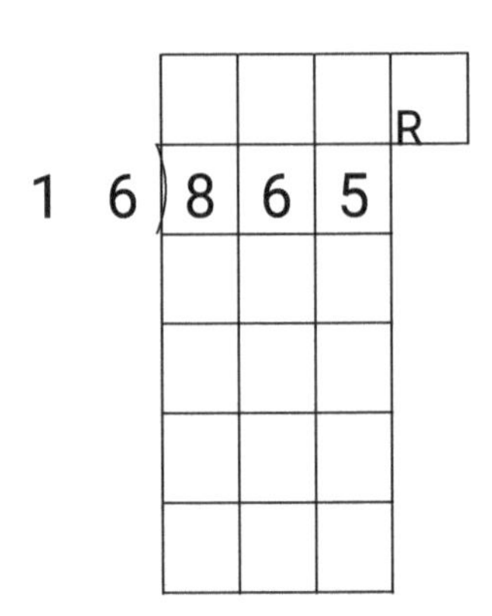

11) 28)136 R

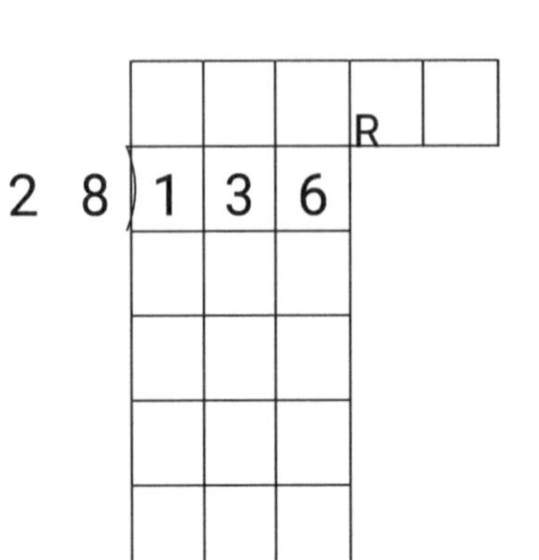

12) 33)838 R

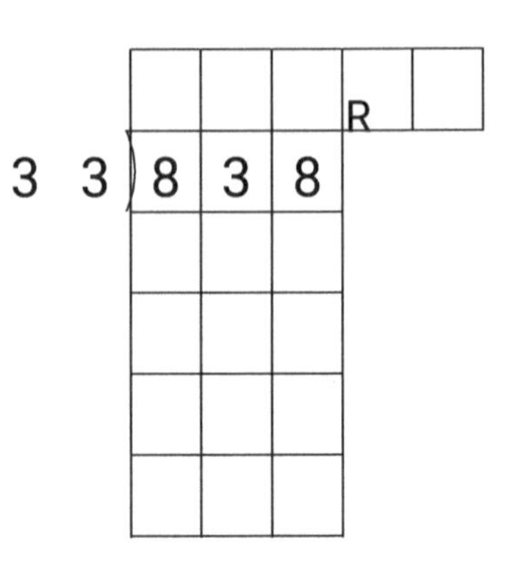

DAY 90

Division: 3-Digit by 2-Digit with Reminders

1) 40) 310 R

2)
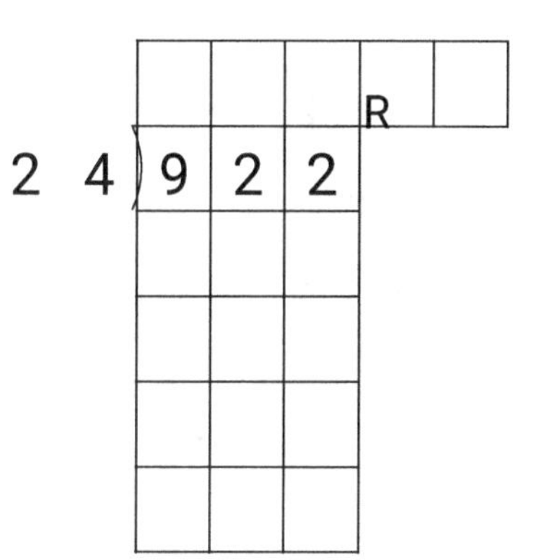

3)
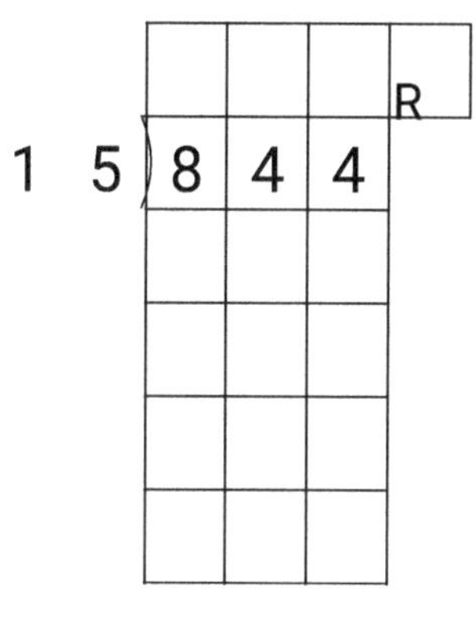

4)
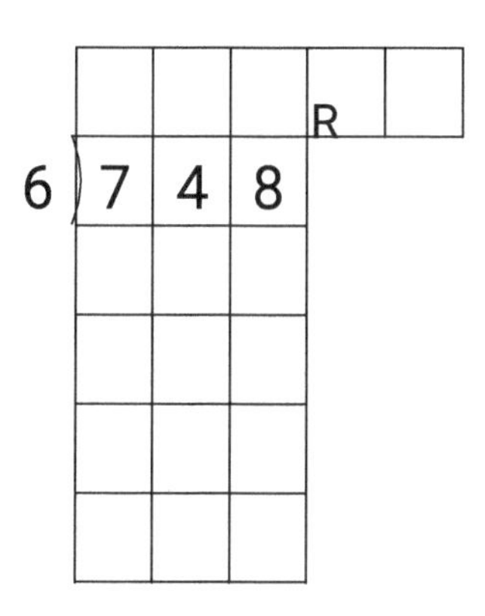

5)
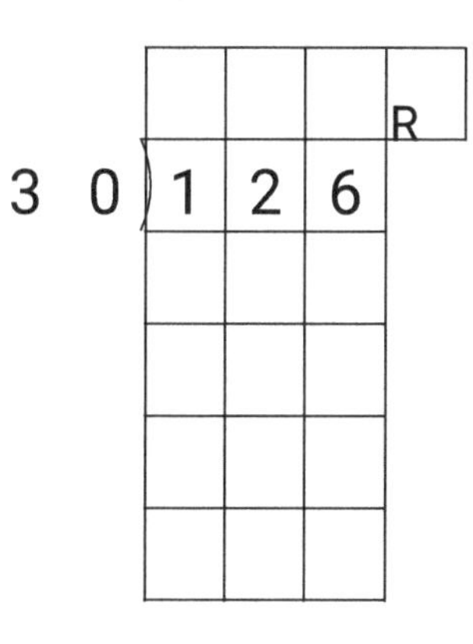

6)
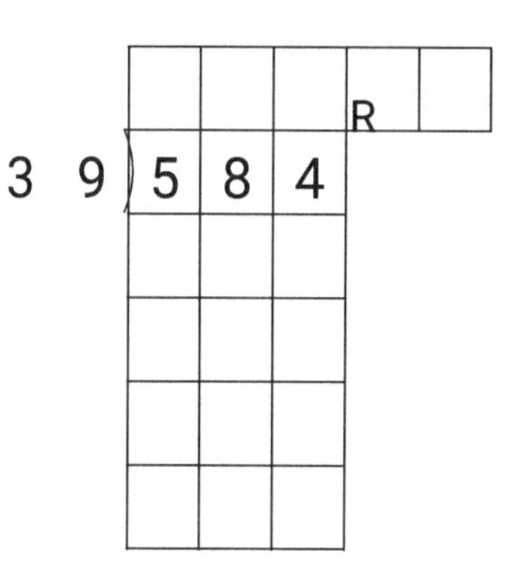

7)
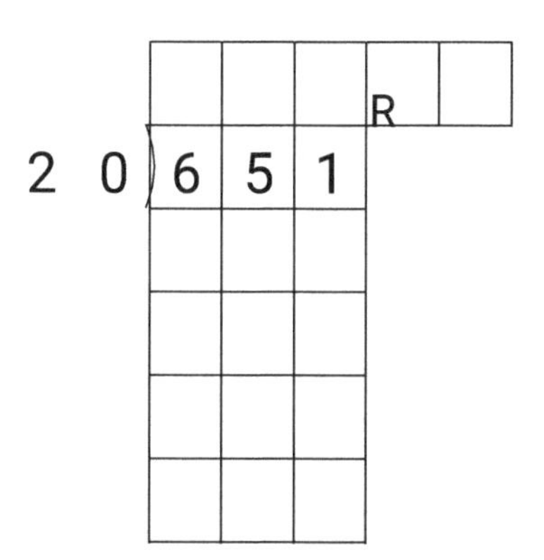

8)
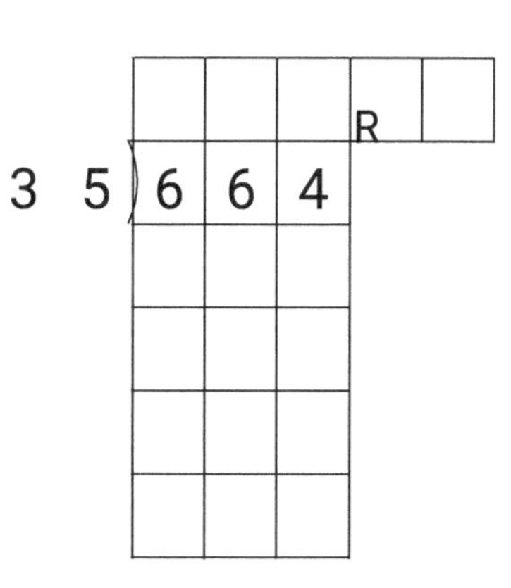

9)
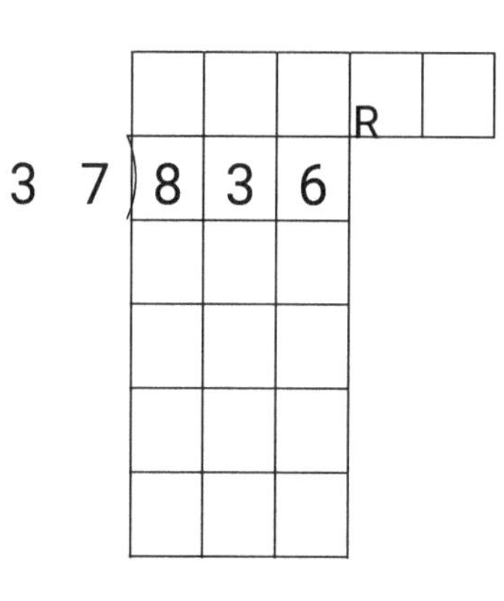

10)
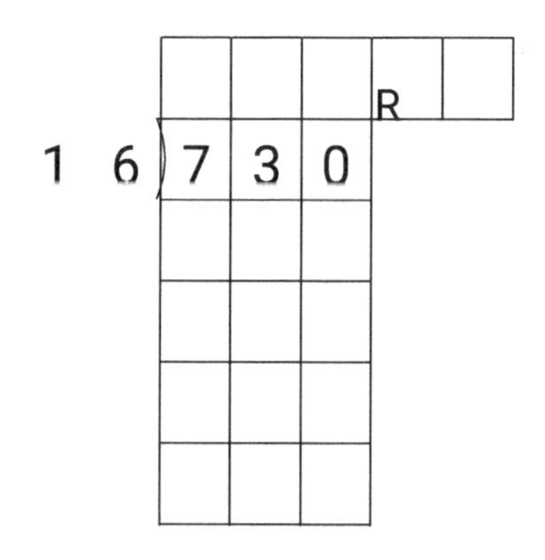

11)
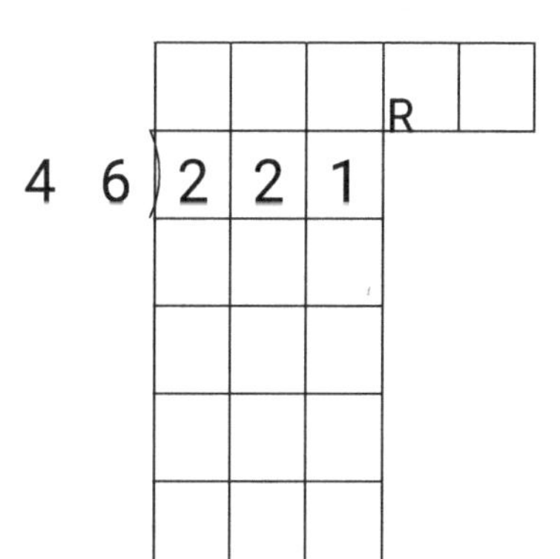

12)
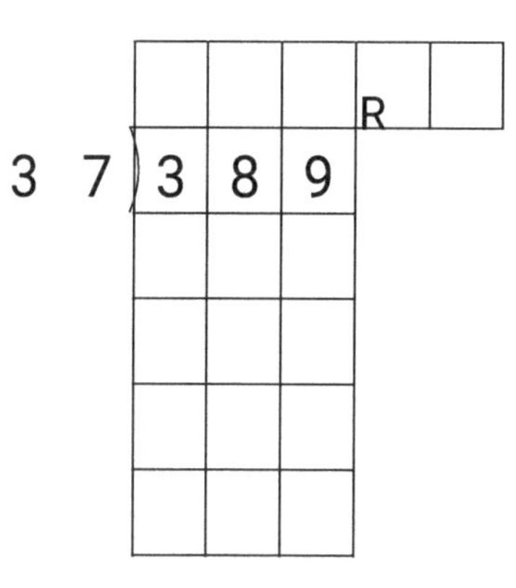

KEEPING TRACK OF THINGS

Let's take a journey back in time to the amazing Inca civilization, nestled high up in the snowy mountains of South America. These clever folks had a super cool way of keeping track of things—it's called quipu!

Imagine this: instead of using pencils and paper, the Incas used colorful strings with knots to write down numbers and important stuff. These magical strings were like secret messages that only they could read.

Each string had different colors and knots, kind of like a secret code! A special string might show how many llamas they had, or how much yummy corn they collected. It's like turning numbers into a beautiful rainbow dance!

And guess what? These magical quipus helped the Incas keep everything in order, just like how we use notebooks and computers today. Isn't that awesome? It's just one of the cool facts I learned on my adventures!

DAY 91

Division: 4-Digit by 2-Digit with No Reminders

1) $24 \overline{)8664}$

2) $94 \overline{)1128}$

3) $62 \overline{)4340}$

4) $23 \overline{)7452}$

5) $15 \overline{)2055}$

6) $46 \overline{)7498}$

7) $61 \overline{)4697}$

8) $33 \overline{)3531}$

9) $16 \overline{)1968}$

10) $38 \overline{)2660}$

11) $26 \overline{)4472}$

12) $13 \overline{)7813}$

DAY 92

Division: 4-Digit by 2-Digit with No Reminders

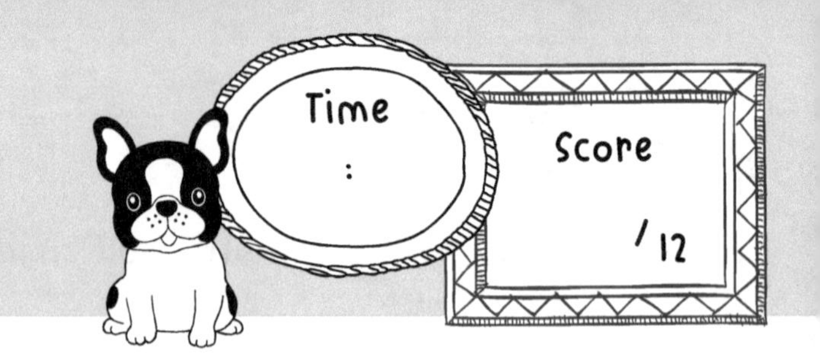

1)

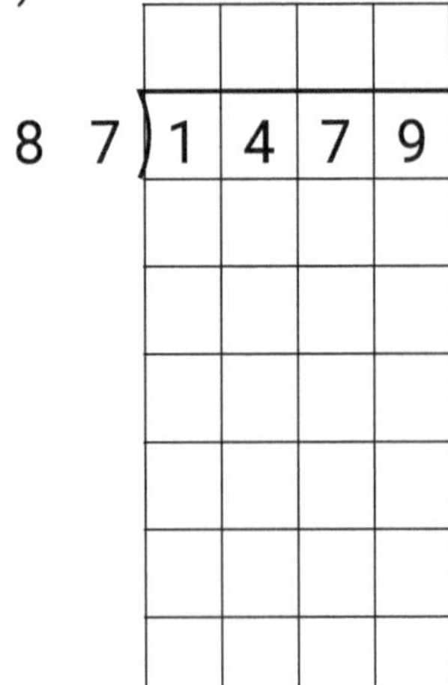

2)

21)8043

3)

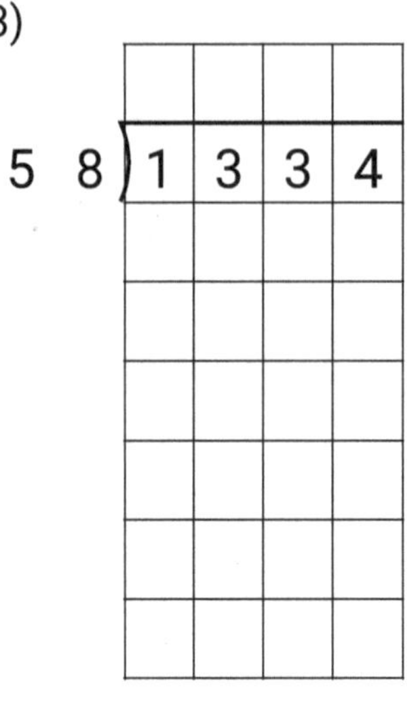

4)

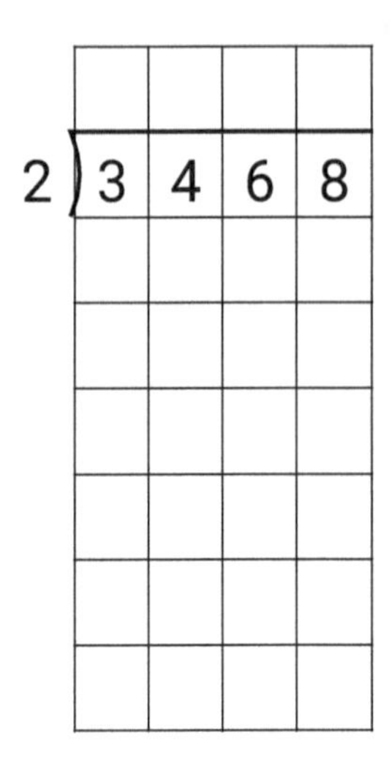

5)

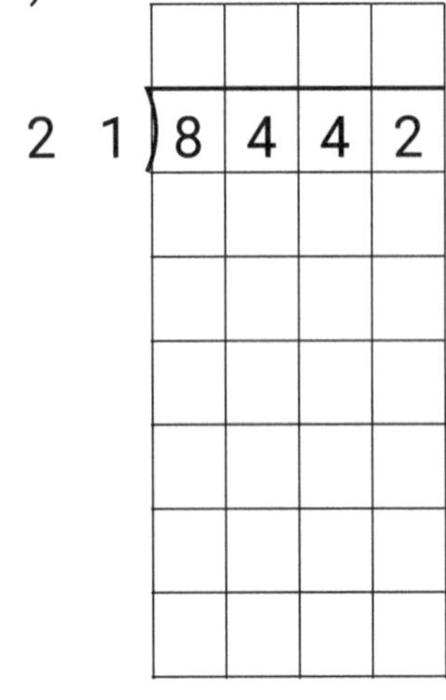

6)

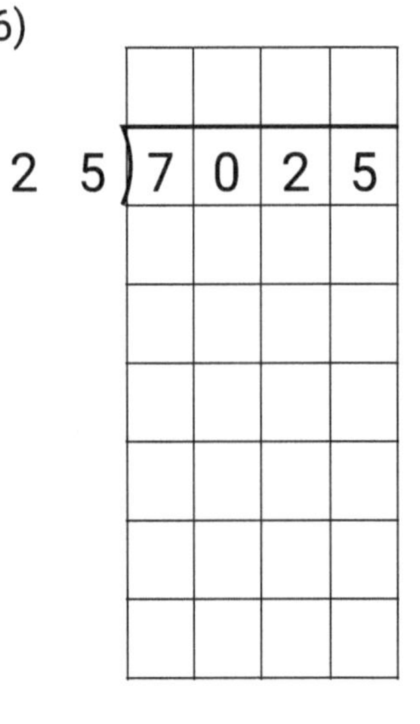

7)

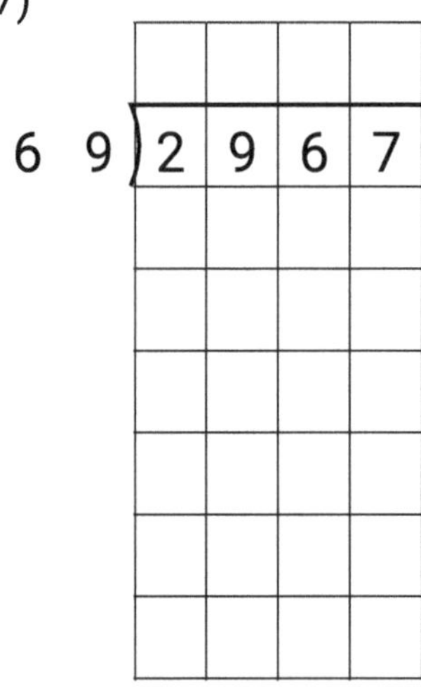

8)

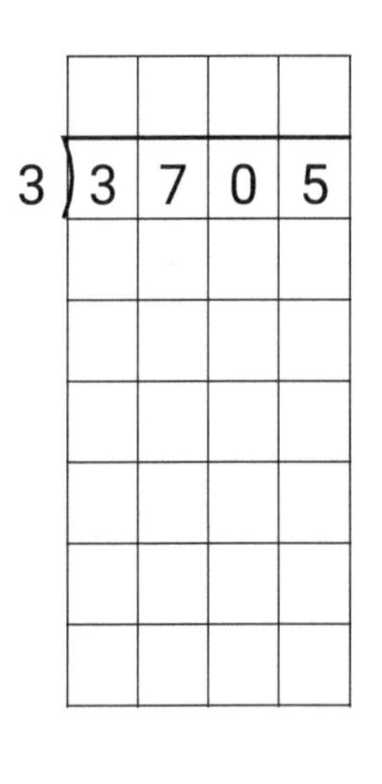

9)

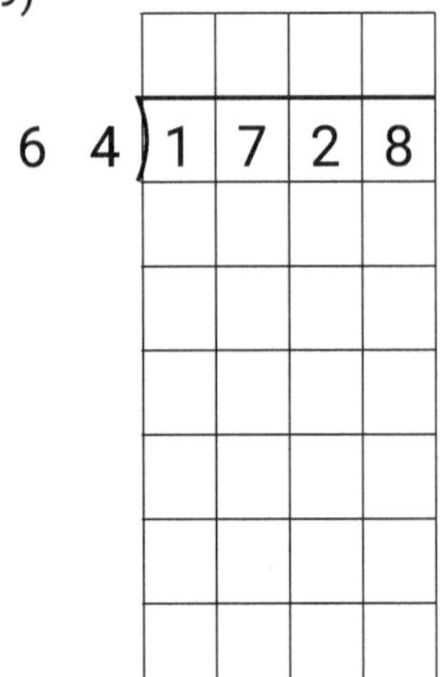

10)

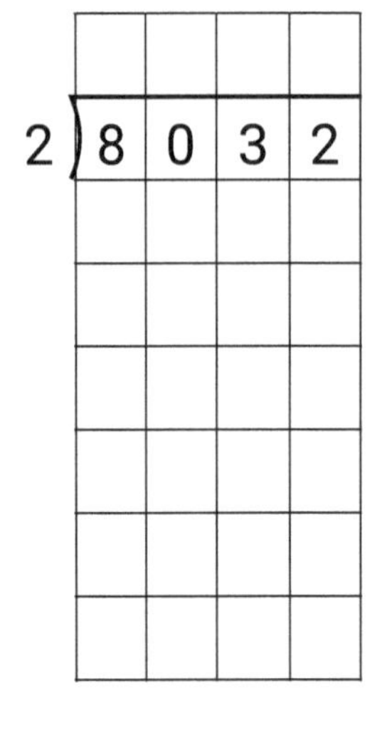

11)

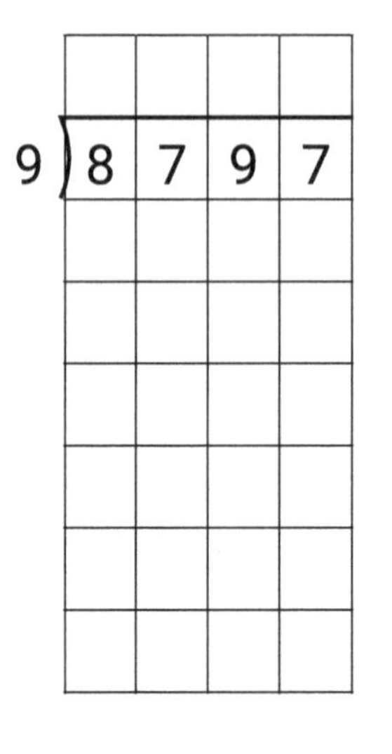

12)

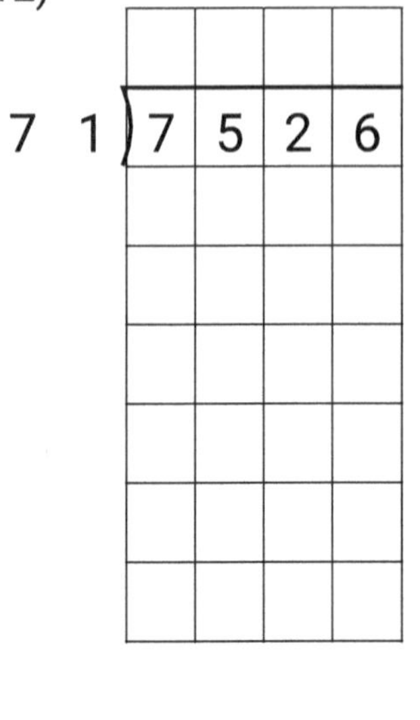

DAY 93

Division: 4-Digit by 2-Digit with No Reminders

1) 67) 3685

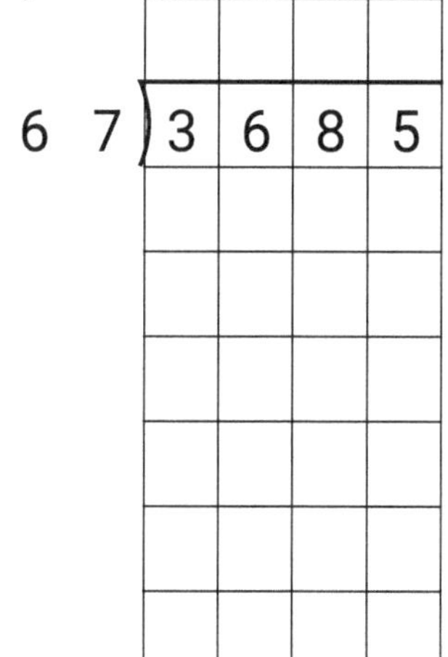

2) 13) 9711

3) 26) 5330

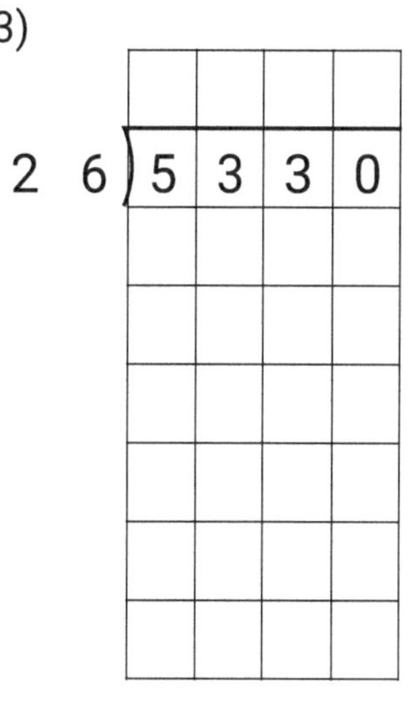

4) 18) 6066

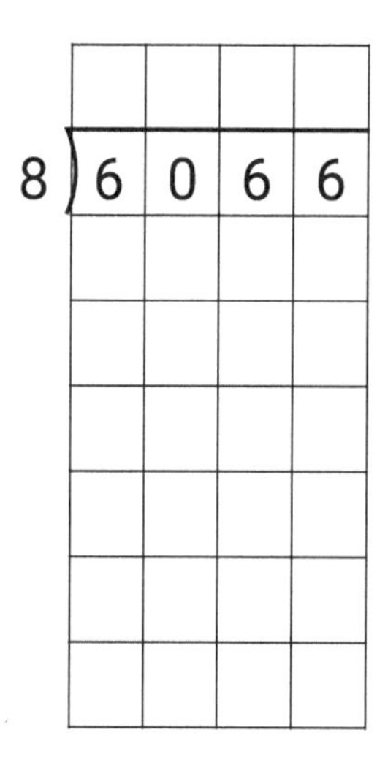

5) 45) 7380

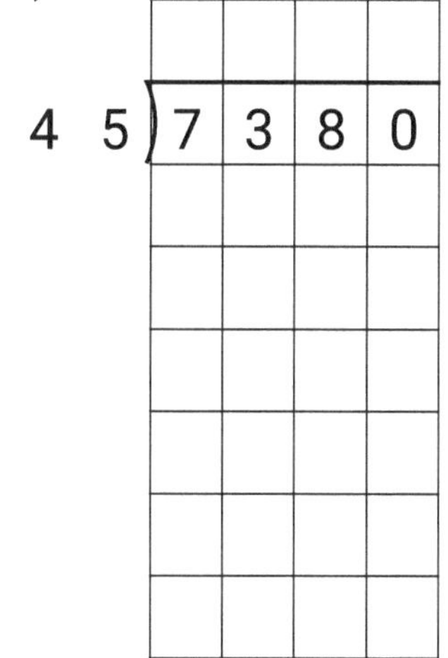

6) 17) 8806

7) 13) 2418

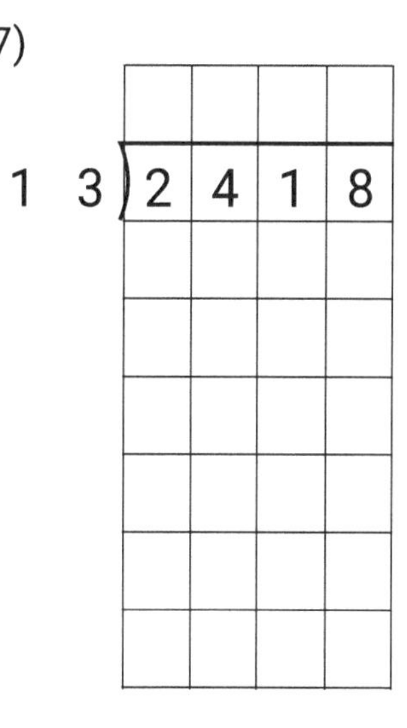

8) 57) 8607

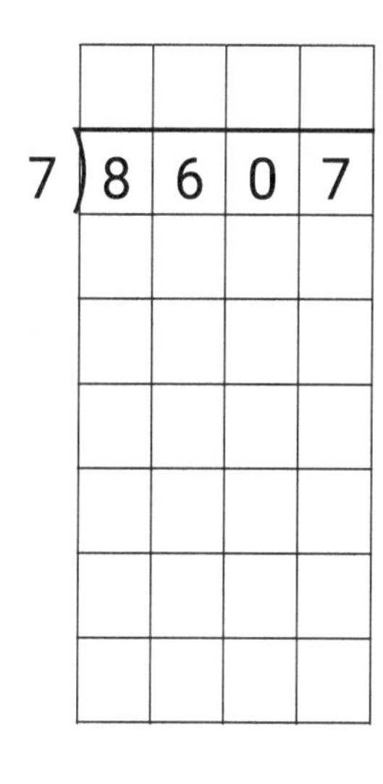

9) 53) 3339

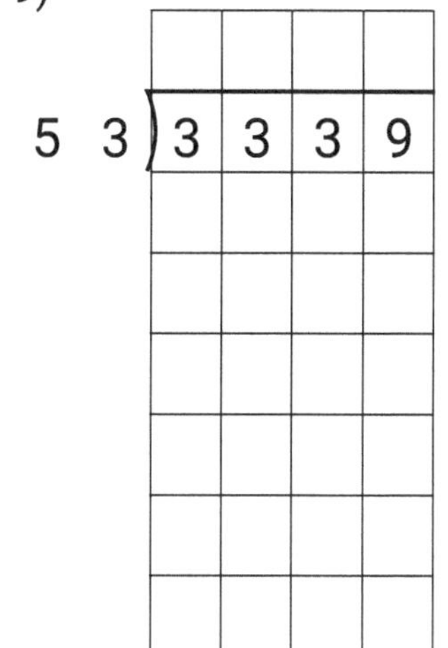

10) 11) 9119

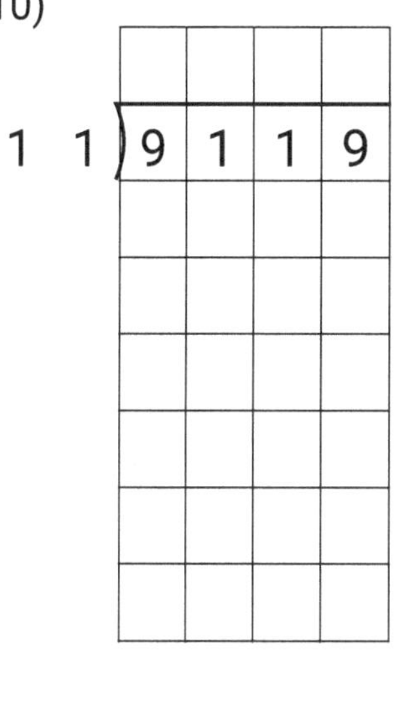

11) 21) 1869

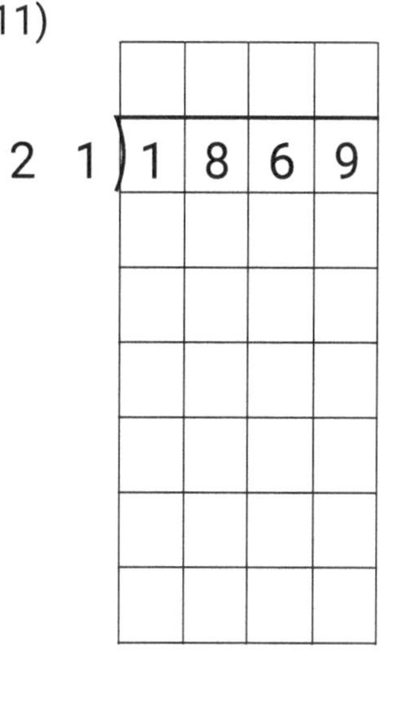

12) 21) 3948

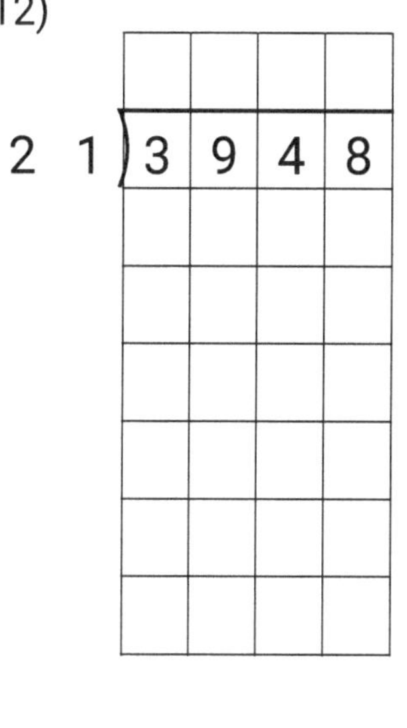

DAY 94

Division: 4-Digit by 2-Digit with No Reminders

1)

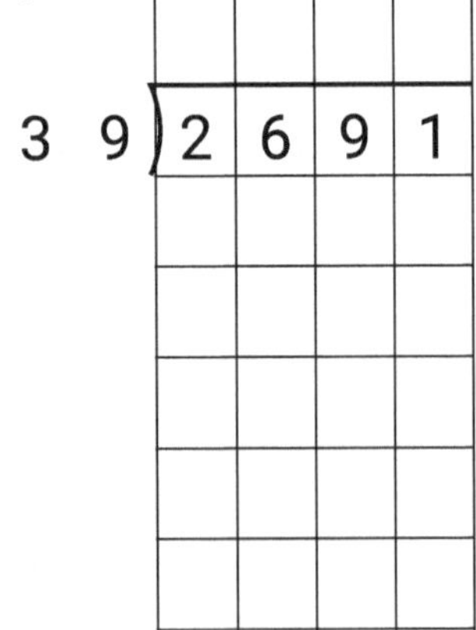

2)

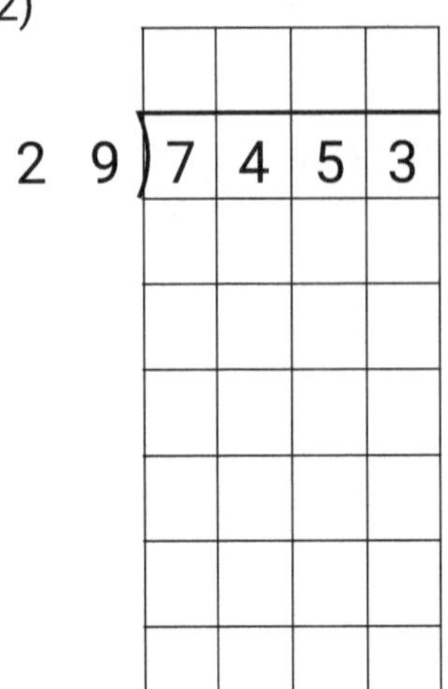

3)

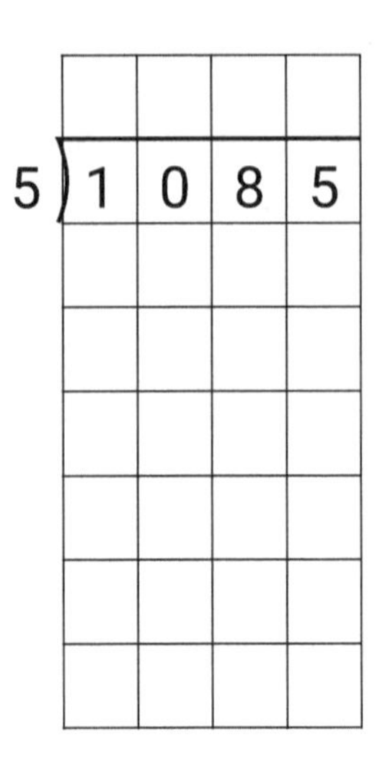

4)

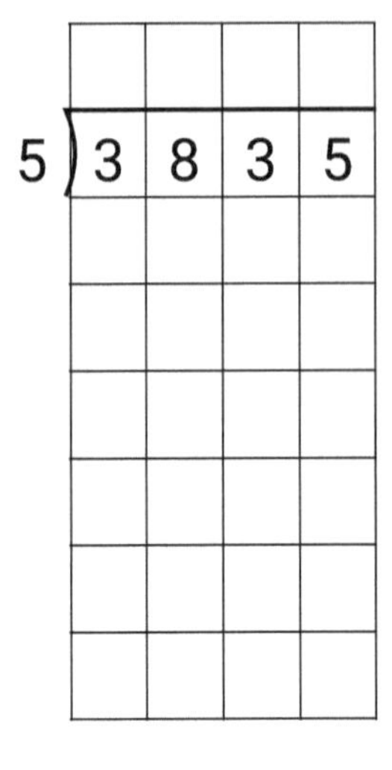

5)

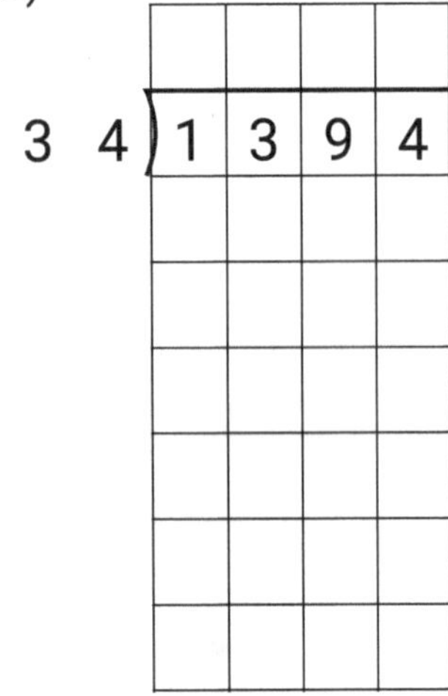

6)

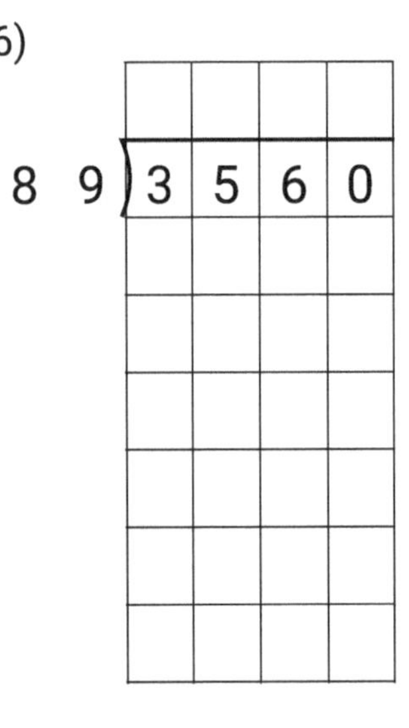

7)

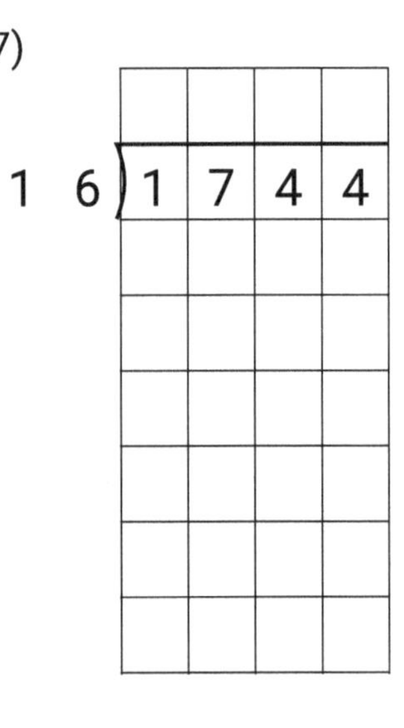

8)

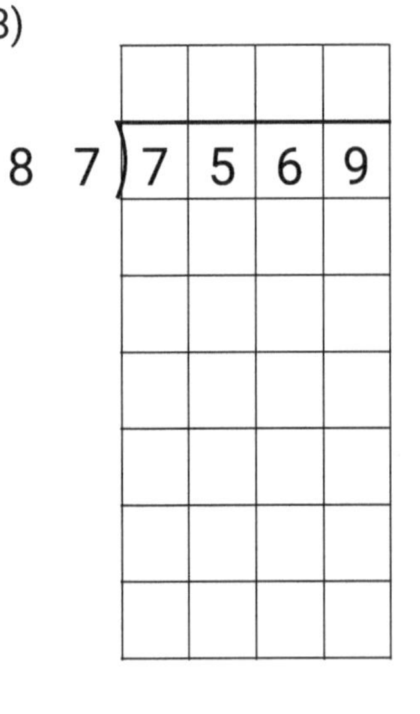

9)

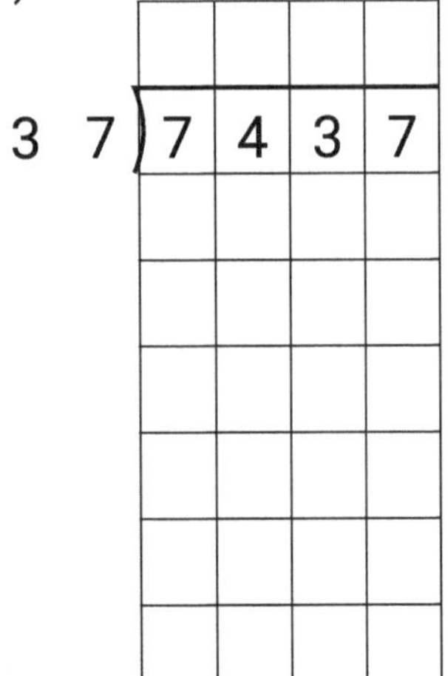

10)

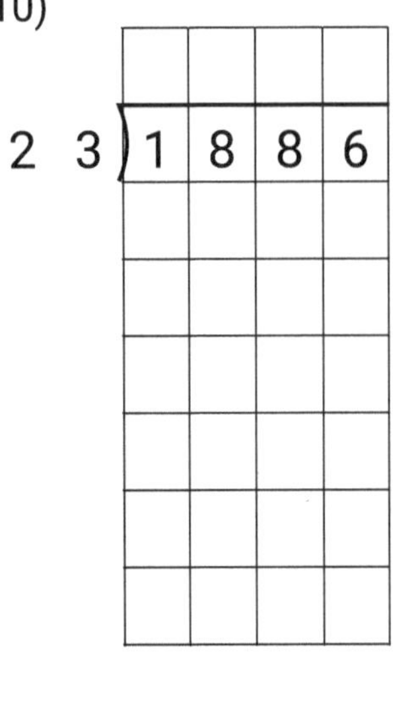

11)

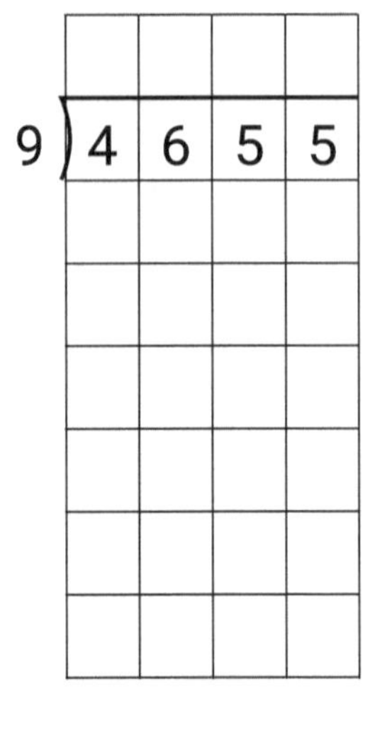

12)

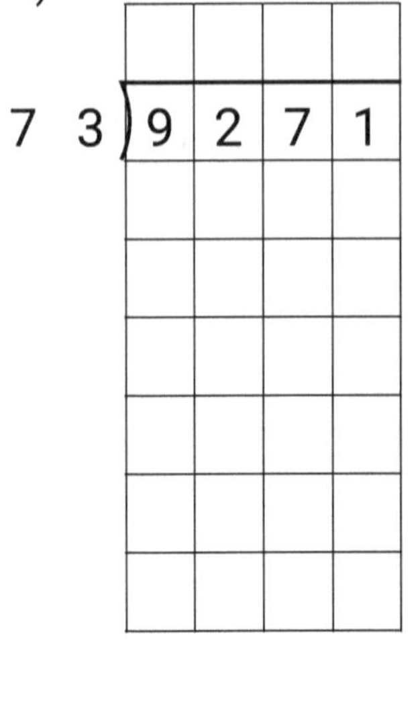

DAY 95

Division: 4-Digit by 2-Digit with No Reminders

1)
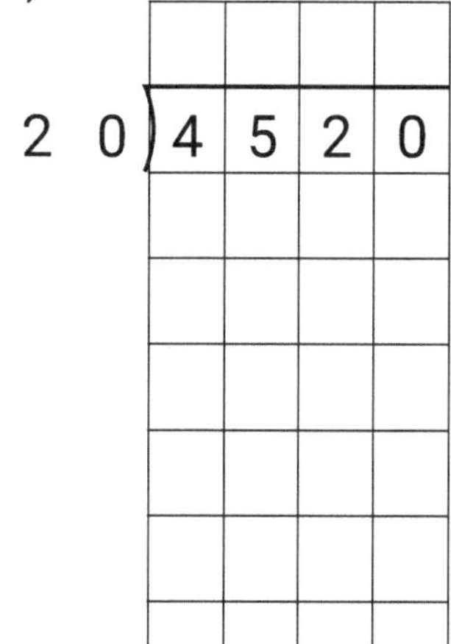

2)
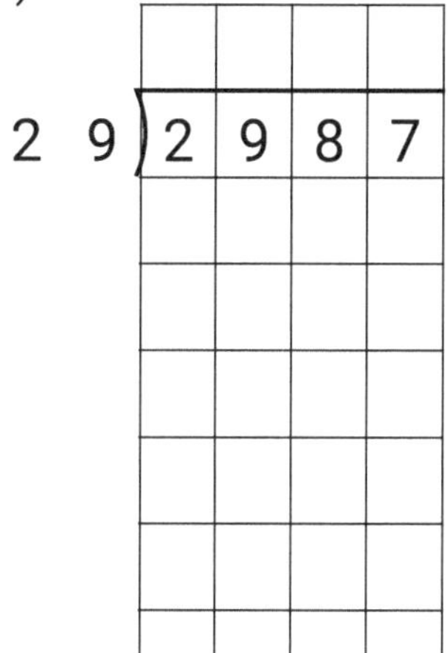

3)
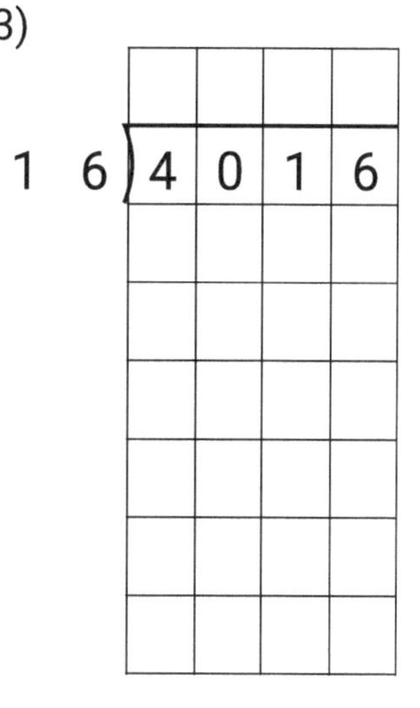

4)
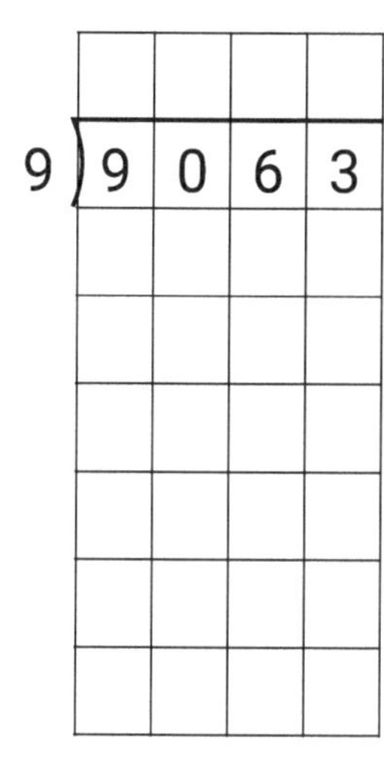

5)
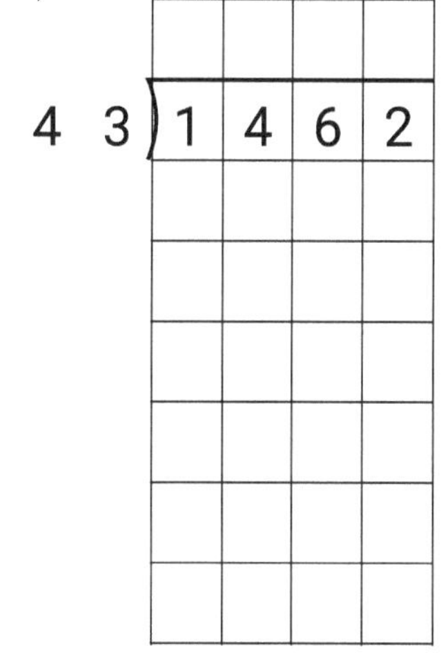

6)
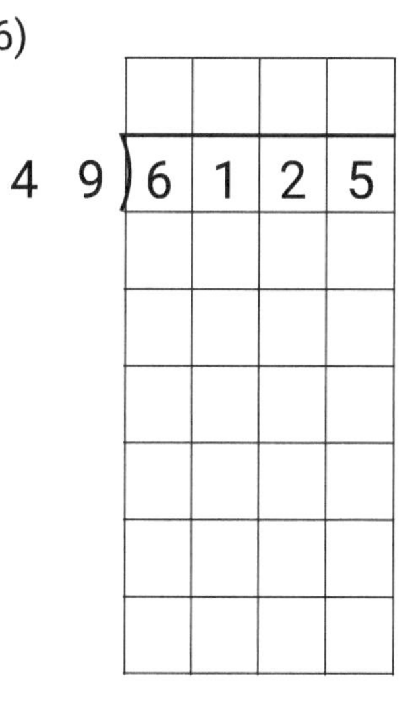

7)
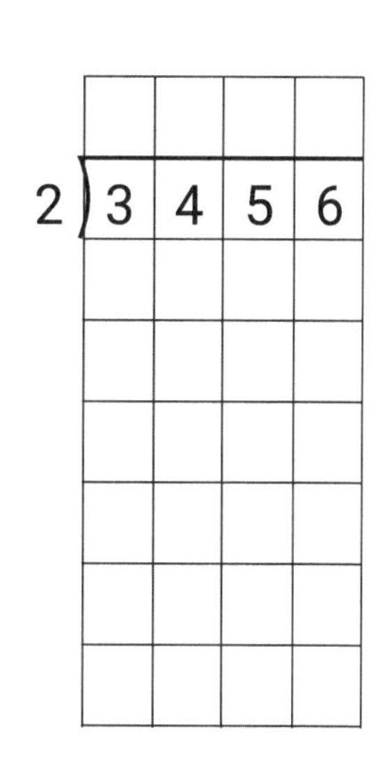

8)
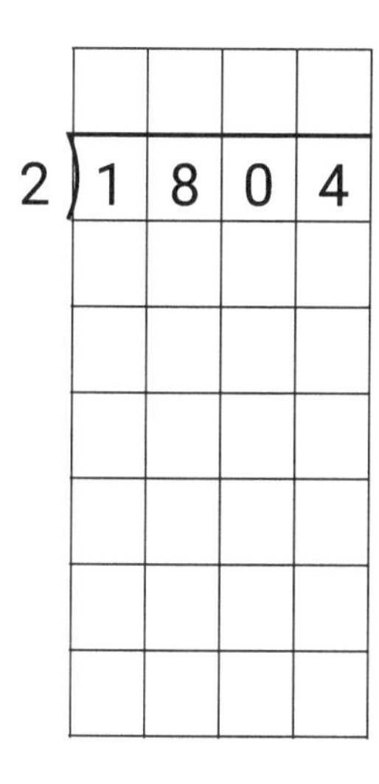

9)
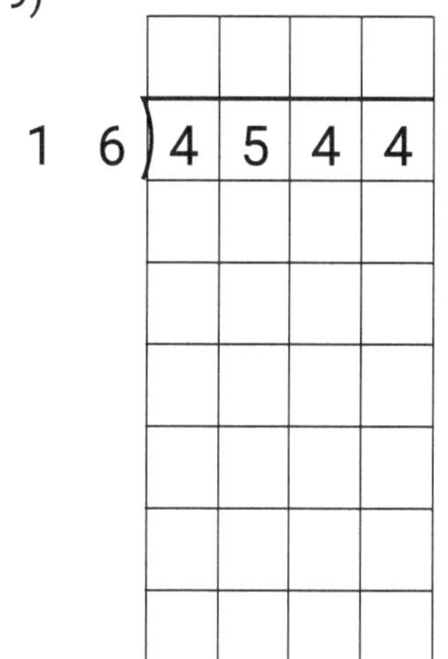

10)
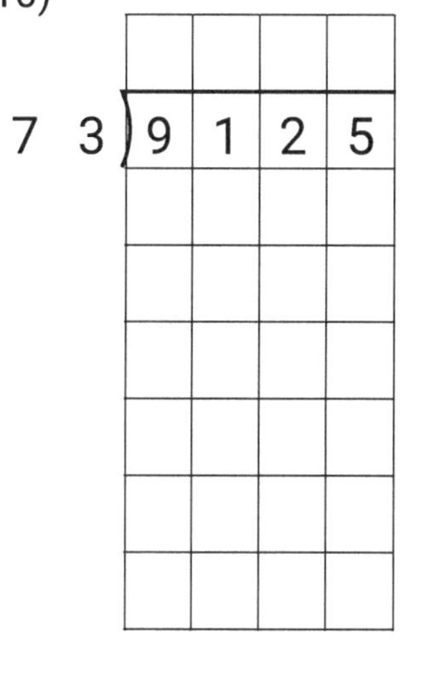

11)
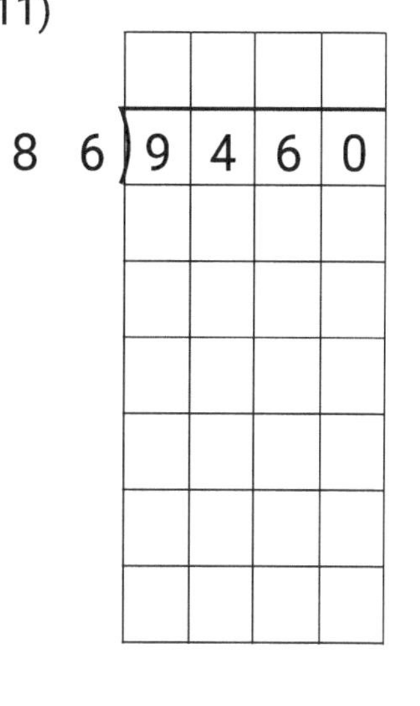

12)
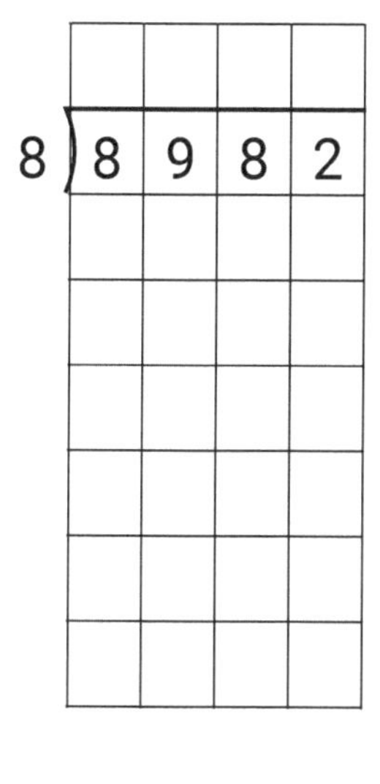

DAY 96

Division: 4-Digit by 2-Digit with Reminders

1) 20) 9132 R

2) 48) 4615 R

3)

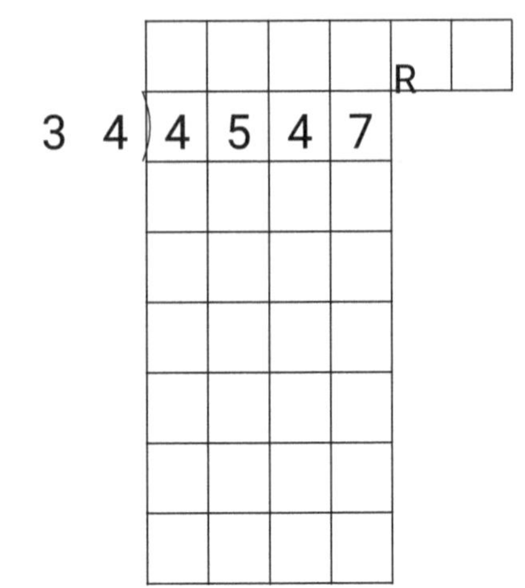

4) 35) 7347 R

5)

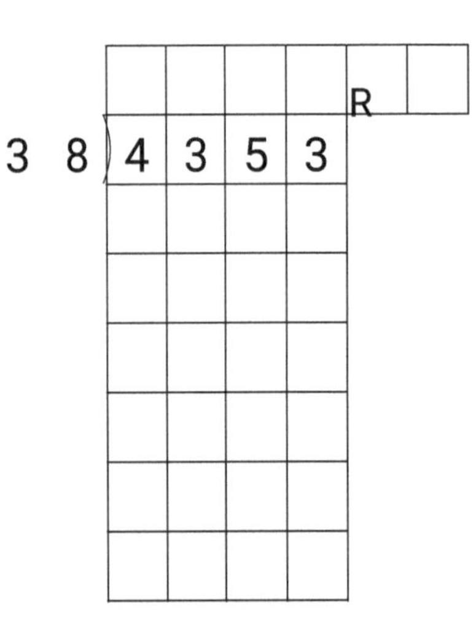

6)

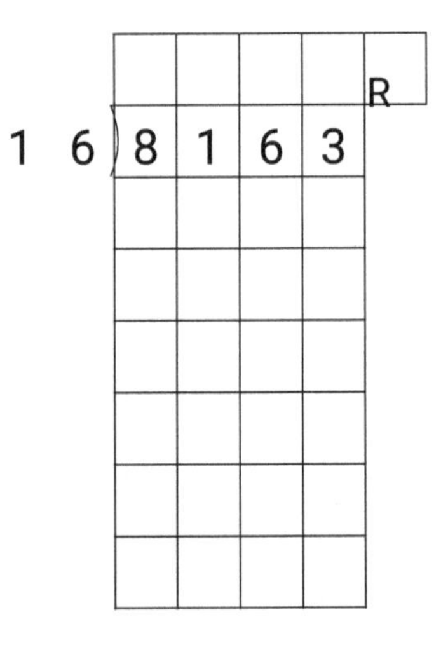

7) 33) 6942 R

8)

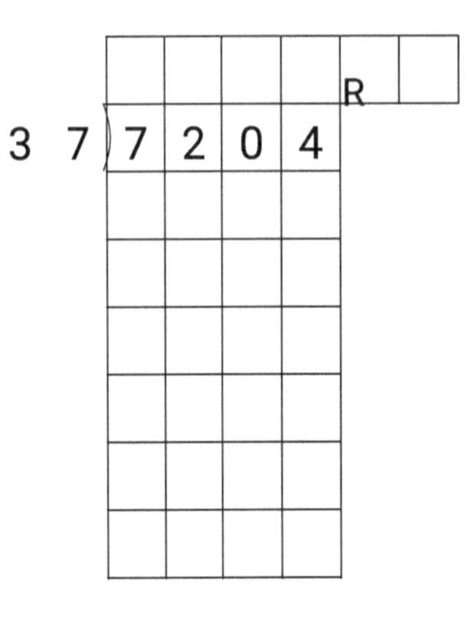

9)

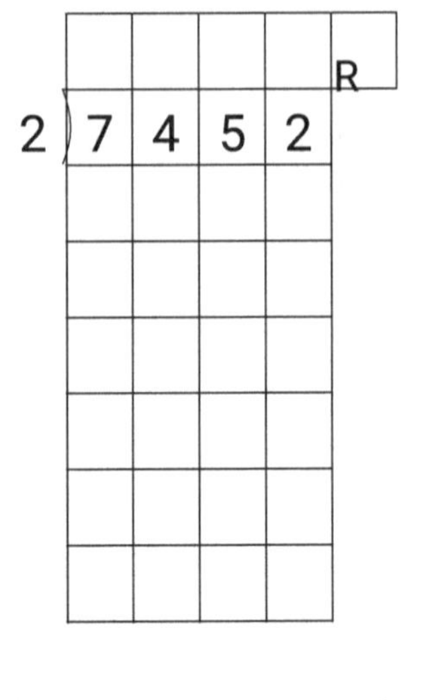

DAY 97

Division: 4-Digit by 2-Digit with Reminders

Time :

Score / 9

1) $46\overline{)1134}$ R

2) $29\overline{)5516}$ R

3) $27\overline{)7988}$ R

4) $43\overline{)1261}$ R

5) $31\overline{)8159}$ R

6) $15\overline{)3528}$ R

7) $39\overline{)6381}$ R

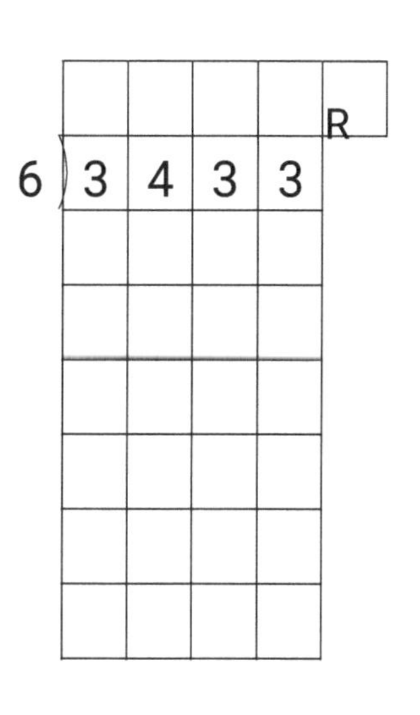

8) $16\overline{)3433}$ R

9) $25\overline{)8573}$ R

DAY 98

Division: 4-Digit by 2-Digit with Reminders

1) $37 \overline{)4885}$ R

2) $17 \overline{)7861}$ R

3) $35 \overline{)7309}$ R

4) $40 \overline{)5668}$ R

5) $33 \overline{)1904}$ R

6) $37 \overline{)3420}$ R

7) $24 \overline{)3480}$ R

8) $15 \overline{)3468}$ R

9) $35 \overline{)3714}$ R

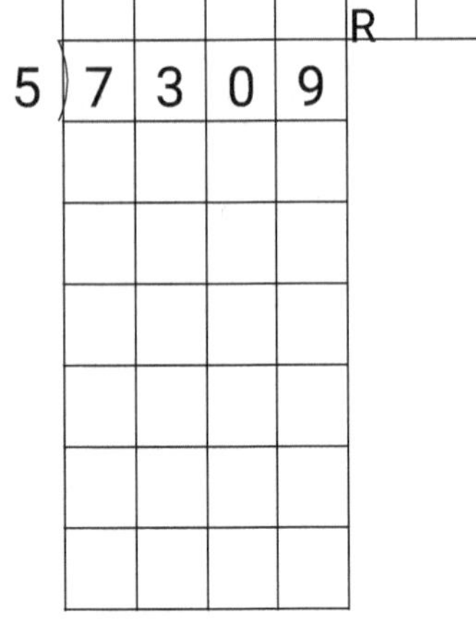

DAY 99

Division: 4-Digit by 2-Digit with Reminders

1) 34)1302 R

2) 29)9609 R

3) 47)7813 R

4) 20)6193 R

5) 42)6616 R

6) 37)2743 R

7) 23)7480 R

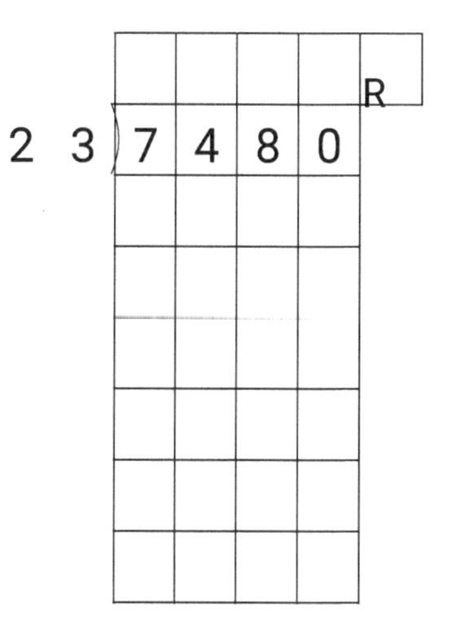

8) 34)5288 R

9) 25)4133 R

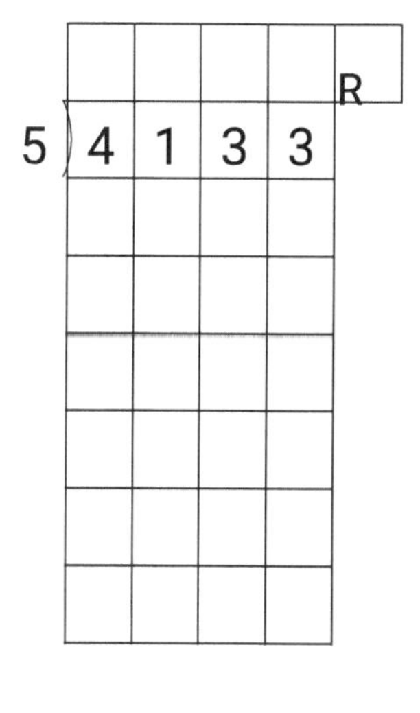

DAY 100

Division: 4-Digit by 2-Digit with Reminders

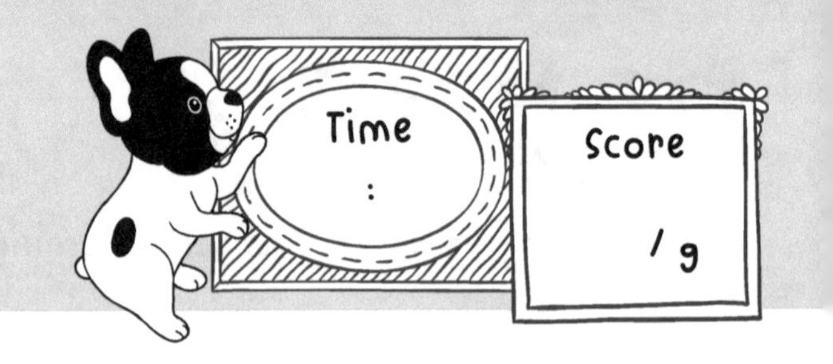

1) 26) 5 5 4 3 R

2) 28) 6 5 9 5 R

3) 39) 9 1 2 4 R

4) 37) 5 9 3 9 R

5) 37) 9 4 0 5 R

6) 25) 9 2 1 5 R

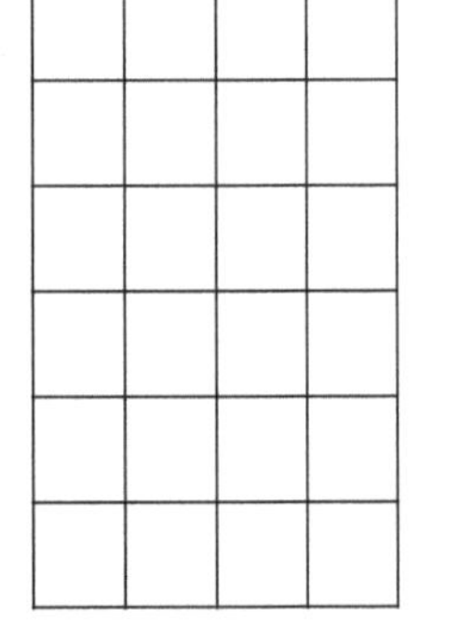

7) 28) 6 8 0 3 R

8) 43) 4 5 6 2 R

9) 40) 9 1 7 8 R

CONCLUSION

Oh wow! You've mastered math, and now you're almost as fantastically smart as me! Get ready to share snacks equally between your buddies, calculate how many books you can squeeze onto a shelf, and so much more using my excellent methods that make math easy!

And remember, a banana daily makes math nice and easy!

ANSWER KEY

DAY 1
(1)384 (2)344 (3)679 (4)810 (5)450 (6)189 (7)486 (8)480 (9)385 (10)126 (11)140 (12)84 (13)544 (14)376 (15)252 (16)621 (17)711 (18)864 (19)170 (20)70

DAY 2
(1)546 (2)120 (3)602 (4)711 (5)564 (6)330 (7)158 (8)435 (9)702 (10)328 (11)294 (12)196 (13)405 (14)425 (15)84 (16)657 (17)357 (18)168 (19)426 (20)270

DAY 3
(1)144 (2)135 (3)288 (4)720 (5)219 (6)630 (7)152 (8)416 (9)44 (10)369 (11)90 (12)118 (13)141 (14)385 (15)228 (16)219 (17)120 (18)104 (19)490 (20)564

DAY 4
(1)161 (2)603 (3)156 (4)322 (5)576 (6)399 (7)396 (8)285 (9)156 (10)74 (11)408 (12)172 (13)432 (14)320 (15)189 (16)324 (17)360 (18)380 (19)420 (20)216

DAY 5
(1)240 (2)198 (3)632 (4)434 (5)392 (6)188 (7)280 (8)225 (9) 189 (10)225 (11)104(12)424 (13)58 (14)128 (15)297 (16)48 (17)276 (18)198 (19)414 (20)637

DAY 6
(1)255 (2)128 (3)126 (4)252 (5)120 (6)290 (7)520 (8)396 (9)160 (10)213 (11)440 (12)48 (13)320 (14)188 (15)158 (16)110 (17)207 (18)118 (19)265 (20)344

DAY 7
(1)285 (2)111 (3)378 (4)90 (5)486 (6)174 (7)891 (8)249 (9)248 (10)190 (11)301 (12)72 (13)124 (14)270 (15)134 (16)292 (17)260 (18)312 (19)212 (20)336

DAY 8
(1)123 (2)520 (3)106 (4)203 (5)624 (6)246 (7)63 (8)480 (9)305 (10)212 (11)711 (12)156 (13)602 (14)88 (15)255 (16)148 (17)265 (18)91 (19)504 (20)651

DAY 9
(1)284 (2)441 (3)621 (4)162 (5)686 (6)36 (7)312 (8)34 (9)126 (10)124 (11)90 (12)640 (13)396 (14)69 (15)282 (16)693 (17)518 (18)350 (19)240 (20)183

DAY 10
(1)141 (2)300 (3)135 (4)198 (5)196 (6)152 (7)188 (8)385 (9)84 (10)420 (11)99 (12)106 (13)110 (14) 165 (15)532 (16)144 (17)332 (18)60 (19)170 (20)180

DAY 11
(1)33 (2)47 (3)41 (4)29 (5)10 (6)26 (7)11 (8)23 (9)11(10)33 (11)38 (12)20 (13)14 (14)31 (15)37

DAY 12
(1)6 (2)14 (3)11 (4)19 (5)2 (6)8 (7)11 8)18 (9)26 (10)4 (11)25 (12)4 (13)11 (14)10 (15)2

DAY 13
(1)19 (2)3 (3)7 (4)2 (5)29 (6)12 (7)27 (8)13 (9)22 (10)26 (11)6 (12)13 (13)17 (14)12 (15)31

DAY 14
(1)19 (2)22 (3)5 (4)7 (5)9 (6)10 (7)18 (8)13 (9)12 (10)7 (11)11 (12)12 (13)9 (14)8 (15)8

DAY 15
(1)11 (2)6 (3)19 (4)13 (5)17 (6)4 (7)13 (8)7 (9)23 (10)8 (11)32 (12)31 (13)35 (14)43 (15)18

DAY 16
(1)1 R 3 (2)37 R 1 (3)10 R 3 (4)6 R 8 (5)10 R 0 (6)12 R 6 (7)10 R 3 (8)5 R 8 (9)15 R 3 (10)3 R 6 (11)12 R 3 (12)43 R 1 (13)4 R 5 (14)16 R 2 (15)11 R 5

DAY 17
(1)19 R 1 (2)9 R 0 (3)6 R 2 (4)6 R 7 (5)16 R 0 (6)30 R 1 (7)14 R 2 (8)7 R 1 (9)17 R 2 (10)11 R 1(11)19 R 0 (12)4 R 1 (13)39 R 0 (14)4 R 6 (15) 7 R 5

DAY 18
(1)10 R 0 (2)4 R 5 (3)12 R 3 (4)8 R 3 (5)13 R 0 (6)16 R 2 (7)37 R 0 (8)11 R 4 (9)13 R 1 (10)17 R 2 (11)5 R 1 (12)6 R 3 (13)36 R 1 (14)13 R 5 (15)22 R 1

DAY 19
(1)25 R 1 (2)9 R 0 (3)26 R 0 (4)5 R 2 (5)22 R 1 (6)11 R 4 (7)32 R 0 (8)10 R 6 (9)7 R 0 (10)12 R 0 (11)24 R 2 (12)9 R 0 (13)21 R 2 (14)37 R 1 (15)3 R 0

DAY 20
(1)22 R 2 (2)10 R 4 (3)6 R 2 (4)47 R 1(5)7 R 0 (6)10 R 5 (7)43 R 1 (8)6 R 6 (9)7 R 5 (10)16 R 1 (11)6 R 2 (12)9 R 3 (13)8 R 1 (14)14 R 1 (15)12 R 6

DAY 21
(1)396 (2)1794 (3)1972 (4)1196 (5)1077 (6)528 (7)720 (8)3668 (9)5593 (10)2504 (11)5346 (12)1490 (13)242 (14)4383 (15)3983 (16)4736 (17)600 (18)933 (19)624 (20)2658 (21)924 (22)807 (23)1484 (24)3096

DAY 22
(1)1148 (2)2244 (3)8064 (4)1152 (5)3205 (6)3897 (7)548 (8)5571 (9)4102 (10)1508 (11)3282 (12)3460 (13)4113 (14)2240 (15)807 (16)2290 (17)510 (18)6560 (19)286 (20)2682 (21)3048 (22)1324 (23)5346 (24)2880

DAY 23
(1)1584 (2)708 (3)7875 (4)1296 (5)3824 (6)2305 (7)612 (8)2382 (9)3129 (10)3573 (11)1102 (12)1545 (13)5000 (14)810 (15)990 (16)2058 (17)7704 (18)3432 (19)2756 (20)8514 (21)1510 (22)5022 (23)4542 (24)5904

DAY 24
(1)1324 (2)5096 (3)3268 (4)3265 (5)3899 (6)6784 (7)6472 (8)730 (9)632 (10)1544 (11)3444 (12)1655 (13)2304 (14)7479 (15)3480 (16)3735 (17)288 (18)4840 (19)6008 (20)2175 (21)5016 (22)6848 (23)405 (24)4650

ANSWER KEY

DAY 25
(1)1636 (2)4788 (3)2096 (4) 1984
(5)1222 (6)3120 (7)4425 (8)2912
(9)4086 (10)1899 (11)3913 (12)1248
(13)1150 (14)272 (15)1896 (16)1188
(17)905 (18)543 (19)5397 (20)5397
(21)3025 (22)2352 (23)2548 (24)1206

DAY 26
(1)672 (2)4290 (3)2890 (4)302
(5)1260 (6)6230 (7)4578 (8)1440
(9)6282 (10)2785 (11)1304 (12)4064
(13)3656 (14)1235 (15)2768 (16)1353
(17)576 (18)3954 (19)1630 (20)5778
(21)4557 (22)2124 (23)6860 (24)1605

DAY 27
(1)669 (2)1208 (3)4385 (4)3120
(5)939 (6)2200 (7)852 (8)2022
(9)5040 (10)1420 (11)1414 (12)6132
(13)4149 (14)5404(15)753 (16)3059
(17)1100 (18)5040(19)8433 (20)3960
(21)1729 (22)1728 (23)8469 (24)981

DAY 28
(1)6720 (2)2520 (3)2695 (4)1416
(5)2292 (6)762 (7)1636 (8)1482 (9)791
(10)1590 (11)1184 (12)400 (13)1900
(14)3312 (15)1105 (16)1060 (17)3135
(18) 1696 (19)672 (20)7641 (21)3159
(22)2103 (23)4941 (24)1056

DAY 29
(1)4086 (2)4797 (3)1494 (4)1914
(5)3360 (6)1023 (7)402 (8)2655 (9)2529
(10)1266 (11)2760 (12)1689 (13)706
(14)1815 (15)6909 (16)3168 (17)5958
(18)3990 (19)3600 (20)2084 (21)1119
(22)904 (23)1756 (24)3024

DAY 30
(1)1338 (2)1098 (3)2384 (4)1860
(5)5502 (6)2545 (7)1160 (8)2152
(9)5202 (10)2840 (11)2104 (12)6776
(13)720 (14)6680 (15)596 (16)1293
(17)1312 (18)1666 (19)2500 (20)1718
(21)5456 (22)4235 (23)1520 (24)4452

DAY 31
(1)237 (2)89 (3)101 (4)125 (5)58 (6)363
(7)83 (8)165 (9)76 (10)408 (11)229
(12)307 (13)64 (14)163 (15)457

DAY 32
(1)263 (2)285 (3)108 (4)55 (5)308 (6)39
(7)25 (8)175 (9)271(10)325 (11)199
(12)103 (13)87 (14)299 (15)154

DAY 33
(1)115 (2)71 (3)442 (4)299 (5)141
(6)346 (7)103 (8)41 (9)151(10)53
(11)42 (12)201 (13)43 (14)103 (15)65

DAY 34
(1)213 (2)469 (3)59 (4)55 (5)459 (6)431
(7)49 (8)49 (9)361(10)242 (11)110
(12)61 (13)142 (14)162 (15)217

DAY 35
(1)310 (2)67 (3)384 (4)163 (5)40 (6)112
(7)256 (8)124 (9)31(10)83 (11)46
(12)114 (13)157 (14)307 (15)155

DAY 36
(1)95 R 2 (2)54 R 4 (3)112 R 3 (4)359 R 0
(5)47 R 1 (6)46 R 0 (7)96 R 7 (8)190 R 0
(9)50 R 0 (10)19 R 1 (11)62 R 4 (12)116 R 0

DAY 37
(1)84 R 6 (2)185 R 1 (3)27 R 7
(4)114 R 6 (5)64 R 3 (6)93 R 3
(7)57 R 3 (8)30 R 1 (9)216 R 1
(10)112 R 1 (11)20 R 3 (12)19 R 5

DAY 38
(1)111 R 3 (2)143 R 4 (3)108 R 1
(4)30 R 2 (5)129 R 0 (6)76 R 0
(7)187 R 3 (8)87 R 0 (9)38 R 2
(10)53 R 0 (11)309 R 0 (12)57 R 5

DAY 39
(1)118 R 6 (2)43 R 4 (3)43 R 7
(4)123 R 2 (5)156 R 0 (6)399 R 1
(7)16 R 8 (8)109 R 2 (9)70 R 4
(10)139 R 0 (11)261 R 2 (12)293 R 0

DAY 40
(1)45 R 5 (2)65 R 0 (3)101 R 2
(4)87 R 3 (5)96 R 5 (6)59 R 4
(7)36 R 5 (8)83 R 7 (9)74 R 3
(10)70 R 4 (11)65 R 5 (12)93 R 0

DAY 41
(1)23400 (2)18104 (3)36045 (4)56504
(5)13300 (6)38151 (7)21552 (8)18228
(9)4694 (10)41244 (11)17185 (12)38405
(13)20412 (14)5823 (15)31875 (16)7503
(17)80964 (18)34808

DAY 42
(1)14008 (2)29384 (3)19125 (4)49042
(5)87759 (6)4380 (7)31552 (8)5424
(9)15258 (10)64435 (11)27512 (12)45395
(13)11650 (14)36444 (15)5576
(16)19908 (17)69685 (18)14035

DAY 43
(1)54800 (2)10325 (3)67131 (4)20946
(5)5160 (6)6646 (7)54864 (8)18856
(9)16625 (10)33968 (11)61434 (12)61479
(13)77967 (14)53472 (15)3716 (16)3954
(17)8010 (18)66720

DAY 44
(1)31015 (2)15435 (3)9810 (4)13440
(5)17528 (6)33820 (7)64304 (8)23410
(9)13959 (10)18200 (11)43281 (12)46287
(13)17213 (14)43974 (15)21296
(16)22212 (17)54243 (18)32249

DAY 45
(1)29022 (2)56490 (3)19474 (4)67176
(5)8800 (6)5816 (7)8162 (8)23992
(9)47748 (10)10080 (11)48377 (12)17028
(13)37492 (14)54279 (15)49975
(16)16672 (17)18090 (18)54732

DAY 46
(1)34272 (2)27937 (3)20480 (4)10912
(5)19038 (6)5328 (7)7427 (8)34710
(9)51776 (10)38680 (11)9452 (12)40736
(13)17036 (14)71289 (15)18180
(16)35200 (17)16083 (18)54066

DAY 47
(1)77800 (2)9160 (3)56154 (4)34416
(5)55454 (6)57015 (7)35792 (8)40971
(9)40430 (10)34734 (11)52578 (12)19566
(13)25005 (14)10798 (15)14706
(16)64071 (17)12214 (18)66661

DAY 48
(1)48525 (2)16108 (3)13704 (4)38375
(5)48344 (6)18042 (7)74133 (8)13152
(9)22692 (10)38628 (11)9954 (12)23328
(13)34515 (14)22032 (15)47440
(16)33956 (17)49740 (18)39843

ANSWER KEY

DAY 49
(1)29460 (2)28768 (3)28296
(4)7770 (5)12712 (6)7808
(7)4098 (8)61173 (9)16905
(10)29043 (11)22736 (12)19215
(13)33312 (14)21765 (15)30128
(16)7760 (17)45150 (18)8640

DAY 50
(1)58872 (2)48492 (3)43284
(4)33456 (5)27210 (6)23427
(7)48660 (8)75204 (9)12174
(10)18456 (11)17172 (12)55836
(13)64989 (14)63640 (15)36747
(16)3558 (17)53270 (18)18472

DAY 51
(1)509 (2)407 (3)703 (4)1145
(5)1093 (6)2340 (7)1975 (8)1625
(9)703(10)3715 (11)1965 (12)1600

DAY 52
(1)2267 (2)4248 (3)597 (4)806 (5)2633
(6)1427 (7)761 (8)1523 (9)4372
(10)313 (11)2051 (12)3947

DAY 53
(1)1706 (2)630 (3)510 (4)4818 (5)3151
(6)319 (7)2092 (8)581 (9)457
(10)2127 (11)2953 (12)508

DAY 54
(1)4703 (2)2659 (3)3643 (4)1585
(5)2729 (6)2479 (7)1323 (8)1747
(9)1193 (10)1891 (11)486 (12)1434

DAY 55
(1)223 (2)997 (3)1307 (4)1852 (5)3587
(6)967 (7)1878 (8)1720 (9)762
(10)4867 (11)1433 (12)1258

DAY 56
(1)2409 R 1 (2)1682 R 2 (3)797 R 2
(4)132 R 7 (5)379 R 1 (6)1172 R 2
(7)207 R 0 (8)2025 R 0 (9)1019 R 1
(10)1666 R 0 (11)818 R 5 (12)1538 R 0

DAY 57
(1)916 R 3 (2)615 R 0 (3)586 R 0
(4)460 R 6 (5)291 R 2 (6)2025 R 0
(7)1668 R 3 (8)195 R 3 (9)1013 R 1
(10)1259 R 2 (11)1234 R 3 (12)656 R 7

DAY 58
(1)2704 R 1 (2)545 R 1 (3)1907 R 0
(4)1421 R 4 (5)1396 R 1 (6)1190 R 2
(7)531 R 0 (8)714 R 1 (9)2176 R 3
(10)924 R 5 (11)749 R 7 (12)484 R 1

DAY 59
(1)445 R 7 (2)439 R 3 (3)888 R 2
(4)2459 R 1 (5)338 R 2 (6)1241 R 0
(7)579 R 2 (8)467 R 5 (9)791 R 0
(10)646 R 2 (11)186 R 5 (12)153 R 3

DAY 60
(1)1215 R 1 (2)2848 R 0 (3)1547 R 0
(4)439 R 4 (5)244 R 3 (6)1994 R 4
(7)596 R 3 (8)466 R 1 (9)551 R 1
(10)252 R 1 (11)551 R 2 (12)1557 R 1

DAY 61
(1)5980 (2)6776 (3)5508 (4)3485
(5)3381 (6)3528 (7)5670 (8)9108
(9)2120(10)6840 (11)1856 (12)4840

DAY 62
(1)4424 (2)7920 (3)3250 (4)4876
(5)7209 (6)4148 (7)4183 (8)2535
(9)4150(10)3774 (11)2754 (12)2010

DAY 63
(1)2736 (2)3666 (3)2262 (4)3344
(5)5184 (6)5429 (7)2726 (8)3696
(9)6336(10)2982 (11)3872 (12)6930

DAY 64
(1)7227 (2)5445 (3)3960 (4)2530
(5)2528 (6)6132 (7)3905 (8)1628
(9)960 (10)2331 (11)5723 (12)1520

DAY 65
(1)3990 (2)1681 (3)6256 (4)9409
(5)4290 (6)2940 (7)7980 (8)6240
(9)1632 (10)2760 (11)2208 (12)3510

DAY 66
(1)2268 (2)4617 (3)2350 (4)1950
(5)5396 (6)8280 (7)6570 (8)3024
(9)7708 (10)5896 (11)4345 (12)3321

DAY 67
(1)4473 (2)1364 (3)3634 (4)4838
(5)2688 (6)3036 (7)5934 (8)4000
(9)2250 (10)1800 (11)5785 (12)1760

DAY 68
(1)3021 (2)4186 (3)5796 (4)4692
(5)3713 (6)2624 (7)2190 (8)3465
(9)3577 (10)1911 (11)5865 (12)6090

DAY 69
(1)1054 (2)3002 (3)2240 (4)4968
(5)2948 (6)3339 (7)7030 (8)4087
(9)2470 (10)2886 (11)2294 (12)3784

DAY 70
(1)5063 (2)4268 (3)4428 (4)3264
(5)1521 (6)5808 (7)3010 (8)2562
(9)7820 (10)6417 (11)3696 (12)2457

DAY 71
(1)12692 (2)21516 (3)39865 (4)78816
(5)15453 (6)17050 (7)37269 (8)16827
(9)68796 (10)17433 (11)1782 (12)6111

DAY 72
(1)10626 (2)95642 (3)31208 (4)25676
(5)18096 (6)77778 (7)38270 (8)46299
(9)2640 (10)25308 (11)1166 (12)5994

DAY 73
(1)19668 (2)14832 (3)14042 (4)35955
(5)17427 (6)2575 (7)40356 (8)14562
(9)15540 (10)21238 (11)17877 (12)3336

DAY 74
(1)7260 (2)76896 (3)5499 (4)20064
(5)31302 (6)13068 (7)3157 (8)22500
(9)19756 (10)11046 (11)20398 (12)42778

DAY 75
(1)17020 (2)29308 (3)29094 (4)61362
(5)22128 (6)81180 (7)15138 (8)25069
(9)14070 (10)15050 (11)20720 (12)51792

ANSWER KEY

DAY 76
(1)20272 (2)10560 (3)30645 (4)17550
(5)26078 (6)22880 (7)51328 (8)56064
(9)4191 (10)39694 (11)15908 (12)9450

DAY 77
(1)36946 (2)20454 (3)7975 (4)31086
(5)9842 (6)4152 (7)62216 (8)2354
(9)12735 (10)44978 (11)9030 (12)9715

DAY 78
(1)34272 (2)82665 (3)5082 (4)15750
(5)13498 (6)22356 (7)11024 (8)21560
(9)30600 (10)65219 (11)27436 (12)6040

DAY 79
(1)5954 (2)5916 (3)33026 (4)18040
(5)44812 (6)51212 (7)20412 (8)24376
(9)17250 (10)24050 (11)11880 (12)23760

DAY 80
(1)11880 (2)15196 (3)14511 (4)79380
(5)5880 (6)11253 (7)17640 (8)10962
(9)10155 (10)27048 (11)59013 (12)11880

DAY 81
(1)2 (2)14 (3)20 (4)5 (5)8 (6)62
(7)31 (8)9 (9)11 (10)6 (11)7
(12)5 (13)73 (14)46 (15)37

DAY 82
(1)11 (2)6 (3)35 (4)35 (5)4 (6)3 (7)4
(8)3(9)11 (10)15 (11)5 (12)28
(13)2 (14)5 (15)43

DAY 83
(1)23 (2)3 (3)5 (4)12 (5)47 (6)7
(7)21(8)4 (9)21 (10)17 (11)19
(12)4 (13)11 (14)6 (15)47

DAY 84
(1)9 (2)17 (3)6 (4)55 (5)9 (6)49
(7)7 (8)38 (9)17 (10)3 (11)5 (12)37
(13)2 (14)10 (15)9

DAY 85
(1)29 (2)8 (3)11 (4)63 (5)4 (6)16
(7)14 (8)62 (9)20 (10)47 (11)45
(12)60 (13)82 (14)26 (15)5

DAY 86
(1)14 R 21 (2)87 R 3 (3)6 R 15
(4)7 R 0 (5)56 R 6 (6)27 R 0
(7)58 R 0 (8)31 R 16 (9)14 R 6
(10)30 R 4 (11)46 R 2(12)45 R 4

DAY 87
(1)34 R 9 (2)32 R 23 (3)27 R 9
(4)5 R 2 (5)10 R 3 (6)29 R 11
(7)14 R 7 (8)69 R 5 (9)24 R 16
(10)8 R 37 (11)8 R 16 (12)22 R 14

DAY 88
(1)9 R 12 (2)24 R 23 (3)9 R 28
(4)18 R 7 (5)6 R 28 (6)41 R 19
(7)8 R 46 (8)2 R 18 (9)24 R 1
(10)22 R 0 (11)76 R 1 (12)19 R 28

DAY 89
(1)10 R 17 (2)32 R 25 (3)18 R 0
(4)18 R 6 (5)25 R 25 (6)5 R 18
(7)17 R 16 (8)17 R 1 (9)6 R 14
(10)54 R 1 (11)4 R 24 (12)25 R 13

DAY 90
(1)7 R 30 (2)38 R 10 (3)56 R 4
(4)20 R 28 (5)4 R 6 (6)14 R 38
(7)32 R 11 (8)18 R 34 (9)22 R 22
(10)45 R 10 (11)4 R 37 (12)10 R 19

DAY 91
(1)361 (2)12 (3)70 (4)324 (5)137
(6)163 (7)77 (8)107 (9)123
(10)70 (11)172 (12)601

DAY 92
(1)17 (2)383 (3)23 (4)289 (5)402
(6)281 (7)43 (8)285 (9)27
(10)251 (11)463 (12)106

DAY 93
(1)55 (2)747 (3)205 (4)337 (5)164
(6)518 (7)186 (8)151 (9)63
(10)829 (11)89 (12)188

DAY 94
(1)69 (2)257 (3)31 (4)59 (5)41
(6)40 (7)109 (8)87 (9)201
(10)82 (11)245 (12)127

DAY 95
(1)226 (2)103 (3)251 (4)477 (5)34
(6)125 (7)288 (8)82 (9)284
(10)125 (11)110 (12)499

DAY 96
(1)456 R 12 (2)96 R 7 (3)133 R 25
(4)209 R 32 (5)114 R 21 (6)510 R 3
(7)210 R 12 (8)194 R 26 (9)621 R 0

DAY 97
(1)24 R 30 (2)190 R 6 (3)295 R 23
(4)29 R 14 (5)263 R 6 (6)235 R 3
(7)163 R 24 (8)214 R 9 (9)342 R 23

DAY 98
(1)132 R 1 (2)462 R 7 (3)208 R 29
(4)141 R 28 (5)57 R 23 (6)92 R 16
(7)145 R 0 (8)231 R 3 (9)106 R 4

DAY 99
(1)38 R 10 (2)331 R 10 (3)166 R 11
(4)309 R 13 (5)157 R 22 (6)74 R 5
(7)325 R 5 (8)155 R 18 (9)165 R 8

DAY 100
(1)213 R 5 (2)235 R 15 (3)233 R 37
(4)160 R 19 (5)254 R 7 (6)368 R 15
(7)242 R 27 (8)106 R 4 (9)229 R 18

Made in United States
Troutdale, OR
01/13/2025